C000151256

With Respect to Old Age:
Long Term Care – Rights and Responsibilities

Alternative Models of Care for Older People

Research Volume 2

A Report by
The Royal Commission on Long Term Care

Chairman: Professor Sir Stewart Sutherland

Presented to Parliament by
Command of Her Majesty

March 1999

Cm 4192-II / 2

£65
3 volumes not sold separately

Alternative Models of Care for Older People

The Main Report

by

Anthea Tinker, Fay Wright, Claudine McCreadie, Janet Askham, Ruth Hancock & Alan Holmans

Age Concern Institute of Gerontology

King's College London

The Authors and Collaborators

The authors of this paper are:

Professor Anthea Tinker, Professor of Social Gerontology and Director of the Age Concern Institute of Gerontology, King's College London. Social Policy analyst

Dr. Fay Wright, Research Fellow at the Age Concern Institute of Gerontology, King's College London. Social Policy analyst

Claudine McCreadie, Research Associate, Age Concern Institute of Gerontology, King's College London. Social Policy analyst

Professor Janet Askham, Professor of Gerontology and Deputy Director of the Age Concern Institute of Gerontology, King's College London. Sociologist

Ruth Hancock, Senior Research Fellow, Age Concern Institute of Gerontology, King's College London (and now Senior Research Fellow, Nuffield Community Care Studies Unit, University of Leicester and Visiting Senior Research Fellow at ACIOG) Economist

Dr. Alan Holmans, University of Cambridge and previously Chief Housing Economist, Department of the Environment. Economist

The collaborators of this paper, to whom go many thanks, are:

Professor Robin Means, Associate Dean (Primary and Community Care) University of the West of England. A Social Policy analyst and qualified Social Worker. He was commissioned by ACIOG to write a paper on Housing and Housing Organisations and this forms Appendix 3.

Dr. Alan Turner-Smith and **Dr. Donna Cowan**, Centre for Rehabilitation Engineering, King's College London. A Physicist/ Engineer and Engineer respectively. They were commissioned by ACIOG to write a paper on Assistive Technology and this forms Appendix 4.

Age Concern England, under the leadership of **Evelyn McEwen** made available the expertise of their Library, Information and Policy Staff.

The Focus Groups of Older People and Carers
This forms Annex E.

The authors are also grateful to **Working Group B (Models of Care)** of the Royal Commission for their support and comments. They would like to express their thanks to the members of the Secretariat, especially **Patrick Hennessy**, for all their help and support. There are many others who helped us and we list them after the references.

(This report has been a team effort. However Anthea Tinker took overall responsibility for editing it into its final form and also the main responsibility for Chapters 5 and 6. Other chapters where a main responsibility can be identified were: Chapter 3, Claudine McCreadie; Chapter 4, Fay Wright; Chapter 7, Janet Askham; Chapter 8, Alan Holmans; Chapter 9, Ruth Hancock and Annex E, Claudine McCreadie and Fay Wright. All benefited from contributions from the team as a whole.)

The responsibility for the report and for any errors and expressions of opinion belong, of course, to the authors

Contents

The authors and collaborators . . . . inside front page

Abbreviations and terminology v

Executive Summary 1

Chapters:

1 **Introduction and Methods** 15

2 **Staying at Home in Context** 21

3 **The Models: Intensive Home Support** 33

4 **The Models: Co-Resident Care** 49

5 **The Models: Very Sheltered Housing** 67

6 **The Models: Assistive Technology** 81

7 **The Vignettes** 93

8 **Costing Care and Support** 103

    Annex A: Details of costings of services in ordinary homes 117

    Annex B: Details of costings of externally provided services in very
    sheltered housing 123

    Annex C: Costs of ordinary housing 126

9 **Paying for Care and Support** 129

    Annex D: Detailed examples of incidence of resource costs (Tables)
    and the effects of increasing income on contributions to total health
    and care costs (Figures) 142

10 **Findings and Issues** 175

    Annex E: Illustrations of schemes 183

Acknowledgments 227

References 229

Appendices:

1 **Focus Groups. Discussions with Older People
   and their Carers** 245

2 **Helping Older People to Stay at Home — The
   Role of Supported Accommodation** 265

3 **Housing and Housing Organisations: A Review of
   their Contribution to Alternative Models of Care for
   Elderly People** 299

4 **The Role of Assistive Technology in Alternative
   Models of Care for Elderly People** 325

Alternative Models of Care for Older People

Abbreviations and Terminology

AA	Attendance Allowance
ACE	Age Concern England
ACIOG	Age Concern Institute of Gerontology
ADL	Activities of Daily Living
ADS	Alzheimer's Disease Society
ADSS	Association of Directors of Social Services
AT	Assistive Technology
COST	European Co-operation in the field of Scientific and Technical Research
CNA	Carers National Association
CPA	Centre for Policy on Ageing
CPN	Community Psychiatric Nurse
DETR	Department of Environment, Transport and the Regions
DoE	Department of the Environment
DoH	Department of Health
DSS	Department of Social Security
EPICS	Elderly Persons Integrated Care System
ESRC	Economic and Social Research Council
GB	Great Britain
GHS	General Household Survey
GP	General Practitioner
GSS	Government Statistical Service
HA	Housing Association
HAS	Health Advisory Service
HB	Housing Benefit
IS	Income Support
JRF	Joseph Rowntree Foundation
LA	Local Authority
MRC	Medical Research Council
NHS	National Health Service
NISW	National Institute of Social Work
ONS	Office of National Statistics
OPCS	Office of Population, Censuses and Surveys
OT	Occupational Therapist
PSSRU	Personal Social Services Research Unit at Universities of Kent, Manchester and the London School of Economics

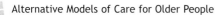

PSI	Policy Studies Institute
RICA	Research Institute for Consumer Affairs
RPI	Retail Price Index
SAR	Sample of Anonymised Records
SERPS	State Earnings Related Pension Scheme
SPRU	Social Policy Research Unit, University of York
SSI	Social Services Inspectorate
TELEMATE	Telematic Multidisciplinary Assistive Technology Education
TIDE	Telematics for Elderly and Disabled People
UK	United Kingdom

The term 'older people' is used throughout the paper unless the reference is to the research of others where a different description is given.

'Home' is used to denote house, flat, bungalow or any other kind of housing unless the reference is to research where a specific description is given.

Executive Summary

CHAPTER 1: INTRODUCTION AND METHODS

This review was undertaken for the *Royal Commission on the Funding of Long Term Care for the Elderly*. The terms of reference for the Royal Commission were: 'to examine the short and long term care for elderly people, both in their own homes and in other settings, and to recommend how, and in what circumstances, the cost of such care can be apportioned between public funds and individuals' (Department of Health Press Release, 4.12.97).

The aims of this review were:

- to examine existing research and practice on alternative models of care for the more dependent older people in the community and those at the margins of institutional care;

- to identify particular types of scheme, facility or service that are integral to those models;

- to assess those models in terms of feasibility, acceptability to users and carers, outcomes and costs;

- to identify who meets the costs in different circumstances.

Since the research had to be completed in less than six months it was not possible to undertake much empirical research. However, besides reviewing the literature on research and practice we investigated a substantial number and variety of current schemes (detailed in Annex E). We also held seven focus group discussions on alternative models of care in late age (Appendix 1, p. 245); the groups included older people and carers. It was not possible to make more than a very few cross-national comparisons. We also drew on two specially

commissioned papers concerned with housing issues (Appendix 3, p. 299) and assistive technology (Appendix 4, p. 325) and one on research on housing for the Department of Health (Appendix 2, p. 265).

It was decided to focus on four models of care:

- intensive home support;

- co-resident care;

- very sheltered housing; and

- assistive technology.

These models have been examined as though they were alternatives, although in reality of course there are no distinct boundaries between them. For example, people living in a co-resident caring situation or very sheltered housing or in an assistive technology setting may need intensive home support to remain at home. Equally a husband or wife with high needs for support may move with a spouse into very sheltered housing.

The review of the models examines their:

- feasibility (whether they can be put into operation successfully);

- acceptability (to older people, carers, and service providers);

- outcomes (whether they meet key objectives such as keeping people at home for longer than would otherwise have been the case); and

- economic costs.

To help with the last of these, we devised six vignettes – hypothetical cases – of frail older people living in the community but on the margins of institutional care. They were chosen with reference to what is known about the age, gender and living circumstances of people who enter institutional care. But six examples cannot represent the full range of relevant characteristics of people who are in this situation. They are simply illustrative. Each vignette was assigned to one or more settings (i.e. own home, with or without a co-resident carer, or very sheltered housing) with an appropriate package of care. The combinations and volume of different forms of care allocated to the vignettes were those which research and practice suggested were likely to be sufficient to keep people out of institutions. However, systematic evidence about the precise level of service or facility necessary to keep someone out of an institution is not available. The packages of care are therefore no more than rough estimates of what is likely to be needed to keep people out of institutions, but do not address the issue of comparisons of quality of life in the different settings.

The value of the economic resources used in meeting the care services provided in each vignette was then estimated. These costs were subsequently apportioned between the individual and the different public bodies involved, under alternative assumptions about how the individual's contribution to care costs is determined. An important caveat is that the cost of informal care has **not** been included.

CHAPTER 2: STAYING AT HOME IN CONTEXT

The four alternative models for dependent older people on the margins of institutional care have to be seen in context. This includes the evidence that most older people want to remain in a home of their own and an understanding of what 'home' means.

Making predictions about the numbers on the margins of institutional care is hazardous, but women, very old people and widows are all more likely to enter institutional care.

Crucial to staying at home for many people is the involvement of carers together with the key role of health (acute, hospital discharge arrangements, rehabilitation and primary services) and social care. Prevention is also important. Housing is another key element and one which is neglected as a component of community care at national, local and individual level.

Key principles underlying the models are that they should promote independence, promote a 'normal' as opposed to a stigmatised lifestyle, guarantee rights to safety and freedom from exploitation, respond to the individual's preferences and choices, and not 'worsen' an individual's living situation.

CHAPTER 3: THE MODELS: INTENSIVE HOME SUPPORT

Intensive home support at its best can deliver care to the standard of the 'best relatives' and enables people, if they so wish, to continue to live as normal a life as possible in their own home. Experimental projects cited in Annex E show just how effective and successful this approach can be.

However, for it to work as a national norm, a great many pieces have to fall into place – the adequacy of people's housing, information, comprehensive assessments, access to a wide range of services, co-ordination of these services, availability, affordability, appropriateness, reliability, continuity, and quality of support. These are strenuous requirements when viewed against service divisions, resource constraints, funding differentials and local diversity of standards and social conditions. They are examined further below.

Housing has to be given attention, not as a specialist provision, but simply as being suitable in terms of adaptability and warmth to the needs of older people. Episodes of illness or accidents, as well as long-term disability, have to be addressed through health services, and particularly rehabilitation, in a way that links them to other forms of support in the home. The Elderly People's Integrated Care System (EPICS) scheme and other similar initiatives quoted in Annex E show how this is practicable and feasible if certain conditions are met.

People have to be able to access services and this in itself creates a need for an infrastructure of advice and information services. Currently, the NHS is the first port-of-call and the principal provider for most people for health care in later, as in earlier, life. But social services are effectively residual, available to those unable to access private help with private means. This hampers substantially the integration of services, already divided by professional and cultural factors.

Care management is a method for trying to provide this integrating function when intensive support is needed, and in the experimental projects evaluated for the DoH, some impressive results were shown. It is early days to be too judgmental about the policy, but the evidence points to considerable confusion. Projects which target resources in a very focused way at particular individuals in need, as in some of the schemes outlined in Annex E, do not represent the everyday realities of life in the services addressing the needs of older people.

When people are on the margins of residential care, they need services more or less immediately if they are to be able to return to, or remain in, their own home. Ready availability of appropriate services – which in turn requires appropriate assessment – is therefore essential. Currently, the national picture is that there are widespread shortages of all kinds of services, including assessments. Rationing services by targeting them at those most in need risks leaving those with less complex needs without help at all, which may be short-sighted. Concentrating support on those who are living on their own can place intolerable strains on caregivers.

Despite the resource shortages, there are illustrations of outstanding practice around the country. Some of these, such as the projects to help people with dementia remain in their own home, are outlined in Annex E. Good professional practice does not seem to relate to the social conditions of an area. In this model, as in all settings, the crucial if obvious element is the quality of the people who manage and deliver the service. Older people are notoriously grateful for the services that they do receive, but they place significant importance on their relationships with staff, along with the reliability and adaptability of the service to fit their particular needs.

It is important to recognise that the costs of intensive home support will be very variable between different users and that any individual may have very varying needs over a period of time. The greater their dependency, the higher the costs of providing support, whether these fall on formal services or family carers.

Key conditions for the intensive home support model to work:

- integration of health, social care and housing services;

- communication and co-ordination between service providers;

- comprehensive assessment;

- the need for someone to have a co-ordinating role;

- quality of staff and relationship with users/carers;

- flexible, reliable services;

- continuity of services;

- addressing the specific needs of dementia sufferers and their carers.

CHAPTER 4: THE MODELS: CO-RESIDENT CARE

Over half of co-resident care is provided by a spouse, and married people are far less likely to enter institutional care than the widowed or never-married. Over a fifth of co-resident care is given by an offspring or daughter/son-in-law. At its best co-resident care gives both the person being cared for and the caregiver a good quality of life in which support is given in the context of a loving relationship. In reality co-resident caregiving often inflicts a heavier care burden on the carer than is the case for a carer living in a separate household. Conversely a co-resident carer is far less likely than a carer living in a separate household from the cared-for person to share the care burden with health or social services. Some kinds of practical help, such as with basic housework, may not be available or appropriate.

There are often positive reasons for spouses and offspring wanting to continue caregiving in the community. But there may be considerable difficulties in continuing to provide that care. Spouses in particular, themselves usually above retirement age, may have serious health problems. A wide literature indicates that it is common for carers to have high stress levels. Living with a dementia sufferer is likely to generate considerable stress.

There have been significant developments in recognising the situation of carers and their needs for support. Two major national organisations, the Carers' National Association and the Princess Royal Trust for Carers, have established substantial frameworks both to champion the cause of carers at a national and local level and to develop support services. There has been considerable expansion in the network of carer support workers and of carer support groups.

Carers emphasise their need for more information and training and more guaranteed breaks from caring. Day care, in its many forms, remains an appreciated service. Nevertheless the amount of support given is limited and few dependent people have more than one or two days of the week in day care. The demand for short-term breaks far outstrips the supply. Placements may be free to the user if in a hospital but high charges may be made for care in a local authority or independent sector care home. Spouses may find it difficult to get, or be induced to take, a break of some days from caring; visits from a care assistant, where available, may be more acceptable. Charges by local authorities for community services may also be a particular problem for spouse carers.

Many spouses and offspring continue to care for a dependent older person to the end, or virtually to the end, of that person's life. It is likely to be particularly difficult to maintain a dementia sufferer in a co-resident caring situation and the cost to the person providing such care may be very high.

CHAPTER 5: THE MODELS: VERY SHELTERED HOUSING

Sheltered housing is accommodation which is grouped with some communal facilities (a common room and usually also a laundry and guest room), a warden (resident or non-resident) and an alarm system which links the people there with a warden. Very sheltered usually has, in addition, extra communal facilities (such as a special bath), 24-hour cover by a warden and meals (sometimes two a day but sometimes only one).

Only 5% of people over the age of 65 live in sheltered and very sheltered housing. Of the half a million units of sheltered housing only 3.5% is very sheltered. Despite a good deal of satisfaction with both forms of housing, problems are developing particularly with sheltered due to lack of facilities, location and greater choice for people to remain in their own homes. There has been a dramatic fall in provision of all kinds of sheltered housing and in 1997 only 402 units were built in England.

The essence of sheltered and very sheltered housing is that a people have a home of their own with their own front door; they are either owners or tenants with the security of tenure that this brings. It is disquieting that most research finds that a growing percentage of tenants have no physical or mental disabilities, although at the same time a growing proportion have a high level of dependency. It may be that providers are making a conscious decision to have the traditional mix of fit and frail.

Although there is a high level of satisfaction with very sheltered housing from tenants a minority would have preferred to have remained in their own homes and felt rushed into making decisions. There is little research on the views of carers or of staff. It is difficult to obtain evidence about outcomes of living in very sheltered housing but encouragingly it appears that a growing number of people are moving into it from institutions. The evidence is mixed about the ability of current schemes to provide an alternative to institutions with some evidence of a lack of care services. It is, for most of the situations described in Chapters 7 and 8, more expensive in terms of resource costs to the economy than staying at home options.

Ways of meeting a potential demand for very sheltered housing and of making better use of sheltered include turning the latter into very sheltered, making greater use of communal facilities and enhancing the role of the warden. However there needs to be clear agreement about allocation procedures in the public sector with a likely emphasis on more dependent older people. The different models of providing care i.e. in house or from outside need more research and evaluation and some interesting new ways are being developed.

Very sheltered housing is therefore one of a range of options and not a panacea. However, the dramatic drop in recent provision, and the remodelling which is taking place for existing tenants, do suggest that there is a case for some expansion to meet the needs of people who are in mainstream housing

CHAPTER 6: THE MODELS: ASSISTIVE TECHNOLOGY

The assistive technology described in this chapter includes communications equipment such as telephones and alarms, equipment to aid problems of mobility, personal and domestic care, 'smart homes' and telemedicine/telecare. They can answer problems of communications, mobility, manipulation, orientation and cognition. Some will answer more than one problem, e.g. an alarm for both communication and security, and may greatly enhance the quality of life. However they cannot take the place of social interaction.

Issues of feasibility are around those of cost and production on a large scale, the degree of subsidy and the contribution of the public sector, the fact that some equipment is bulky and expensive, and the lack of accessibility. On acceptability much depends on the perception of the person – for example mobile phones are very acceptable and do not have a stigma. In general there is satisfaction with some types of AT such as alarms but sometimes a reluctance to use them. However this may change in the future, with a new generation of older people who are more accustomed to electronic devices. There is little evidence about acceptability to carers or service providers. On outcomes one cannot generalise but some have the potential to restore mobility, give greater independence and save lives as well as improve the quality of life. There is not a great deal of data on costs but the development of a market in the EU would undoubtedly bring prices down.

CHAPTER 7: THE VIGNETTES

The hypothetical cases which formed the basis for the costings were as follows:

- **Vignette 1.** Man aged 65-74, married and living with a spouse. His dementia is severe enough that he cannot safely be left alone in the house. He is often awake and active at night. During the day he uses the toilet frequently and needs some help and supervision. His wife has arthritis and finds it difficult to get up the stairs. He has short-interval needs (i.e. 'unable to perform one or more domestic tasks which require to be undertaken frequently, that is more often than daily'). He received higher rate Attendance Allowance.

- **Vignette 2.** Woman aged 75-84, recently widowed and living alone. She has a supportive neighbour who is in full-time employment. She has some restrictions on mobility and moderate confusion. She is unwilling to go outside by herself now and is unable to go shopping alone or to collect her pension. She does not receive the Attendance Allowance. She has long-interval needs (i.e. 'unable to perform one or more domestic tasks which require to be undertaken occasionally but less often than daily').

- **Vignette 3.** Woman aged 75-84, living alone, is mentally capable and has become wheelchair-bound after e.g. a stroke. She finds her situation demoralising and needs to be encouraged to socialise and take holidays. She has the lower rate Attendance Allowance. She has critical-interval needs (i.e. 'unable to perform crucial self-care tasks which need to be undertaken frequently and at short notice').

- **Vignette 4.** Woman aged 85+, has moved to live with her married daughter who works part-time. She is mentally capable but has developed diabetes in recent years and now has terminal cancer. She has become doubly incontinent. She has the higher rate Attendance Allowance and her daughter has the Invalid Care Allowance. Her daughter cannot provide her with 24-hour-a-day care but is able to provide care at the weekend. She has critical-interval needs.

- **Vignette 5.** Man aged 85+, living alone. He is prone to falls and is a recent widower, not used to performing any domestic tasks. Cooking, cleaning and doing the laundry are problematic for him. He is lonely. He has short-interval needs. He does not receive Attendance Allowance.

- **Vignette 6.** Woman aged 85+, living alone, and has become anxious and clinically depressed. Physically quite active but needs encouragement to leave the house and to socialise. Needs some support with domestic and self-care tasks. She has long-interval needs. She does not receive Attendance Allowance.

CHAPTER 8: COSTINGS OF PACKAGES OF CARE SERVICES FOR OLDER PEOPLE IN THEIR OWN HOMES

The costings of packages of services for men and women depicted in the six vignettes provide some comparisons of the cost of care in ordinary homes and in very sheltered housing. Both can be compared with costs and charges for full-time residential care. Some parts of the calculations depended on assumptions about the staff time involved in, for example, managing packages of care, and others on incomplete information about how much of the time of (for example) community nurses is spent with those who receive their services. The average costs quoted are therefore approximate estimates. Defensible alternative assumptions could sometimes result in different figures for costs; differences of a few hundred pounds a year cannot in consequence demonstrate a material cost advantage or disadvantage.

A comparison is made in Table 8.6 between the cost of full-time residential care as estimated in Table 8.5 and care in older people's own homes (Table 8.3). Whether like is being compared exactly with like especially in terms of quality is not certain, so the comparison must be interpreted with caution.

Subject to these provisos, the costings summarised in Table 8.6 show that there is no general rule for all the vignettes about whether care in ordinary housing, adapted if necessary, costs more or less than care in very sheltered housing. Nor is there a general rule about either being less costly than full-time residential care. It depends on how many hours of home care, including day and night sitting, are needed and on how far such care is provided by the staff of very sheltered housing. For vignettes 2, 5 and 6 care in an ordinary home is cheaper than care in very sheltered housing. But for vignette 3 the opposite is true. The person depicted in this vignette requires large amounts of home care; in an ordinary home it has to be provided by a home carer one to one but in very sheltered housing it can be provided partly by the staff who need not be in a one to one ratio with the residents. For the same reason, full-time residential care is substantially cheaper than either care in an ordinary home or in very sheltered housing for the woman depicted in vignette 4.

	Vignette no.					
	1	**2**	**3**	**4**	**5**	**6**
Care in people's own homes						
Ordinary houses	17,253 or 20,031	13,969	41,740	26,206	11,291	17,370
Very sheltered housing	18,188	19,377	37,322	–	18,316	27,124
Full time residential care						
Local authority basis	21,399	21,285	21,285	21,038	21,038	21,038
Private sector basis	16,646	16,532	16,532	16,285	16,285	16,285

Table 8.6: Summary of costs of different structures of care (£/year) 1997/98 prices

In the summary to Chapter 8, each of the vignettes is considered in detail in relation to each of the models, in order to show the particular strengths and weaknesses of the models in different care-need circumstances.

CHAPTER 9: PAYING FOR CARE AND SUPPORT

For each of the vignettes, the resource costs of the various possible care packages were identified in Chapter 8. It was then necessary to determine who would meet these resource costs: a statutory authority or the individual.

1. The method
The method involves a base scenario and variations from it:

■ in the base scenario both ordinary and very sheltered housing is provided by a Housing Association. The implications of ordinary housing being owner-occupied and the consequent possibility for drawing on housing wealth are also examined;

■ the whole of the care element in very sheltered housing is treated as 'eligible rent' for Housing Benefit purposes in the base scenario but a variant in which only half is eligible is also examined;

■ the LA sets a full charge equal to the resource cost of externally provided non-health care services and assesses users' contributions to that charge on the basis of the net income they have in excess of their net housing costs and the relevant Income Support threshold ('available' income) and savings. Under the base scenario the whole of any available income is required to be put towards the LA charge. A variant in which the LA takes only 65% of available income is also examined;

■ health services are assumed to be free to all users and a charge on the NHS budget;

■ the following contributions to components and sub-totals of resource costs are then identified: the individual from private sources; DSS through Attendance

Allowance, Housing Benefit and for living expenses, Income Support; the Local Authority; the NHS, the Housing Association providing the accommodation;

■   detailed examples are presented in Tables D.1 to D.12 of Annex D for each of the vignettes and care packages on the basis of a modest income level and savings below £3,000. For selected vignettes the effect of varying income, alternative charging regimes and treatment of the care component of rent in very sheltered housing are shown in figures D.1 to D.19. The implications of assuming savings of £10,000 are shown in Table D.13.

2. The findings

Under the baseline assumptions the relative contributions of the state and the individual to health and care resource costs do not vary very much, with the state incurring between 90 and 100%. At the modest income levels assumed, the outcome for the older person concerned in terms of how much income is left after meeting housing and care costs is virtually the same under each care package. Yet the burden on the budgets of each statutory authority varies considerably.

Allowing only 50% of the care component of rent in sheltered housing to be considered eligible rent for Housing Benefit purposes considerably reduces the cost borne by the DSS. Through the calculation of available income it increases the cost borne by LAs to some extent. It also makes very sheltered housing unaffordable to older people on low incomes.

A LA charging system which takes only a proportion of available income in charges obviously places more cost on LA budgets but allows those who have earned higher retirement incomes to retain some of the benefits.

Assuming that the older people having savings of £10,000 reduces the cost borne by the state but where LA charges are high, this saving is short-lived. For one vignette, the extreme case, it would be only 3 weeks before her capital fell below the £8,000 threshold and 12 weeks before it fell below £3,000.

Unlike tenants, low income owner-occupiers are not eligible for help with their housing costs through Housing Benefit. The net housing costs of older owner-occupiers can therefore be higher than those of tenants. If the LA makes an allowance for this in calculating available income, it may find itself able to charge owners less than it charges tenants for care services.

Owner-occupiers have the possibility of using housing wealth to pay for care by taking out an equity release scheme. However, the extra income generated is taken into account in assessing Income Support entitlement. If LAs also include it in available income, calculations show that there is little incentive for those on low incomes to release equity in this way.

3. Conclusions

It is not uncommon for means testing to produce what appear to be anomalous results. But for older people the funding of care in community settings produces anomalies that are extreme by any standards. If it is health rather than social care, the costs are borne by the NHS regardless of the users' financial resources. If it is care included with accommodation costs in very sheltered housing it *may* be met in part or in full by DSS through Housing Benefit depending on the income or savings of the older person concerned but this is under review. The role of Attendance Allowance may also be crucial in helping with costs. If it is social care provided via a Local Authority, the older person may make a contribution depending on his or her financial resources and on the charging system used by the Local Authority. There is currently no national framework for such charges. For older people with modest financial resources, it is not the division between private and public costs which varies most: it is the apportionment of public costs between the NHS, Local Authorities and DSS. However, a cost has not been put on informal care: had this been possible, those situations where much of the care was provided by a co-resident carer would have shown more of the costs being borne by the private sector.

Cost-shunting remains a key issue in paying for care and support for older people. Debate over the division of costs between the state and the individual sector is in danger of missing key issues in relation to the incidence of costs within the public sector.

Some consistency in the charging policies of LAs is surely necessary. This need not rule out local discretion to take account of individual circumstances, but it must be possible to establish some general, publicly-stated principles. If these principles imply means-testing, then the regime must take due account of interaction with means-testing in the social security system without the haphazard adoption of isolated features of Income Support or Housing Benefit.

Prospects for the growth of private care insurance are not independent of developments in public sector charging. The challenge, as always, is to try to avoid penalising those who have chosen to make private provision while giving security to those unable to do so. The treatment of housing wealth is likely to remain a contentious area. It too could benefit from a review from first principles, paying attention to fairness between owner occupiers and those who rent their homes.

CHAPTER 10: FINDINGS AND ISSUES

This review has raised a host of different issues. The most important seem to us to be the following:

(a) The views of people on the margins of institutional care and their carers

- although the evidence is clear that ***most older people want to remain in a home of their own*** these findings are based on the current generation of older people and current forms of institutions. In the future more older people may not have families to turn to (e.g. because they have no children), or they may choose to live in an institution because circumstances change (e.g. areas may be perceived as dangerous). ***Much depends on what choice is being offered.*** The Wagner Report (1988) pointed to the need for a 'Positive Choice' and institutional settings may become more like hotels which offer choice and comfort;

- potential *conflicts* between older people and their carers when, for example the older person wants to remain at home and the carer would prefer them to move or *vice versa*;

- how services can best be provided for *older people with dementia* and their carers.

(b) Information

- how older people, their carers and professionals obtain *information about service availability* (both statutory and independent) and *access to help* and social security entitlements;

- how professionals not only obtain information but are able and willing to communicate it.

(c) Assessment

- how needs should be assessed (*preferably a common assessment* for the different kinds of housing and care) and their separation from the costs of meeting those needs, the ability to pay on the one hand, and the ability to provide the service on the other;

- the need for *assessment* before discharge from hospital (a precipitous discharge to an institution without an examination of all the options – both long and short term – may mean that the person never returns home);

- the value of *reassessment* (e.g. after admission to a residential care home where needs may have changed).

(d) Services and how they are provided and organised

- the *availability and appropriateness of care services* as currently constituted; how very dependent older people can be maintained in homes of their own *without their homes becoming like institutions*;

- the *role of different services and professionals* and how they *collaborate*;

- the way *services are organised, particularly primary care* and its potential role in bringing together health and social care;

- the *neglect of housing* and its role in community care at a national, local and individual level;

- the need for *effective rehabilitation* services following an episode of ill health including the role of convalescent facilities;

- the importance of *planning not just for older people but for everyone* (such as by good design of housing and the environment);

- ways in which *quality* (including the reliability) of services, or at least a standard below which services may not fall, can be guaranteed to older people whether they are in their own homes or a communal setting;

- *targeting* services for frail older people *versus the need for preventive services* for other older people;

- the *failure to follow good practice* when this is well known (e.g. over hospital discharge);

- there are specific *issues to do with sheltered and very sheltered housing*: e.g. people may go in because of emotional/psychological problems such as depression. Their health may improve. Is this a positive or negative outcome? Should they then remain there if they have no 'need'?

(e) How services are funded

- *current financial mechanisms* drive services apart rather than together;

- the extent to which policy should focus on making *cash payments to individuals* and encourage them to make their own care arrangements, with the consequent need both for determining entitlement to such cash payments and for regulation of private suppliers.

(f) Lack of knowledge

- the *limits which current knowledge* still places on the extent to which it is possible to identify the circumstances in which providing services in a community setting, even when it is more costly than in a residential setting, is more *cost effective* bearing in mind:

  - the quality of life each delivers; and

  - that for community services, the variation in costs over time for one individual and between individuals is likely to be very much greater in the community than it is in residential settings;

- the *lack of evaluation* of innovatory schemes which are thought to be 'good' but where evidence is lacking;

- *problems in assessing outcomes* of services and interventions. While it is relatively easy to obtain measures which are service based 'and deal with the nature, number and intensity of the components of care packages' it is more difficult to focus 'on the impact of such packages on individuals themselves' (Petch *et al.*, 1996, p. 137). As Baldock has pointed out: 'There are many ways of measuring the benefits of interventions, all of them imperfect; do they prevent entry into institutional care, do they affect the expressed satisfaction of users and carers, do they reduce the chance of falling and other accidents and problems, do they affect measures of depression and anxiety, do they slow the increase in disabilities, and, ultimately, do they extend life?' (Baldock, 1997, p. 87). DoH are currently sponsoring a significant research initiative in this difficult area (DoH, OSCA, 1998).

The review has shown the complexities of provision and funding and the many anomalies that exist. Clear coherent strategies would help, but we would also stress that many older people and their carers have modest requests which would make all the difference in their ability to remain at home. We cite small

adaptations to the home, help with house cleaning and good practice in hospital discharge as examples.

We would also emphasise that, for some people, the kinds of housing and care we have examined may be needed for a short time only. Older people in receipt of very intensive levels of support may not live for very long, or may not need them for many years. In this respect, the long-term costs of disability are rather different from the long-term cost of ageing.

The needs of older people on the margins of institutional care are complex and depend on many different factors. They need advice and support and those who help them make decisions need to be both sensitive and knowledgeable, not only about the services available, but also about their costs. We hope this report will contribute to the Royal Commission's deliberations.

Chapter 1
Introduction and Methods

INTRODUCTION

This report is a review of models of care in the community which are alternatives to institutional care for dependent older people in need of extensive support. It has been undertaken for the *Royal Commission on the Funding of Long-term Care for the Elderly*. The terms of reference for the Royal Commission were: 'to examine the short and long term care for elderly people, both in their own homes and in other settings, and to recommend how, and in what circumstances, the cost of such care can be apportioned between public funds and individuals' (Department of Health (DoH), Press Release, 4.12.97).

Older people generally prefer to remain in their own homes and it is not until a very late age that one in four are living permanently in institutional care (see Chapter 2).

AIMS

The aims of this review were to:

■ examine existing research and practice on alternative models of care for the more dependent older people in the community and at the margins of institutional care;

■ identify particular types of scheme, facility or service that are integral to those models and assess those models in terms of feasibility, acceptability to users and carers, outcomes and costs.

CONTENT AND SCOPE OF THE REVIEW

This was a challenging brief in that there are large numbers of schemes, services and facilities (both in the United Kingdom (UK) and overseas) designed to support older people. The review has concentrated mainly on the UK (but has included interesting developments elsewhere if they were not mirrored in this country), as well as the major literature on alternative models of care. Although in this report some types of services or facilities receive much greater attention than others, the team have reviewed the services in Table 1.1.

Table 1.1: Services and facilities reviewed	
1. Housing-related services and facilities	sheltered and very sheltered housing half-way houses/hostels granny flats shared housing retirement villages adaptations to ordinary housing or improvements to sub-standard housing
2. Services and facilities in the home	intensive home care packages live-in carers neighbour care hospital discharge schemes the use of technology facilities to make an older person safer/more independent
3. Services outside the home	day care night care outside the home adult foster care rehabilitation schemes
4. Services specifically to support family carers	respite care counselling/preparation/relaxation services home sharing support groups

Some community support schemes involved more than one of the services listed above. Attention was paid to collaboration between different kinds of service providers e.g. links between health, housing and social services (see Annex E, Appendices 2 and 3).

METHODS

1. The models

Four alternative models of care in the community were chosen. Three clearly have the potential to keep dependent older people who might otherwise move to institutional care at home; the fourth is currently attracting a good deal of interest:

- intensive home support, where the essence of the model is that people remain at home but with a good deal of care or services coming into the home;

- living with a carer, who will probably (though not necessarily) be a relative, and where 'living with' is interpreted fairly loosely, and so would include arrangements such as 'granny flats';

- very sheltered housing, where the essence of the model is that people live in specialised housing with care services and facilities provided;

- a technological model, where technical support is the focus rather than human care services.

The reality of people's lives is, of course, much less straightforward than a simple model can reflect. There is a good deal of overlap between the four models. Many of the types of services described in the previous section are components of all four models. Certain support services are common such as the need for effective primary health care services (e.g. the General Practitioner (GP) or the community nurse). The restrictions we have had to apply should be carefully noted for the purpose of comparisons between the models. The 'intensive home support' model, for example, has been discussed mainly in connection with people living on their own, whereas in reality intensive home support schemes may be appropriate for those who live with a relative, particularly one who is frail or in employment.

Each model is discussed in terms of:

Feasibility

Important aspects of feasibility include aspects of delivery of the services involved in each of the models such as the collaboration between agencies or of recruiting the staff needed to run them. For example a scheme which cannot recruit sufficient staff to run it is not effective, nor is one in which barriers between organisations make communication difficult. Nor is one which does not take account of the willingness, availability and capacity of carers.

Acceptability

Satisfaction with individual services involved is discussed from the perspective of service recipients, carers and staff. It will include things like the quality and reliability of the service. Satisfaction may be different for recipients and carers; for instance, carers may be enthusiastic about respite care but recipients may dislike leaving home.

Outcomes

The most pertinent outcome is whether a service helps keep people at home. Services that are liked but which do not really make a difference to dependent older people remaining at home cannot be the answer to the problem. But other outcomes such as the restoration of mobility or improvements to the quality of life are relevant.

To enable us to cost the different kinds of care we devised **six vignettes** of older people with different levels of disability, in different environments and living in different models of care.

Costs

Costs for individual schemes and services are included where possible. The following types of costs were calculated where possible for these people:

- The full economic or opportunity cost, i.e. all the economic resources which were used to provide the accommodation and care which could otherwise be put to some other use (land, buildings, labour);

- The public expenditure costs, which may be defined broadly as the difference between the full economic costs and what people pay towards these costs from their private resources. Each component of public expenditure was calculated separately;

- The contribution to these costs made by the older person concerned (which depended on their financial circumstances and eligibility for social security benefits).

Obtaining the views of older people was an important part of the research. Some modest empirical research was undertaken (see section 4). It was not possible in the time available to undertake extensive new research such as a survey of older people in the community at the margins of institutional care and their carers.

2. The team

The research was carried out by a multi-disciplinary team of researchers from the Age Concern Institute of Gerontology (ACIOG), King's College London. All those involved had extensive recent and current experience in relevant research areas.

In addition to the core members of the team others were involved. Dr. Alan Holmans, an economist at the University of Cambridge, was in the lead on the costings and is a co-author of this report. Professor Robin Means (a qualified social worker), Associate Dean (Primary and Community Care), University of the West of England, was asked to bring in his expertise on links between housing, health and social services and on the specific contribution of housing associations. His paper was drawn on for this report and is presented in full (Appendix 3, p. 299). Dr. Alan Turner-Smith, Reader in Rehabilitation and Engineering (a physicist and engineer), and colleagues at the Centre for Rehabilitation and Engineering, King's College London, examined technical aspects of Assistive Technology and also provided a paper (Appendix 4, p. 325) which was drawn on for the report.

3. Sources and data used

Extensive sources of information were used including the Centre for Policy on Ageing (CPA) database (Ageinfo), the King's Fund, Age Concern England's library and cuttings service, libraries at the DoH, the National Institute of Social Work (NISW) and King's College London. Unpublished reports which specifically evaluated schemes were obtained by contacting some providers directly. The Royal Commission provided access to their evidence which included reports and unpublished details of many schemes.

In addition:

- voluntary organisations assisting the research included the Carers National Association (CNA), the Alzheimer's Disease Society (ADS), the Princess Royal Trust for Carers and Age Concern England;

- the Age Concern England Information Service provided data on the sorts of enquiries received on topics relevant to the research and the Policy and Information Teams gave advice about current issues giving rise to concern;

- over 50 University Departments and Research Institutes were contacted to find out about relevant research. Particular attention was paid to the important research undertaken by the Personal Social Services Research Units (PSSRU) at the Universities of Kent, Manchester and the London School of Economics; the Social Policy Research Unit (SPRU), University of York; the Institute of Health, Community Care Division, University of Leeds; the Policy Studies Institute (PSI); and the Nuffield Community Care Unit, University of Leicester.

4. Focus group discussions

To explore older people's and carers' views about alternative models of care in late age, seven focus group discussions were held in April and May 1998 (in Bournemouth, London, St. Neots and Kent). Participants included 44 older people and 24 people currently in a caring situation (Appendix 1, p. 245).

5. Work beyond the scope of this review

In the limited time available it was not possible to undertake:

- cross national comparisons;

- new research (beyond the focus group discussions) into the needs of older people in the community at the margins of institutional care and of their carers;

- networking local authorities (LAs) or National Health Service (NHS) providers;

- a review of the literature on younger people with physical or mental disabilities.

6. Timing

The research started in mid-March 1998 and the report was submitted to the Royal Commission at the beginning of September 1998.

Chapter 2
Staying At Home In Context

INTRODUCTION

Chapters 3-6 examine four models of care which could provide alternatives to institutional care. Dependent older people living in the community but on the margins of institutional care are central to these models. This chapter provides the context for these models by examining:

- the evidence that most older people want to remain in a home of their own;

- the importance of home to older people;

- the likelihood of admission to a care home and the likely numbers of older people in the community at the margins of institutional care;

- the involvement of carers;

- other innovatory developments;

- the principles underlying the models and common components and themes.

EVIDENCE FOR THE VIEW THAT MOST OLDER PEOPLE WANT TO REMAIN IN A HOME OF THEIR OWN

A common finding of research is that older people want to stay in their own home. Before looking at some of these findings it must be recognised that some of these studies are not of people on the margins of institutional care. The large national Department of the Environment (DoE)/DoH study of innovatory schemes to enable older people to remain at home *Staying at Home: Helping Elderly People* concluded 'even if it is not in the best condition, there was little evidence of a desire to move' (Tinker, 1984, p. 118). This was a consistent finding throughout the 1980s. For example older people in very poor private rented housing expressed a similar view (Smith, 1986) as did the very old in a study in Wales (Salvage, 1986). In the latter study of the over 75s most wanted to stay in their own homes and remain independent, over half could not think of any circumstances under which they would consider residential care and the older they were the less likely they were to think of such circumstances.

In the 1990s similar findings have been reported (McCafferty, 1994, Sykes and Leather, 1998). In the DoE research when asked about housing preferences four-fifths of those living in mainstream housing opted for their own home (69% exactly as it was and 15% with minor repairs and adaptations) (McCafferty, 1994). Of the remainder 8% wanted a smaller property, 4% wanted alternative accommodation of the same size, 2% wanted somewhere larger and 1% wanted to live with relatives or friends as part of their household (McCafferty, 1994, p. 96). There was a small but steady increase in proportions wanting to remain in their present homes by the age of the respondent (*Ibid.*). Evidence about the desire to stay put becoming stronger with age is borne out in later research as is the dislike of moving in with friends or relatives (Leather and Sykes, 1996).

Research currently being undertaken in ACIOG on older owner occupiers endorses the wish of older people to remain in their own homes (Askham *et al.*, forthcoming). One of the policy changes which has helped, besides home support, is the increased emphasis on home improvements and adaptations. In particular home improvement agency schemes, where advice and practical assistance is given to householders to repair and maintain the fabric of their homes, have been proved by research to be successful on a satisfaction and cost criteria basis (Mackintosh and Leather, 1993, Mackintosh *et al.*, 1993, Fielder *et al.*, 1994). The title of one study summed up the intention of such schemes *Staying Put – the best move I'll never make* (Randall, 1995) (Tinker, 1997, p. 1865). Home Improvement Agencies are now struggling with rising demand for adaptation and repair and long delays are common (Audit Commission, 1998, p. 28). There is also evidence that there has been a striking reduction in expenditure on renovation grants between 1996 and 1998, that information about housing grants is neither clear nor accessible and that there is great variation between local authorities (see Means 1998, Appendix 3).

Some studies which **have** looked at people on the margins of care – for example Allen *et al.* (1992) – found that those who **would** consider institutional care cited illness or loss of a carer. The majority did want to remain at home.

Ageing in place is being developed across the world in response to a number of factors including the demands of older people (Heumann and Boldy, 1993). One of the key themes is of 'Independent living' which is a term particularly used by the disability movement (see Tinker, 1998, Appendix 2). The concept of 'home' is important (see next section).

There is also evidence that a proportion of older people move to residential care (and to sheltered housing) when they neither need nor want to. For some people staying at home means that they want to remain outside institutional care although they might be prepared, or even want, to move; for others 'home' means their current home and no move would be welcomed. However home may be a prison and staying literally in one's own home may not be the right solution. A move to smaller accommodation to be near relatives or amenities, or to sheltered housing, may be the answer for some. It is also likely that if the alternatives to staying at home were more attractive (e.g. like hotels with choice) many more people might opt for this.

What is difficult to assess, in the absence of research, is whether people want to stay in their own home when they need such intensive care that their homes are a highway for professional staff, or the stress on their carers puts their relationship at risk.

THE IMPORTANCE OF HOME TO OLDER PEOPLE

Recent research endorses the importance of home to older people (Gurney and Means, 1993; Langan *et al.*, 1996). A recent qualitative study of the meaning of home to older people showed its importance in terms of security, refuge, a place where they could express individuality and above all where they could retain control over their lives and not be dependent (Means, 1997, Appendix 3). 'We were struck not only by the modesty of what most of the respondents wanted . . . they included the need for help with housing issues and a major preoccupation with concerns about mobility and transport' (Langan *et al.*, p. 29)

Four focus group discussions held with older people as part of ACIOG's work confirmed the desirability of maintaining a home of one's own (Appendix 1). They considered whether a woman in her eighties with mobility problems and increasing confusion should consider moving from her home to live with her daughter in the same neighbourhood. Group members were unanimous that it was crucial to her well-being to stay in her own place and be in control of what she wanted to do. Members of the three carers' groups had a different perspective. Despite some reservations, many thought that for the older person moving in with a daughter would be preferable to moving to a residential home.

The positive concept of 'home' contrasts with the negative concept of a residential home. Residential care in this country has always been seen as a provision of 'last resort' (Means and Smith, 1985). As Oldman and her colleagues point out, in contrast to many other countries, for example USA, Australia, Germany and Holland, the predominant cultural attitude to residential care in this country is a negative one (1998). A DoH review of research evidence about why people entered care homes concluded that the main message was that most older people, given the choice and the necessary support, would prefer to live in their own homes for as long as possible (Warburton, 1994). If people find it difficult to cope physically or psychologically at home, their views of residential care may be more positive than those of people without those problems. A study of older people with both physical and mental problems and at the margins of residential care in three areas concluded that the idea of residential care was not as abhorrent to them as might have been imagined (Allen *et al.*, 1992). Although 55% said they would not consider it, as many as 33% said they would and 12% were not sure. Nearly 40% of the 85-89-year-old age group said they would consider it. Women were more likely to consider residential care than men.

THE LIKELIHOOD OF ADMISSION TO A CARE HOME AND NUMBERS IN THE COMMUNITY AT THE MARGINS OF INSTITUTIONAL CARE

The likelihood of becoming resident in a long stay residential or nursing home is far greater for women than for men. The life time risk of long-stay entry into a care home based on 1995/6 admission rates for men is 16% at birth rising to 19.6% at the age of 65 (Bebbington *et al.*, 1996). For a woman it is higher with a life time risk of 32.2% at birth rising to 36.4% at age 65. Gender differences in survivorship in the community are well established; 1995 figures show that 29% of men but 43% of women survived to 80 (*Ibid.*, Table 6.1). Women particularly in the 85+ age group predominate in both residential and nursing homes.

Table 2.1: Rates of living in a nursing home/residential home per 1000 population by gender — Great Britain

	Age groups			
	to 74	75-84	85+	Total
Nursing homes				
Men	2.79	12.07	46.05	8.25
Women	3.71	20.71	79.31	18.95
Total	3.30	17.53	71.25	14.67
Residential homes				
Men	6.26	23.03	94.84	16.72
Women	7.15	40.54	166.21	38.33
Total	6.75	34.11	148.77	29.68

Source: 1991 2% Sample of Anonymised Records (SAR)

Women tend to enter care homes at a later stage in the ageing process than men: the men in both residential and nursing care homes are likely to be younger than the women. A further significant gender difference is in marital status. A far higher proportion of the men than the women are single and unmarried (31.4% compared with 21.5%) (Office of Population, Census and Surveys (OPCS), 1993, Table 3). On the other hand, a far higher proportion of the women than the men are widowed (69.0% compared with 41.2%). This gender difference is attributable not only to women living longer than men but also to their propensity to marry men older than themselves. Most married men can expect to be cared for at home by their wives in the last stage of life. Their widows, however, are less likely to have the support of a co-resident carer in the last stage of life and may have to enter a care home to get the care and support needed.

As part of the implementation of the NHS and Community Care Act 1990 DoH commissioned a review of research evidence explaining why some older people enter residential homes while others remain in the community (Warburton, 1994). Its conclusions were that it was a combination of key factors (such as carer circumstances, the carer/dependant relationship and the availability of community based services).

It is not possible to know how many older people currently living in the community are so physically or mentally disabled that they are on the margins of moving into institutional care. Using figures calculated by Nuttall *et al.* (1994) from the mid-1980s OPCS Surveys of Disability, the Joseph Rowntree Foundation

(JRF) Inquiry produced an estimate of roughly 1.5 million people aged 60 or more needing regular or continuous care in 1991 (1996, Table 2). On this basis the number of people in this age group with this level of need would have increased to approximately 2 million by 2011 (*Ibid.*). However, making predictions is hazardous. Changes in medical science could revolutionise the situation. New drugs, for example those affecting the progress of dementia, may have an enormous impact on dependency.

THE INVOLVEMENT OF CARERS

The General Household Survey (GHS) identified carers as 'adults who looked after, or gave special help to, someone in the same household who was sick, handicapped or elderly or who provided some regular service or help to someone who was sick, handicapped or elderly living in a different household'. On this definition the 1995 GHS reported that 13% of adults, approximately 5.7 million people, were carers (Government Statistical Service (GSS), 1998). Co-resident carers constitute approximately 25% of all carers i.e. 1.9 million adults. Carers whether co-resident with, or living in a different household from, a dependent older person are highly important in that person continuing to live at home in the community.

Older people provide much of the care for other older people. A re-analysis of the GHS showed that people aged 65 and over provide 35% of the care for people of that age (Arber and Ginn, 1990).

OTHER INNOVATORY DEVELOPMENTS

Before discussing the models other innovatory developments must not be ignored. For example adult placement schemes, half way houses and shared home arrangements may enable the kinds of older people we are concerned with to obtain enough support to remain outside institutional care (see for example Annex E sections 1C, 2B and 3C).

THE MODELS

1. Underlying principles

Key principles should underline the quality of care in residential homes (CPA, 1996). Similar principles should inform service responses in the community. These should:

- promote independence for the older person;

- promote 'normal' as opposed to 'stigmatised' lifestyle;

- guarantee rights to safety and freedom from exploitation;

- respond to the individual's preferences and choices;

- not 'worsen' an individual's living situation.

2. Common components

If dependent older people are to be retained in the community the four suggested models have to be underpinned by key components.

(a) Health and social care services

(i) Acute health care

Very few people aged 65 and over (less than 1% in the 1991 census) are in hospital at any one time (Tinker, 1996). However, people over the age of 65 account for 60% of all days spent in hospital in the four largest specialties – general medicine, general surgery, trauma and orthopaedics and urology (Audit Commission, 1995). NHS hospitals are crucial in the treatment of older people recovering from acute episodes of ill-health such as a stroke or a broken bone following an accident. The shortness of hospital stays for older people continues to be a matter for widespread concern. The DoH circular *NHS Responsibilities for Meeting Continuing Health Care Needs* (1995) reminded health authorities of the importance of provision for older people who may need a longer period than those who are younger to reach their full potential for recovery and to regain confidence. A recent Health Advisory Service (HAS) report drew attention to the contractual currencies used by purchasers, such as the number of consultant contacts with patients, which appear to have contributed to generating perverse incentives such as over emphasising the importance of speeding the through-put of elderly people in acute wards (1998).

(ii) Hospital discharge

Discharging an older person from hospital before sufficient recovery has been made may well result in the revolving door phenomenon i.e. readmission to hospital at an early date. An answer to a parliamentary question revealed that there are now about 100,000 emergency readmissions to hospital annually of people over 75 within 28 days of discharge (quoted in Harding, 1998). Many older people enter a care home directly from hospital. An Association of Directors of Social Services (ADSS) survey highlighted the growing importance of hospital stays in the process of permanent admission to a care home. In the financial year post-April 1993 45% of long-stay residents had entered care homes straight from hospital whereas in 1992/93 this was the case for only 26% (1994). When older people who have previously been supported at home enter care homes following a hospital discharge, the inevitable question is whether appropriate convalescent facilities or rehabilitation might have enabled them to return home. At one stage there used to be extensive convalescent facilities separate from the main hospital to ease the transition of patients back to the community. Convalescent places, however, have declined sharply. The proportion of nursing homes offering convalescent care has plummeted from 29% in 1989 to only 17% in 1995 (Laing and Buisson, 1997, Table 6.7).

The 1995 circular *NHS Responsibilities for Meeting Continuing Health Care Needs* emphasised that 'the NHS and local authorities have complementary responsibilities for continuing care. Proper arrangements should be in place for hospital discharge and particular care should be taken in cases where the responsibility for care of frail and vulnerable people is being transferred between agencies'. A more recent study has shown some improvements (DoH/SSI, 1998b).

A study of older people leaving hospital concluded that despite all the subsequent guidance given, hospital discharge is not necessarily a well-managed process (Clark *et al.*, 1996). As two Social Services Inspectorate (SSI) inspections of hospital discharge arrangements have shown, in many areas there are concerns about hospital consultants either pre-judging the outcome of assessments or pressing for discharge (DoH/SSI, 1995a; 1995b). A recent Audit Commission study in nine hospitals of the treatment of hip fractures examined the records of 480 patients and drew attention to the variation between them. At one end of the spectrum only about 5% were discharged to a long-stay residential or nursing home (1995, exhibit 3); at the other end of the spectrum, this was the case for almost half of the patients at another hospital. One of the conclusions of this report was that few hospitals generally start discharge planning early enough, resulting in long waits and other problems. The Clinical Standards Advisory Group has recently made recommendations to help overcome these problems (Clark, 1998).

(iii) Rehabilitation

There is widespread concern among doctors, nurses, social workers and others about the shortage of rehabilitative or recovery provision (*Ibid.*). Rehabilitation potentially has an important role to play in the successful return home of an older person once the medical intervention has ended. In evidence to the House of Commons committee the ADSS argued that rehabilitation could create greater independence for older people and reduce the demand for long-term institutional care (House of Commons, 1996, p. 141). In addition the SSI has been encouraging local authorities to consider developing short stay social rehabilitation schemes to enable older people to return to their own homes after a stay in hospital instead of entering long-term care (House of Commons Health Committee, 1995/6 vol. 1, p. xix). Typically such schemes based in adapted residential care homes allow an older person a rehabilitation period of about six weeks after hospital discharge before returning home.

Little guidance based on research, however, is currently available as to the best approaches to rehabilitation (Medical Research Council (MRC), 1994). The MRC itself has called for an evaluation of randomised trials of the effectiveness and cost-effectiveness of whole packages of rehabilitation and of elements within community care packages (*Ibid.*, p. 65).

(iv) Primary health and social care services

Good primary health care is important to maintaining older people with care needs in the community. This includes all those services provided outside hospitals by the family practitioner services (family doctors, dentists, retail pharmacists and opticians) and by the community health services (community nurses, health visitors, occupational therapists, physiotherapists and chiropodists).

Social services departments are equally important. Their role includes developing and implementing community care plans, assessing the needs of users and carers (in conjunction with medical, nursing and other agencies), and designing packages of care in the most cost effective way. There must be concern about the reduction in the number of households receiving home helps (DoH, 1998, p. 2), many problems with home support services (Henwood, 1998) and a lack of appreciation of 'low level' services like housework, laundry etc. (Clark *et al.*, 1998).

(v) Preventive strategies

Preventive strategies, including measures to prolong an active and healthy life, are not the focus of this study but it is important to stress that this is a neglected area. Research indicates the importance older people themselves place on this (Clark *et al.*, 1998; Hanson, 1997).

(b) Appropriate housing

It appears from both empirical research and from expert opinion that housing is neglected in policy, practice and research (see Tinker, 1998, Appendix 2). At a local level there is evidence that community care plans do not always take account of housing and at the individual level housing does not always feature in packages of care for older people. Extensive research (summarised in Tinker, 1998, Appendix 2) shows that inter-agency co-ordination still focuses on health and social care and that there is poor collaboration with housing (Audit Commission, 1998). At a national level there is need for a much stronger national framework. However, the new initiative *Better Government for Older People* has stated that housing will be a priority.

The impact of housing is shown in the clear links with health. Substantial proportions of older people have problems with cold homes, condensation and draughts which can lead to cold related problems. A major contributory cause to accidents, especially falls, is the condition of the home. The consequences of accidents to older people are physical and mental but they may also be a reason for entry into institutional care (Warburton, 1994).

If people are to be enabled to remain in their own homes attention needs to be paid to their design and condition. Older people and those just starting their housing careers are most likely to live in poor conditions (Leather and Morrison, 1997). For those over the age of 75 this is much more likely (*Ibid.*, p. 46). For the *current* generation of older people a high priority should be enabling them to repair and improve their homes. There is now extensive research on how this can be done (see Tinker, 1998, Appendix 2; and Means, 1998, Appendix 3 for details). They include extending the number of home improvement agencies, giving emergency grants and emphasising prevention by persuading owner occupiers that they need to save for repairs. The value of aids and adaptations has been shown and there is need for speed with their provision. Widespread delays are reported by Age Concern England (ACE, 1998). Handypersons' schemes, which assist with small repairs and minor adaptations, have provided a valuable service but are 'unable to meet demand and face an uncertain future whilst mainstream funding is difficult to secure' (Appleton, 1996; and Annex E 1B).

For older people who want to move, ordinary housing, such as a flat or bungalow, may be the right solution. In a recent study one quarter of older households wanted to move, mainly to smaller accommodation (Leather and Sykes, 1996). A bungalow is usually the first choice.

For the *future* generation of older people attention to design is crucial. Many features such as the automatic provision of a downstairs lavatory would help. The widespread provision of 'Lifetime' homes (which incorporate features such as a level or sloping approach to the home and room for a future chair lift) would not only enable people with a range of disabilities to stay there but would enable them to visit friends and relatives (Cobbold, 1997; JRF, 1997). There is also need to take into account the growing number of older people who will be owner occupiers.

The conclusions of research undertaken for the DoH on supporting frail older people at home (see Appendix 2) were that:

- there is need for a higher profile for housing;

- more attention must be devoted to policies which support the growing number of owner occupiers;

- housing must be taken seriously and improving housing conditions seen as part of preventive strategies;

- there must be choice in housing and a recognition that different groups of older people may have different needs;

- older people need advice and support when making decisions about whether to stay in their own home or move;

- there is need for the provision of a full range of different types of housing and for clarity about the role and limits of different kinds of housing/care;

- a co-ordinated approach both at a micro and macro level is essential.

In addition, Age Concern England (1998) argues for some new housing for older people partly to cater for the one million additional pensioner householders expected in the next 20 years and expresses concern at the diminishing amount of social rented accommodation.

Please note that although very sheltered housing has been chosen as one model for an alternative to institutional care, it should be stressed that 90% of older people live in ordinary, mainstream housing and more attention should be paid to this in policy and practice than is currently the case (See Appendices 2 and 3).

3. Common themes in the models

Older people are as diverse and individual as those who are younger. Some have poor and others good health. Some are gregarious and others prefer their own company. Older people have widely different incomes. Some of the wealthiest people in our society are over the age of 65 but many older people have limited income and depend on income support. Ageing is a continuous *process,* not a state. It is marked by discontinuities such as illness or bereavement.

Different people have very different possibilities of support from neighbours or from relatives. When people need support, accessing appropriate help is an important issue. They have to acknowledge to themselves that support is needed. Some people are articulate and well informed and will find out how to get the support needed. Others will need family members or expert help to identify their needs for support and access it.

Older people's needs vary. The kind of help which may be needed, either in the short term (where a temporary problem has occurred) or over the long term (where disability has compromised the individual's capacity for independence), may include:

- help with personal tasks e.g. getting in and out of bed, dressing, bathing, foot care, medication, personal finance, toileting;

- help with domestic tasks e.g. for help with housework, the garden, pets, meal preparation;

- treatment for chronic illness and disability, e.g. medical and nursing services, physiotherapy, continence advice and supplies;

- help with adapting housing, i.e. provision and use of aids and equipment (e.g. Annex E, 1F);

- social contact, support and companionship, e.g. via day care, home visiting

- safety and care, e.g. through community alarms, homeshare arrangements (e.g. Annex E, 2B);

- (where the older person is being helped by a member of the family, other relative or friend) support for the carer, e.g. via respite care, counselling, support groups (e.g. Annex E, 4).

For many of these needs the family will be the main provider. For specialist services such as chiropody the need is likely to be for a professional. A large number of older people make provision themselves by buying services (such as home help) or funding accommodation independently. As a result of the 1990 NHS and Community Care Act, the private sector has become far more important in the provision of care in the community. One of the claims is that private care enables older people to be more in control and to have a greater say in what tasks are done and their timing. But it not known whether this is reality or myth. In many areas of private care such as domiciliary care or chiropody little is known about standards.

SUMMARY

The four alternative models for dependent older people on the margins of institutional care have to be seen in context. This includes the evidence that most older people want to remain in a home of their own and an understanding of what 'home' means. The likelihood of admission to a care home is greater for women, for very old people and for widows. It is usually a combination of factors which leads to admission. Making predictions about the numbers on the margins of institutional care is hazardous.

Crucial to staying at home for many people is the involvement of carers together with the key role of health (acute, hospital discharge arrangements, rehabilitation and primary services) and social care. Prevention is also important. Housing is another key element and one which is neglected as a component of community care at national, local and individual level.

Key principles underlying the models are that they should promote independence, promote a 'normal' as opposed to a stigmatised lifestyle, guarantee rights to safety and freedom from exploitation, respond to the individual's preferences and choices and do not 'worsen' an individual's living situation.

Chapter 3
The Models:
Intensive Home Support

INTRODUCTION

Note

Since the literature in this field is enormous no attempt has been made to be comprehensive. The principles guiding choice of sources have been recent publications until July 1998 and authoritative work, either because of research quality, or because the organisation concerned has expertise about users' experience, about service provision, or about policy implementation.

1. The need for intensive home support

The need for support at home that is intensive arises for a diversity of reasons, both short and long term. In the short term, help may be needed after discharge from hospital or for the treatment of illness, thus avoiding hospital admission. Rehabilitation may require services for rather longer. Chronic physical illness and disability may give rise to a need for help with daily living tasks and activities over the remainder of a person's life. Psychological problems, arising particularly from depression, can have a severe impact on physical health and the ability to cope with ordinary everyday activities. Two studies of inner city populations have found high levels of serious depressive disorder among older people living in the community (Banerjee and Macdonald, 1996; Livingston *et al.*, 1997). The issues raised by dementia underline the fallacy of treating older people as an homogeneous group when considering the appropriateness of different forms of support and help. Dementia gives rise to high levels of need for services on the part of both user and any supportive relative. An early study of user preferences where there was widespread antipathy in general to residential care, found that:

> '*All the family care options with or without professional help receive very little support. In respect of confused elderly persons, there is the strongest evidence of a public preference for service and professional involvement of the most intensive kind.*'
> (West *et al.*, 1984)

The family circumstances of individuals are also very diverse, giving rise to the need for different types and variety of help, in some instances involving a combination of health, social care and housing services, in others one component from one of these. A recipient of home support may be isolated, or may have involved relatives or neighbours. If there is support from others in the community, the need may be for some home support rather than a full package.

2. Relationship of model to schemes

There have been a substantial number of innovatory projects around the country. Successful on-going schemes are invariably due to the commitment and vision of individuals who have managed to cut through many of the barriers which defeat colleagues elsewhere. The following schemes illustrate various aspects of the intensive home support model (details in Annex E, 2A and C).

Intensive home support packages

- Kent (Thanet) Community Care and Related Schemes (experimental Care Management)

- Belfast Intensive Domiciliary Care

- Dementia Home Support Scheme, Ipswich and Newham (experimental)

- Newcastle upon Tyne Care Management for People with Dementia Pilot Study

- Newcastle upon Tyne Dementia Care Initiative Pilot Project

Short-term support

- Wakefield Immediate Support at Home

- Marlow Elderly Persons Integrated Care System (example of an EPICS scheme)

- South Derbyshire Hospital at Home Pilot Schemes

- Gloucester Hospital at Home

Rehabilitation

- Stone Rehabilitation Centre

- Victoria Project: Community Occupational Therapy Rehabilitation Service

3. Variations in social service provision and general problems of unmet needs

The volume of change since the 1990 NHS and Community Care Act has been immense, and it is only in the last two to three years that the organisational and strategic changes envisaged by the reforms have begun to make an impact on the allocation of resources (Davies, 1998). There remain substantial differences between areas in the quantity, range and quality of services delivered, although there is no straightforward relationship between the levels of social deprivation in an area and the provision of services (HAS, 1997; Audit Commission, 1997; 1998). Moreover, there is considerable variation between different agencies and between individual practitioners within authorities, as well as between them. The upshot is that it is extremely difficult to generalise across the whole of the UK.

Although there has been a general trend towards needs-led and more flexible services, this has been compromised by resource constraints (Henwood, 1995). While there is evidence of imaginative and complex packages of care (Henwood, 1995; Johnson, 1995) there is much more evidence of shortages, limited availability, rationing and the absence of the kinds of package of service that would address complex needs. (Henwood, 1995; Johnson, 1995; Langan *et al.*, 1996; House of Commons, 1997; Petch *et al.*, 1997; Phelps, 1997; Hanson, 1997; DoH/SSI, 1997a and 1997b). An Audit Commission/SSI review of Sefton social services found that the authority could only respond to 1 in 19 priority requests from older people and that 291 older people, including 100 in hospital, were waiting for funding to be agreed for either residential or home-based care (Audit Commission/ SSI, October 1997, p. 19). There is evidence that there are still high unmet levels of need for support for dementia sufferers and their carers from nearly all mainstream services particularly home care, day care, respite care, meals, sitter services and GP and consultant services (Philp *et al.*, 1995; Svanberg *et al.*, 1997). Services provided are mostly those provided for older people generally rather than designed for people with dementia (DoH/SSI, 1997a).

Older people with serious mental health problems other than dementia also lack focused support and appropriate housing (Adams and Wilson, 1997; JRF, 1996; Green *et al.*, 1997). Although there are genuine attempts to address the needs of black and ethnic minority elders, the SSI found that choice is limited, that 'the nature of service provision mean that many black elders had difficulty in having their needs met' (DoH/SSI, 1997c, para 2.2).

4. Eligibility for services

Health services are rationed very largely according to need, with ability to pay entering when people have private insurance. The position with social care (and housing) is very different. Services are rationed in relation to ability to pay, savings levels and criteria of need, such as risk to health. These eligibility criteria and the charging policies which accompany them vary considerably between areas (Baldwin and Lunt, 1996; Leicester and Pollock, 1996; HAS, 1997; Laing and Buisson, 1997; Phelps, 1997). Local authorities are setting increasingly stringent eligibility criteria. The criteria may not relate to those set by the local health authority for receipt of continuing care services . Research for the Scottish Office found that 'eligibility criteria operated by service providers created a significant barrier to meeting needs in many cases' (Petch *et al.*, 1996 p. ix). Variations in charging policies mean that 'two people on identical incomes receiving identical services in two different authorities can find themselves facing very different charges' (Phelps, 1997, para 4.8).

Ability to pay is increasingly being taken into account when assessing charges, but treatment of income, including benefit income (e.g. an attendance allowance) and savings varies enormously (Baldwin and Lunt, 1996). Three-quarters of London boroughs now levy a means-tested charge for home care and the number of authorities providing free day care has dropped considerably (Pettit, 1997). Many local authorities set ceilings on the cost of home care packages (Laing and Buisson, 1997; HAS, 1997; *Ibid.*, 1997). One result is that those who might benefit most from a service like respite care are unable to access it, because the costs of their package of care have already reached the allowed limit (see also Chapter 9).

FEASIBILITY OF INTENSIVE HOME SUPPORT

Key issues of feasibility concern information, assessment, management, the input of the key components.

1. Information
Research and policy guidance (DoH, 1994a) emphasises the importance of information about potential support and access. The lack of adequate and important information has been and remains a key criticism of services (Audit Commission, 1994, 1997; Henwood, 1995; 1997; Johnson, 1995; Davis *et al.*, 1997; SSI, 1997b). There is variation between areas (Wooldridge, 1997). The more isolated people are, which may be related to their difficulties or to their geographical location, the less likely they are to hear about services and to know about their own eligibility (Clark *et al.*, 1996; Langan *et al.*, 1996; Hanson, 1997; Henwood, 1997; Johnson, 1995). It cannot be assumed that good leaflets are the answer. Personal contact and help with completing forms may be important.

Some personnel remain particularly important as referral agents. GPs, as well as other members of the primary health care team, because they are most likely to be turned to by people in need, remain, in principle, crucial referrers to all services, but they often lack the appropriate information themselves (Tinker *et al.*, 1993). For older people being discharged from hospital, nursing personnel in the hospital and in the community are crucial.

2. Assessment
Assessment is the key to accessing services. It should establish, for user and carer, the most appropriate way of helping them, and what configuration of service provision is needed. There is widespread recognition across the professions of the necessity of comprehensive, multi-disciplinary, holistic assessment, and its importance in enabling people to stay in their own homes. In practice, assessment has different meanings for health, housing and social services personnel, is invariably neither comprehensive nor multi-disciplinary, is often a 'snapshot' at a moment in time and can be administratively very complex (Bennett *et al.*, 1995; Audit Commission, 1996, 1997; Phelps, 1997; HAS, 1997; Clark *et al.*, 1997).

In a social services context, assessment was intended to be 'needs-led', but in practice, it is closely linked to a purchasing role and therefore to the availability of services and is constrained by eligibility criteria (Johnson, 1995; Petch *et al.*, 1996; Phelps, 1997; Allen *et al.*, undated). Needs that cannot be met may be unrecorded, because otherwise the local authority might be found negligent in meeting statutory responsibilities (Midgley *et al.*, 1997).

Furthermore, although it was envisaged that there should be an ongoing review of a person's needs, and the appropriateness of the services, such practice is at best variable (Petch *et al.*, 1996; HAS, 1997). No health authority, whose documentation was reviewed by the HAS, required re-assessment of older people once they had moved into institutional care (HAS, 1997, para. 290).

Users can find assessment procedures daunting or confusing and in consequence may feel inhibited in articulating their needs. Assessment-related problems are common e.g. inadequate assessments, delays, no account taken of carer needs (Johnson, 1995; Davis *et al.*, 1997; Phelps, 1997). Assessment raises particular issues for older people from ethnic minority groups, whose culture may not be properly understood.

People's home environment must also be appropriate and, therefore, assessment of the home and ability to adapt it if necessary is important. However, assessments invariably fail to take into account housing needs (Arblaster *et al.*, 1996). Comprehensive multi-disciplinary assessments before a client is admitted to any form of long-stay care is essential if misplacements are to be avoided (Bennett *et al.*, 1995). Examination of records of 157 residents admitted since 1993 to 25 nursing homes in three south London boroughs (82% from hospital), however, found that there was no recorded medical information about the patients in 40% of cases, no social work information in 70%, no nursing information in 35%, none on occupational therapy in 93% and none on physiotherapy in 90% of cases. The researchers estimated that 35% of those placed had relatively low care needs and most, with appropriate help, could have been in the community (*Ibid.*).

3. The management and co-ordination of care

Crucial to intensive home support is the need for someone to negotiate and access a complex range of support, notably appropriate care from both health and social services, help with housing issues, eligibility for financial help, and guarantees that help will be reliable. Private agencies are beginning to address such problems, so that individuals with their own funds to pay for care can have a privately funded package organised for them, but these developments are still on a very small scale. The major responsibility remains with the statutory services. The organisational device chosen by government to effect this essential co-ordination and 'packages of services' from a diversity of providers is care management and the main locus of responsibility for this has been given to social services. In the influential experimental projects evaluated by the PSSRU (see Annex E, 2A), care management meant that trained workers, usually based in social services, holding a delegated budget, arranged and purchased services for people with complex needs living in their own homes. In practice the meaning given to the term care management has been varied and confusing. 'Rarely, it could be suggested, has there been an area of government policy in which, despite the extent of guidance documents, the detail of implementation has led to such divergent interpretation' (Petch *et al.*, 1996 p. 124).

Despite repeated policy advice, and the introduction of care management, the goal of 'seamless care' appears ever harder to achieve. Collaboration and co-operation have become more, rather than less, difficult, due to the purchaser/provider split, to local government reorganisation and to changing boundaries over long-term care (Goss, 1996; Henwood *et al.*, 1996; HAS, 1997;). Undoubtedly there are examples of collaborative working, and of some highly successful schemes, but these are despite, rather than because of, the changes. The divisions between health and social care, which not only relate to structures and finance but also to different professional perspectives, continue to have a pervasive effect on the delivery of intensive home support. Three way links between health, social services and housing are comparatively unusual (Arblaster *et al.*, 1996). Perhaps this is not surprising when considering the complexity of the relationships unless handled at a very local level (Goss, 1996).

Three areas in particular relate to the boundaries of health and social care. (Henwood *et al.*, 1996). First is the responsibility, both financial and professional for the continuing long-term care of older people. Existing arrangements promote rivalry and the shunting of responsibility between services. Second, and related, is the issue of hospital discharge. Hospital staff are under incentives to discharge patients but the home support required to make this viable may be lacking, and this may relate to housing or social care or primary health care provision. Third, there is a changing divide between community nursing and home care, which has meant a reduction in routine domestic work like cleaning as home carers take on more personal care tasks which might previously have been undertaken by nurses. One consequence has been a withdrawal of domestic cleaning help. As the focus groups with older people run by ACIOG illustrated, a refusal to assist very frail people with essential cleaning is a source of some anger and resentment. Overall, the result of these difficulties is a general lack of co-ordination and communication between services except where some brave individuals, are determined to cut through the structure of different roles and responsibilities (Henwood, 1995; Arblaster *et al.*, 1996; House of Commons, 1996; Audit Commission, 1997; Hanson, 1997; HAS, 1997; Svanberg *et al.*, 1998). The importance of multi-disciplinary training in contributing to improved co-ordination has been stressed (HAS, 1997; Stout and Orr, 1997).

4. The input of key service components

Many kinds of home support can be delivered to older people. In practice, home care (i.e. domestic and personal help) is usually an essential component. Some of the key contributory services, in addition to home care, are nursing, psychiatric nursing, a range of therapies, chiropody, meals provision, sitting services, both day and night, shopping, community alarm provision and day care. In practice, all home support depends on people having appropriate housing in relation to their health and dependency (Audit Commission, 1998). Housing is discussed in detail (see Appendices 2 and 3).

Of particular relevance are home care, health services, housing and day care.

(a) Home care

Home care, that is help with domestic and personal needs, is widely viewed as the backbone of the Intensive Home Support model. An inspection of services for people with dementia at home in the community (in eight areas) found that 'the home care services were of vital importance to service users and their carers and perhaps the most important and significant support many received' (DoH/SSI, 1997a p. 9).

An 'intensive' home care service is judged by the DoH to mean more than five contact hours and six or more visits weekly and in the Audit Commission/SSI reviews to mean seven hours of home care a week (Audit Commission/ SSI, 1997, p. 27). The average number of hours varies by provider with the private sector providing an average 8 hours a week (Laing and Buisson, 1997). The Association of Directors of Social Work in Scotland described the home help services as still 'typically non-intensive' (House of Commons, 1997). Their survey showed that less than 10% of people supported by local authority home helps received 10 or more hours assistance a week (House of Commons, 1997).

Henwood (1997) suggests there are 'major weaknesses' in home care services relating both to the nature of the service, and to the commissioning, organisation and delivery of such services. These may relate to the absence of communication between staff, the irregularity of visits, the appropriateness of the timing of visits for instance in getting people up, or helping them to bed and the referral of people to other sources of support. There is evidence of lack of reliability of provision (Henwood, 1995, 1997; DoH/SSI, 1997b; Audit Commission, 1997), of use of casual staff to cover gaps (Audit Commission/ SSI, review of London Borough of Barnet, 1998) and of occasional chaos:

'extreme examples were encountered of elderly people receiving home visits from the staff of several agencies each day, with the result that the user was bewildered by the numbers of people involved. In some cases they felt exposed to the risks of insecurity.'
(HAS, 1997, para. 217)

Although the SSI inspection of services for older people with dementia found that home care provided by the independent sector led to more choice and flexibility, there were concerns about standards, reliability, and the problems arising when users had home care from more than one source (DoH/SSI, 1997a).

Local authorities are increasingly concentrating home care on those who are most dependent (Laing and Buisson, 1997) in line with the policy of targeting services effectively. However, many commentators have pointed out that there is a conflict between targeting 'intensive' services on very dependent older people and a preventative strategy (House of Commons Health Committee, 1996; Henwood, 1997; Nocon *et al.*, 1997; Pettitt, 1997; Phelps, 1997). Prevention is seen as a core responsibility and key function of home care support. Smale and colleagues (1994) (also Clark *et al.*, 1998)argued that 'a little help to many people in need is of enormous significance, be they individuals living at home or carers struggling to maintain others in the community. It is vital that resources are targeted on these people if the reforms are going to fulfil their aim' (Smale *et al.*, p. 5).

There are important questions about whether home care, with its current focus on tasks and activity, is the most appropriate service for intensive support in people's own homes. Sheffield experimented with a 'community support worker' whose work covered a much wider range of activities than traditional home care (Walker and Warren, 1996). Some of the schemes illustrated in Annex E indicate that the role often needs to be that of a substitute family carer and that a complete rethink of the role may be needed.

(b) Health services input to intensive home support

For older people being discharged from hospital, or those remaining at home with some chronic illness or disability, the health service input, particularly the contribution of community (including psychiatric) nursing staff and therapists, may need to be much stronger. Scottish Office research into the implementation of care management in four Scottish regions (including care for younger disabled people) found that:

> '*the role of health and housing agencies was decisive in a number of cases, limiting the potential for co-ordination by social work practitioner. Practitioners were on occasion able to engage constructively with GPs, but the strict rationing of nursing services caused serious difficulties and led to some admissions to nursing homes.*'
> (Petch *et al.*, 1996 p. ix)

Bathing presents services with a particularly sensitive and challenging area as people may be very uneasy about who helps them with such an intimate area of care (Twigg, 1997). A survey of 25 users unable to bathe without help reported that only one received a bathing service from a district nurse and three had a 'wash-down' from home-carers (Johnson, 1995). A bathing service is unavailable to many individuals in need of such help. Although seven had applied for walk-in showers only one had been fitted five months after assessment (*Ibid.*, 1995).

Hospital discharge schemes are important for older people successfully returning home from hospital. Hospitalisation is a turning point in the lives of many older people. Many very old people are discharged not to their own homes but to residential or nursing home care. There are concerns that people many be being discharged to care homes when they could return to their own homes. As two Social Service Inspectorate inspections of hospital discharge arrangements have shown, in many areas there are concerns about hospital consultants either pre-judging the outcome of assessments or pressurising for discharge (DoH/SSI, 1995a; 1996b).

When older people are discharged from hospital their care is transferred from a hospital setting to the community. In the community the responsibility for supporting newly discharged older patients lies with social services and the primary health care team. Particular importance has been attached to developing effective hospital discharge procedures between social service departments, health authorities and hospitals under the 1990 NHS Community Care Act. The 1995 circular *NHS Responsibilities for Meeting Continuing Health Care Need* reminded authorities of the importance of provision for older people who may need a longer period to reach their full potential for recovery and to regain confidence. It also emphasised that the NHS and local authorities have complementary responsibilities for continuing care. Proper arrangements should be in place for hospital discharge and particular care should be taken in cases where the responsibility for care of frail and vulnerable people is being transferred between agencies (DoH, 1994c). Research carried out by the Nuffield Institute of Health however, describes absence of planning and development between health and social services at national and local levels (Henwood *et al.*, 1996). Hospital discharge remains an area of increasing concern.

Although the importance of chiropody services in helping people maintain their mobility has been stressed (DoH, 1994b), services have been rationed and cut (Salvage, 1998).

Although rehabilitation is recognised as an essential component of provision, however attention has increasingly been drawn to the shortcomings of current services (Medical Research Council, 1994; HAS, 1997; Robinson and Turnock, 1998; Nocon and Baldwin, 1998).

(c) Housing

There are particular delays and shortages in the provision of housing aids and adaptations (DoE, 1996; Laing and Buisson, 1997; Phelps, 1997). The role of occupational therapists (OTs) in assessment is a crucial one, and has particular bearing on housing adaptations and on the need for aids and equipment, but OTs are in short supply (Clark *et al.,* 1996; Laing and Buisson, 1997; HAS, 1997; DoH/SSI, 1997b;) (see Chapter 2). Changes recommended in 1989 by the Blom-Cooper report to shift the balance of the OT service from secondary to primary care have not taken place (Blom-Cooper, 1989).

(d) Day care

The chance of being offered a day care place is far greater in some areas than in others. Wide differences exist between areas in the availability of local authority provided or purchased day care. There is particularly a shortage of day care places in rural areas. Day care requires first of all a willing attender, and not all older people will want to leave their home and attend a day centre or day hospital. The provision also needs to be appropriate to their needs, particularly where dementia is concerned and needs to be available regularly. Transport is critical to day care provision, since inadequate arrangements can undermine the value of services (Audit Commission/ SSI, 1997) or prevent take-up of day care places (Johnson, 1995). Generally, the amount of day care any one individual receives is limited. A study of respite care for all types for confused elderly people in three areas reported that in one area the average amount of day care was only for one day and in the other two areas, for two days (Levin *et al.*, 1994). A review of the literature on day care for adults (Brearley and Mandelstam, 1992) concluded that day care:

- had developed in a piecemeal fashion;

- was not adequately integrated into coherent local planning between agencies;

- did not reach those most in need;

- had not been exploited to the extent of its potential.

ACCEPTABILITY OF INTENSIVE HOME SUPPORT

There are different criteria of acceptability: how people come to get support in the first place, what they get, quality of staff, reliability of service, costs and how they are met. People's responses vary according to the criterion. Many surveys report considerable satisfaction by users with the actual services they receive (Johnson, 1995; Thomas, 1995; Walker and Warren, 1996; DoH/SSI, 1997b, appendix C; Henwood *et al.*, 1998). Virtually all respondents (95%) in a survey by the SSI in nine areas said that care workers showed respect for the person and their home (DoH/SSI, 1997b, appendix C; Audit Commission/SSI Reviews, 1997; 1998). In the same survey, 76% of respondents said that the care or services provided were the ones they really needed and were of most help. Almost all (93%) had help on the days most helpful to them and 80% at the times most convenient. An SSI report on services for older people with dementia living at home in eight areas (50 cases in each area) found that carers were almost universal in their praise for services and for staff (DoH/SSI, 1997a p. 3).

However, older people are often grateful for what they receive, and there is some scepticism about the accuracy of results from questionnaires, as opposed to more detailed studies of consumer reactions (Reed and Gilleard, 1995; Johnson, 1995). Anchor research into their Home Support Services found that many older people found it difficult to express their views (Quilgars *et al.*, 1997). Research by Age Concern Scotland stressed:

> '*gallantry in the face of severe problems . . . the question of shortage of resources comes out again and again in the interviews . . . I became aware – although nobody complained and I asked no questions about it – that some people who were not mobile had to sit for long hours before anyone would come and accompany them to the toilet.*'
> (Thomas, 1995, pp. 7, 9)

Research with older users of domiciliary care services, including those receiving intensive care packages, indicated the importance of the quality of relationship between users and home care staff. This is borne out in the schemes outlined in Annex E. Important aspects of this were flexibility, reliability, competence, good interpersonal skills and continuity. Criticisms related to the absence of these factors (Henwood *et al.*, 1998). Staff are also often pressed for time (Thomas, 1995; Walker and Warren, 1996; Quilgars *et al.*, 1997). 'Virtually all service users and carers remarked on the intense time pressure on care workers' (Henwood *et al.*, 1998, p. 7).

The following examples stand in contrast to one another:

> '*The quality of the relationship between service users and their home carers is especially important, and is one reason why continuity is valued highly. Many of the service users to whom we spoke praised their home carers, and described them in glowing terms. Many clearly regarded them as friends, and eagerly awaited their visits.*'
> (Henwood *et al.*, 1998)

> '*Local authorities are starting to purchase homecare on the basis of tasks performed rather than time spent caring. An example is bathing and toileting consumers; instead of a single carer calling, a team of three carers might visit. This makes the whole process easier and faster, and sometimes safer for consumer and carer, particularly for tasks involving lifting. Local authorities know that the necessary tasks are being done, and they are not paying for cares to stay around longer than is necessary.*'
> (Laing and Buisson, 1997, p. 20).

Issues of charging and people's attitudes to means testing and to receiving financial help from charitable sources may also influence the acceptability of intensive home care.

Research in Leeds found that day care was particularly valued by elders from minority ethnic communities and that it provided a crucial route for accessing other services (Johnson, 1995). It appears also that older people value preventive and rehabilitative services (Hanson, 1997).

OUTCOMES OF INTENSIVE HOME SUPPORT

Outcomes relate to different aspects of the intensive home support – assessment, services provided, quality of services, reliability etc., ongoing appropriateness and so on. Measurement is intrinsically difficult. Outcomes may be satisfactory in one respect and unsatisfactory in others. At one level, the key questions are whether people are enabled to stay in their own homes or return home from hospital. At another the concern must be with the resources that are needed – and their alternative use – in securing a particular outcome. At a third, the crucial measures relate to their experience of the service, and how it affects them. The PSSRU experimental projects (see Annex E) measured levels of depression, dissatisfaction, felt ability to cope, morale, social activity, ability to manage basic tasks and reduction of need for basic services in these projects. The impact of focused intervention in the form of care management was highly positive for the older people for whom this approach was selected. However, it has been subsequently stressed by the researchers that these older people were not actually at the point of entry to residential care, and it may be important to bear this in mind when considering other research. The presence or absence of dementia is important. Scottish research indicated less favourable outcomes than the PSSRU schemes and ascribed this to the fact that 'the users with dementia were no longer on the margins of insitutional care but in urgent need of it' (Bland, 1996, p. 68).

The components of intensive home support are a mixture of goods and services. Some, for example most aids and adaptations, are straightforward consumer goods which can be allocated accurately according to the needs of older people. Outcome, in terms of whether people use the aid, whether they like it or not, whether it enables them to have a bath, or cook a meal, or get up the stairs, is fairly straightforward. The 'people-care' aspects of the package are however very different and vastly more complex (Baldock, 1997). The ways in which services are delivered affect outcomes (Nocon *et al.*, 1997; Henwood *et al.*, 1998). How personal care is experienced depends not only on the quality and capacity of the person delivering the service, but also on how the user – and the carer, if there is one – respond. 'User' responses vary with individual quirks and preferences, which are very diverse, with caring situations, also very diverse, and with changes which are occurring through time, as the health and disability, both mental and physical, of both 'user' and 'carer', wax and wane. They are also related to wider aspects of community life, particularly aspects of neighbourhood amenity such as access to shops and community safety (Tinker *et al.*, 1994; Blunden, 1998). The consequence is that:

> '*Individual differences, varying from person to person and across time and place, will powerfully affect the outcome and therefore the value and success of the intervention . . . Many years of research designed to test "the limits of home care" have failed to discover user characteristics or service inputs that explain long-term success or failure in home care . . . This is partly because the degree to which an old person, and sometimes the carer, are committed to staying at home swamps all other variables . . . it is their unique set of preferences that often explains (home care) success or failure, and the particular characteristics of the intervention are much less important.'*
> (Baldock, 1997, p. 23)

Research is consistent in concluding that 'personal relationships are more significant indicators of the need for services than individual characteristics'

(Smale *et al.*, 1994). The Scottish Office research (Petch *et al.*, 1996) concluded that high risk and the inability of carers to continue caring were closely associated both with practitioner recommendations for residential placement and with subsequent admission. Service response was strongly influenced by factors out of the practitioners' control, in particular by the role of informal carer's role, the preferences of users and the actions of other agencies.

The Scottish research compared 144 older people receiving home care packages with an earlier group of 726 older people receiving home care in 1990-92. The more recent group were older, less likely to have a principal carer and more likely to have a carer who needed regular/permanent support. They were very much more likely to have 'complex needs' i.e. needs in more than one area (daily living, personal, material, at risk, carer needs support). When these different aspects of need were specifically compared, the earlier sample contained 'comfortably higher proportions of people maintained in the community' (Petch *et al.*, 1996, p. 116). However, these results suggest fairly conclusively that those older people who had considerable needs were receiving more services. When the two groups were compared according to the different need criteria and the services they received, the earlier group contained large proportions who either received a domiciliary (i.e. home help) service only, or no service at all. The proportions receiving three or more separate services rose as follows (Petch *et al.*, 1996, Table 7.3):

Table 3.1: Percentages of older people receiving three or more services at home. Scotland, 4 regions. 1990-92 and 1994				
Type of need	**1990-92**		**1994**	
	%	**n**	**%**	**n**
'complex'	22	59	59	27
high carer support	19	116	47	36
assessed at high risk	20	78	67	18
'personal'	18	321	51	53

Petch and colleagues concluded that 'definitive answers to the central question of whether the care management approach succeeded in maintaining people in the community to a greater degree than pre-implementation practice must be qualified' (*Ibid.*, p. 118). They did not find an overall tendency for more people with the higher levels or ranges of need to be supported at home. Their conclusion was that those in particularly vulnerable groups who were enabled to remain at home were provided with significantly more by way of support services than in the past (*Ibid.*).

A recently reported piece of research in Northern Italy (Bernabei *et al.*, 1998) showed fairly conclusively that it was not the package of services themselves but co-ordination, through integrated health and social care management, that reduced admission to institutions, particularly hospitals, and had an impact on both physical and cognitive functioning. The substantially lower rate of admission to hospital (including accident and emergency departments) resulted in substantial cost savings. Significantly this model of care management involved:

■ intensive training for care managers in care management and geriatric assessment skills;

- use of community geriatric evaluation unit as gatekeeper to health services;

- the role of the care managers was to support and integrate the activity of GPs.

The evidence reviewed for the UK suggests that it is the above three conditions that were responsible for the very positive outcomes reported, and that the conclusion for Northern Italy would also hold for the UK. 'The close collaboration between case managers, community geriatric evaluation unit, and general practitioners was critical to the success of the intervention; this may determine the effectiveness of any community based programmes' (Bernabei *et al.*, 1998, p. 1350).

COSTS OF INTENSIVE HOME SUPPORT

Costs, in terms of expenditure per person on services enabling them to stay in their own home, are immensely variable, depending on area, purchaser, provider, volume of service, type of service as well as the needs of the older person. The only research available that examines costs in relation to medical/social characteristics suggests that dementia, activity limitation, increasing age, living alone and depression are key factors in increasing costs (Livingston *et al.*, 1997).

The same expenditure may purchase very different standards (quality) of care. Costs are not independent of quality but nor are they necessarily positively related. Laing and Buisson (1997) point out that local authority provision is more expensive than independent sector provision, partly because 'the terms and conditions on which in-house staff are employed are more generous' (p. 4). Some care managers thought that low pay, lack of employment benefits and security were linked to lack of training and high turnover of independent sector staff (Leat and Perkins, 1998). Anchor Home Support, with costs at the 'top end' of the price range, have tried to reduce costs but research for them concluded that good quality services, delivered by a properly trained, supported and reasonably remunerated staff team would deliver extra benefits to users (Quilgars *et al.*, 1997).

While undoubtedly it was thought in the early days that it would be less expensive to keep someone in their own home with intensive support, and staying at home was what most people wanted, clearly much depends both on the type and extent of care needed and supplied. While it can be a great deal more expensive for some users to remain in their own home, this may well vary over time, and for other users it may be cheaper. **From the point of view of public spending, the overall picture needs to be looked at.**

Care management costs rise with the number of personnel involved in assessment and tend to fall over time (i.e. the longer the 'package' is in place, the lower these costs. (Davies *et al.*, 1995). Expensive packages may be set up only to be made redundant or irrelevant by changes in people's circumstances or preferences (Baldock, 1997). The Scottish Office research (Petch *et al.*, 1996) found no association between the costs of assessment and subsequent costs of home support. Costs were significantly greater for women than men, and for people who died within nine months of assessment, but this included users other than older people. There was considerable variation between the four regions studied.

Accommodation dominated costs, ranging from an average of £144 in one region to £285 in another over a nine-month period. Domiciliary care was the only other significant component in the care, costs ranged from an average of £69 a week in one region to £20 in another. The average amount attributable to services like day care, respite, out-patient care and aids and adaptations was low, ranging from an average of £26 to £4 for day care, and £18 to £2 for respite. Over the nine-month period total costs ranged from £1,747 to £39,686 with a mean of £10,455 (*Ibid.*).

SUMMARY

Intensive home support at its best can deliver care to the standard of the 'best relatives' and enables people, if they so wish, to continue to live as normal a life as possible in their own home. Experimental projects cited in Annex E show just how effective and successful this approach can be.

However, for it to work as a national norm, a great many pieces have to fall into place – the adequacy of people's housing, information, comprehensive assessments, access to a wide range of services, co-ordination of these services, availability, affordability, appropriateness, reliability, continuity, and quality of support. These are strenuous requirements when viewed against service divisions, resource constraints, funding differentials and local diversity of standards and social conditions. They are examined further below.

Housing has to be given attention, not as a specialist provision, but simply as being suitable in terms of adaptability and warmth to the needs of older people. Episodes of illness or accidents, as well as long-term disability, have to be addressed through health services, and particularly rehabilitation, in a way that links them to other forms of support in the home. The Elderly People's Integrated Care System (EPICS) scheme and other similar initiatives quoted in Annex E show how this is practicable and feasible if certain conditions are met.

People have to be able to access services and this in itself creates a need for an infrastructure of advice and information services. Currently, the NHS is the first port-of-call and the principal provider for most people for health care in later, as in earlier, life. But social services are effectively residual, available to those unable to access private help with private means. This hampers substantially the integration of services, already divided by professional and cultural factors.

Care management is a method for trying to provide this integrating function when intensive support is needed, and in the experimental projects evaluated for the DoH, some impressive results were shown. It is early days to be too judgmental about the policy, but the evidence points to considerable confusion. Projects which target resources in a very focused way at particular individuals in need, as in some of the schemes outlined in Annex E, do not represent the everyday realities of life in the services addressing the needs of older people.

When people are on the margins of residential care, they need services more or less immediately if they are to be able to return to, or remain in, their own home. Ready availability of appropriate services – which in turn requires appropriate assessment – is therefore essential. Currently, the national picture is that there are widespread shortages of all kinds of services, including assessments. Rationing services by targeting them at those most in need risks leaving those with less complex needs without help at all, which may be short-sighted. Concentrating support on those who are living on their own can place intolerable strains on caregivers.

Despite the resource shortages, there are illustrations of outstanding practice around the country. Some of these, such as the projects to help people with dementia remain in their own home, are outlined in Annex E. Good professional practice does not seem to relate to the social conditions of an area. In this model, as in all settings, the crucial if obvious element is the quality of the people who manage and deliver the service. Older people are notoriously grateful for the services that they do receive, but they place significant importance on their relationships with staff, along with the reliability and adaptability of the service to fit their particular needs.

It is important to recognise that the costs of intensive home support will be very variable between different users and that any individual may have very varying needs over a period of time. The greater their dependency, the higher the costs of providing support, whether these fall on formal services or family carers.

Key conditions for the intensive home support model to work:

- integration of health, social care and housing services;

- communication and co-ordination between service providers;

- comprehensive assessment;

- the need for *someone* to have a co-ordinating role;

- quality of staff and relationship with users/carers;

- flexible, reliable services;

- continuity of services;

- addressing the specific needs of dementia sufferers and their carers.

Chapter 4

The Models:
Co-Resident Care

INTRODUCTION

1. Overview

The model described in this chapter is co-resident caring i.e. a co-resident carer who may, or may not, be supported by health and social services. Carers (for definition see Chapter 2) are an important resource for maintaining dependent older people in the community. The majority of those with support from a carer are older people. The 1995 GHS shows that over half (54%) of those being cared for by someone in the same household and 85% of those cared for by someone in a different household were aged 65 or over (Rowlands, 1998, Table 15). Women are more likely to be carers than men but the difference is not great, 14% compared with 11%. As there are more women than men in the population, the total number is higher 3.3 million female carers compared with 2.4 million male carers. Co-resident carers constitute approximately 25% of adult carers i.e. 1.9 million people. Middle age, is the peak age for caring responsibilities and 20% of adults aged 45-64 are in this situation. Older people themselves provide much of the care for older people. The 1995 GHS survey showed that 13% of people aged 65 and over were carers. A re-analysis of the 1985 GHS showed that if co-resident and non-resident caring are considered together, people aged 65 and over provide 35% of the care to people of that age. (Arber and Ginn, 1991).

Older people who are married or cohabiting are far more likely to be carers than those who are single or widowed. Although co-resident caring may occur within a wide variety of relationships (Table 4.1) a high proportion (52%) occur in households containing a married or cohabiting couple. One of the most striking changes between the 1990 and the 1995 GHS in Great Britain (GB) was an increase of 11% in the proportion of co-resident carers looking after a spouse. Just over a fifth of co-resident carers look after a parent or parent-in-law and a similar proportion care for children. Granny flats are one way in which an older person with needs for support may live in a self-contained home adjacent to the family home. The idea is that the older person would be able to give and to receive help from their family next door. There is an absence of recent research on granny flats. An evaluation of local authority schemes showed certain problems of flexibility if the family moved or the grandparent died (Tinker, 1976). Private schemes have become increasingly popular as families see advantages in having grandparents next door (Tinker, 1996).

Main dependant's relationship to carer	Carer with main dependant:			
	in same household %		in another household %	
	1990	1995	1990	1995
Spouse	41	52	0	1
Child under 16	8	14	0	0
Child 16 and over	10	8	1	2
Parent	23	17	39	43
Parent-in-law	6	5	15	12
Other relative	10	4	20	20
Friend/neighbour	2	1	25	22

Table 4.1: Dependant's relationship to the carer by whether main dependant lived in the carer's household GHS, 1990, 1995 Great Britain

Source: Rowlands (1998) *Informal Carers*. Office for National Statistics (ONS), Table 14.

Although studies on both sides of the Atlantic have drawn attention to the role of older spouses in providing care (Soldo and Myllyluoma, 1983; Fisher, 1994; Wright, 1995; 1998) they have not received the same research attention as daughters in a caring role. Nevertheless as Parker points out spouses whether wives or husbands are increasingly the carers of first resort (Parker, 1996). Spouses often care for partners with a severe disability. Arber and Ginn, for example, in a re-analysis of the 1985 GHS in the UK calculated that elderly spouses provided care for 51% of severely disabled elderly people in the country as a whole (Arber and Ginn, 1991). Elderly spouses provide much of the care for dementia sufferers in the community. A NISW study of confused older people living in three areas reported that 41% were cared for by a husband or wife (Levin *et al.*, 1989).

Spouse carers are more likely than other types of carers to experience what Parker has described as role overload (Parker, 1996). A spouse carer is likely to have to take on a partner's previous responsibilities. Wives have to take on household maintenance tasks and husbands cooking and other domestic tasks. Studies of caregiving by adult children and spouses, on both sides of the Atlantic, confirm that people supported by a spouse before finally being admitted to a care home reach greater dependency level than those supported by a daughter or son (Wenger, 1984; Wright, 1998).

2. Differences between co-resident and non-resident caring

Many similarities exist between non-resident caring and co-resident caring. But significant differences also exist (Table 4.2). Co-resident carers are far more likely than non-resident carers to be the sole or main carer, to spend 20 hours or more in caring activities (the level generally seen as a significant level of caring involvement), to look after a dependent person with both physical and mental problems, to give personal care and physical help, to give medicines and to look after the dependant's paperwork or financial affairs.

Table 4.2: Significant differences between a co-resident carer and a carer in a different household: for dependants of all ages GHS 1995 Great Britain	
Co-resident carer	**Carer in a different household**
63% spend 20 + hours per week in caring activities	13% spend 20 + hours per week in caring activities
29% with a main dependant having both physical and mental problems	18% with a main dependant having both physical and mental problems
59% give personal care	14% give personal care
58% give physical help	24% give physical help
48% give medicines	16% give medicines

Source: Rowlands (1998), Tables 20 and 21.

3. Relationship of models to schemes

Many of the schemes described in Annex E help support co-resident carers. These include day care (3A), night care (3B), night sitting (2F), counselling/ preparation/ relaxation services (4B) and support groups (4C)

FEASIBILITY OF CO-RESIDENT CARE

1. Capacity to care

The model of co-resident care supported by appropriate health and social services is predicated by a supply of willing carers. Future levels of informal care will be the result of factors such as divorce, mobility of family members and women's employment which are difficult to predict with any precision.

(a) Willingness to care

Social policy changes such as those in the criteria of eligibility for social security benefits may also affect the willingness of people to provide support. Much of the literature on carers emphasises negative aspects of the role. Many carers, however, positively want to provide care. As a SSI report on local authority support for carers commented:

'We were struck by the tremendous caring responsibilities being undertaken by them. Often this stress was unrecognised by carers themselves, the majority of whom did not want this responsibility to be taken away but only to receive more support so they could continue. Many saw what they were doing as an expression of love for the person they cared for and as a natural development of that relationship.'
(DoH/SSI, 1995c, p. 2)

Positive reasons for providing care appear in the wide ranging literature (Askham and Thompson, 1989; Clifford, 1990; Nolan *et al.*, 1996; Levin *et al.*, 1989; 1994; Twigg and Atkin 1994).

Positive reasons for caregiving:

- Love

- Reciprocity for cared-for person's past actions

- Belief that only the carer will give the best possible care

- Sense of achievement

- Doing one's duty

- Appreciation by the dependent person or by others

- Desire to keep the cared-for person out of institutional care

- Desire to keep a married couple living together in the same household (spouses)

Several aspects of personal care for the cared-for person are likely to be problematic for both adult children and spouse caregivers. A qualitative study of caring and disability in marriage when couples were below the age of retirement reported that, despite the intimacy of marriage, both spouses commonly reported distress at one partner's assistance being needed with intimate tasks (Parker, 1993). Having to give or receive personal care could interfere with other aspects of their relationship particularly sexual activity. Bathing or showering, using the toilet, dressing or undressing are all areas of personal care which the cared-for person and the carer may prefer the involvement of a paid worker.

(b) Physical health of carers

As we have seen spouse caregivers are often themselves in their seventies and eighties and many co-resident daughters and sons are either middle-aged or above retirement age. Generally there is an increase in reported ill-health for people in the older age groups. Not only are caregivers as prone to ill health as their peers, the stresses of caregiving may cause or exacerbate illness. Not surprisingly both local and national studies confirm that a high proportion of caregivers in the older age groups are in poor health (Wright, 1986; Green, 1988; Wenger, 1990). In addition there is clear evidence of injury resulting from caregiving. In-depth interviews with 41 carers of people admitted to a regular hospital respite care scheme found that no less than 31 of them had sustained injuries while handling and lifting the cared-for person (Brown and Mulley, 1997). Most had sustained back injuries. In addition, 16 of the people being cared for had been injured while being handled by the carer.

(c) Stress of caring

A wide literature from both sides of the Atlantic indicates that many family caregivers whether co-resident or living in a separate household from the cared-for person suffer both psychological and physical stress as a result of providing support and care in a domestic setting (Nolan *et al.*, 1996; Quereshi and Walker, 1989; Zarit and Toseland, 1989; Twigg *et al.*, 1990; Wright, 1986). A relationship is apparent between the length of time spent caring and stress (Levin *et al.* 1989; 1994). Another relationship is between the gender: of the caregiver and stress levels; female caregivers are likely to have higher levels of stress than male caregivers (*Ibid.*). Although the explanation for such gender differences may lie partly in the stress measures used; significant gender differences in approaches to caregiving are apparent. Although female caregivers are less likely than men to have support services such as home care (Parker and Lawton, 1994) they may be less willing to seek, or to accept, them. Twigg and Atkin report evidence suggesting that men and women have different approaches to caregiving (1994). Men appear to find it easier to separate themselves from the caring role, to set limits on their involvement and to see themselves as 'professional' carers who have a right to support.

(d) Caring for dementia sufferers

A review of research carried out for the Wagner Committee on residential care issues concluded that the difficulties of maintaining a person in the community are greater if dependency stems from dementia rather than from physical incapacity (Sinclair, 1988). Several studies have demonstrated the impact of the behavioural problems associated with dementia on carers' stress levels (Levin *et al.*, 1989; 1994; Askham and Thompson, 1990). A NISW study in three areas re-interviewing carers after an interval of a year concluded that the only two factors resulting in a reduction of a carer's stress levels were a dementia sufferer's death or permanent admission to long-term care (Levin *et al.*, 1994).

2. Support for co-resident carers

The need to support carers has been widely acknowledged in the community care changes which have taken place. The White Paper, *Caring for People*, which preceded the 1990 NHS and Community Care Act, stressed that a key objective of the reforms was 'to ensure that service providers make practical support for carers a high priority' (Secretary of State for Health *et al.*, 1989).

Sir Roy Griffiths' common-sense observation on the importance of supporting carers in his report on community care is worth repeating:

> *'A failure to give proper levels of support to informal carers not only reduces their own quality of life and that of the relative or friend they care for, but is also potentially inefficient as it can lead to less personally appropriate care being offered. Positive action is therefore needed to encourage the delivery of more flexible support which takes account of how best to support and maintain the role of the informal carers.'*
> (1988, p. 7, para. 4.3)

(a) Assessment of carers

The 1995 Carers (Recognition and Services) Act, the conclusion of a campaign by carers' organisations, was a milestone in the recognition of carers' rights. Carers 'providing or intending to provide a substantial amount of care on a regular basis' are now entitled to ask a local authority for an assessment of their own ability to care. The Act requires local authorities to take into account the results of a carer's assessment when deciding about any support service.

Many local authorities have responded to the new legislation. The conclusions of a national postal survey (with a 56% response rate) conducted one year after the introduction of the Act concluded that 46% of responding authorities had developed new procedures for assessing carers' needs (CNA, 1997). Nevertheless central government's failure to allocate additional central funding meant that local authorities had to contain their response to the Act within current budgets.

DoH guidance accompanying the Act outlined what would constitute good practice for social services departments (1996). There should be:

- *greater recognition of carers;*

- *an assessment of the 'caring system'* which considers the range of support available to service users and carers;

- *an integrated, family-based approach* which does not see either the service user or the carer in isolation;

- *improved practice* – providing the opportunity for the carer to have a private conversation with a care manager and trying to ensure that carers are not having to provide the same information repeatedly.

A CNA review of the first year of the Act included a postal survey of 1,655 members and telephone follow-up interviews with 98 of them (1997). A positive conclusion was that more than half of those who had been assessed reported an increase in the services offered. A more sobering conclusion, however, was that carers were only asking for an assessment when they had reached breaking point;

> *'Even when carers do know their rights, they are reluctant to ask for an assessment because they think there is no money available to provide them with services and they have feelings of guilt about asking for anything for themselves.'*
> (*Ibid.*, p. 44)

The three carers' focus groups run by ACIOG sounded a note of caution about the assessment process. Assessments, in some participants' experience, could be superficial and unhelpful. They argued that carers needed to be aware of potential support facilities before an assessment.

(b) National organisations working for carers

Two major national voluntary organisations, the CNA and the Princess Royal Trust for Carers work to give support to improve the situation for all carers.

Princess Royal Trust for Carers

- Provides information, counselling, help and support to carers;

- Has established carers centres have been established throughout the UK, staffed by a small team of professional carer support workers backed by volunteers.

Carers' National Association

- Provides information, advice and support to carers;

- Has offices in England, Wales, Scotland and Northern Ireland providing information and support to carers (has 121 branches);

- Runs a telephone help line for carers, Carers Line;

- Campaigns on issues which have an impact of carers' lives.

(c) Carer support workers

Carer support workers are employed by voluntary organisations, local and health authorities. The CNA estimates that it currently sends an information newsletter to about 1,800 of these workers throughout the UK. Many of these appointments have been made in the voluntary sector and there is enormous geographical variation in their availability. Job specifications will vary widely. There is no way of knowing whether the following specimen job description for a carer support worker employed by Bournemouth social services is typical or atypical of similar appointments.

Role of Carer Support Worker employed by Bournemouth Social Services

1. Working alongside staff in social services:

    - to enable them to 'think carer';

    - assisting staff in assessing carers' abilities to continue caring;

    - in developing carer support groups;

    - by providing a resource and information point on carers issues;

    - promoting carer awareness in staff training and development.

2. Working with individual carers.

3. Working with other agencies both voluntary and statutory.

4. Consultation:

    - acting as a channel between carers and the Department.

(d) Carer support groups

Carer support groups have developed extensively in recent years. They are seen as a way of providing carers with information, education, and emotional support. Many different types exist. Twigg *et al.* (1990) describe broad categories that include self-help groups run by, and for, carers, groups that are an off-shoot of a service facility, groups set up to train or educate carers, therapy groups and groups set up and run by a social worker. Within each of these categories groups vary considerably in their organisation (Mitchell, 1996). (See Annex E, 4C). There is a wide descriptive literature on carer support groups but little systematic research evidence about their objectives, how they are run and their effectiveness.

Evidence suggests that a number of carer support groups, contrary to expectations, experience difficulties in recruiting members (Twigg *et al.*, 1990).

(e) Information, training and counselling needs of carers

Research into carers' views of what they would like, emphasises a desire for more information, more emotional support and skills training (Nolan and Grant, 1989; Allen *et al.*, 1992; Twigg and Atkin, 1994). (See Annex E, 4B and 4C). Carers report that they experience lower levels of stress and anxiety and are better able to cope with their caring role if they have access to good information and support (ADS, 1998).

Carers' needs for more information was a theme of the three focus groups held with carers by ACIOG. Participants emphasised that they entered had usually taken on a caring role with little appropriate local knowledge, often discovering relevant information by accident. One participant, herself above retirement age, described only found out about a bathing service from her GP after 18 years of caring for her 95-year-old mother.

A wide selection literature describes the different types of information that carers need.

Different kinds of information wanted by carers

- The nature and course of the cared-for person's disease or condition

- Advice on handling problems e.g. behavioral problems of dementia sufferers

- Support services available for the cared-for person

- Support available to a carer such as counselling and telephone help lines

- Financial benefits

- Advice about the consequences of giving up work or reducing work hours

- Possible adaptations to a home such as stair lifts, showers or ramps

- Advice about aids which might assist the caring tasks

- Advice about transport schemes available to those with a disability.

The timing of information is important. An SSI inspection of the support for carers in five local authority identified key stages at which carers wanted information: when they took on a caring role, some time later and at points of crisis (DoH/SSI, 1995c, p. 4).

3. Respite from caring

A need for breaks from caring has been frequently expressed by carers, carers' organisations and policy makers. The ADS identifies the provision of a break from caring as one of the most frequent requests made by carers (1998). Although relatives, friends or neighbours may be prepared to look after the cared-for person such respite may be limited and not available to everyone. The NISW study of respite care for confused elderly people in three areas reported that less than half the sample of carers had a relative or friend willing to look after the dementia sufferer for a few hours and only 11% were able to have a break for as long as 24 hours in this way (Levin and Moriarty, 1996). Having privacy or personal space can become difficult for the carer of a dementia sufferer. Half the carers in the NISW study reported never leaving their relatives alone in the house and 90% felt restricted by the caring situation, half of them very much so. Even those carers with respite care spent an average of only 16 hours apart from the cared-for person each week.

A respite service may involve the cared-for person being looked after by someone other than the carer at home or somewhere else (see Annex E, 4A). Although key respite care services in the UK are day care, short breaks and sitting services Night care may also be needed (see Annex E, 3B).

(a) Day care

Day care is care during the day usually in a different venue from the cared-for person's own home. The NHS, local authorities, the voluntary sector, and to a lesser extent, the for-profit sector are all providers. There has been a substantial growth in day care within residential and nursing homes. Not all day care is located in some type of centre. Innovative schemes, such as the provision by an individual householder in their own home, have developed. For older people living alone, day care is seen as a means of providing sociable contact with others and possibly support services such as baths, showers and chiropody (see Annex E, 3A). When an older person is being cared for in a co-resident household, day care gives the carer a break but there is some ambiguity about the benefit to the cared-for person. Although cared-for people may enjoy day care others may feel resentment at leaving home.

Day care raises issues of equity and quality of care. It may be provided free of charge in an NHS hospital setting or, usually at a charge, in public, voluntary of for-profit sector specialist centres or in centres with a client mix. Dementia sufferers may have day care in any of these facilities, the great majority of NHS day hospital attenders, however, are reported to be dementia sufferers (Warrington and Eagles, 1995). Clients attending an NHS day hospital are likely to go more frequently than those using a day centre in the community. Although day hospitals might be expected to provide care for more dependent people, research has consistently shown is little difference in terms of mobility problems and degrees of confusion between people attending day care in this setting and their counterparts at local authority or voluntary sector day centres (Pahl, 1988; Warrington and Eagles, 1996).

The amount of day care any one individual has is generally limited. The NISW study of respite care for confused older people in three areas, for example, reported that in one area the average amount of day care in any one week was for one day and in the other two areas, two days (Levin *et al.*, 1994). The chance of being offered a day care place is far greater in some areas than in others. More unusual day care venues have been reported such as mobile day centres in rural areas and day care in an individual paid carer's own home.

An issue commonly identified in studies of day care is that of transport. If a carer takes the cared-for person to the day centre this shortens the break from caring.

Organised transport, on the other hand, often poses problems of unreliable timing and tedious journeys picking up all the day centre users en route.

(b) Short-term breaks

Access to breaks from caring is a consistent and persistent demand from carers and carers' organisations. Common arrangements to facilitate a carer having a break are either the cared-for person entering an institution (such as a residential or nursing home or a hospital) or staying with someone in another private household (such as a foster family) or a substitute carer coming to stay in the home. Hospital breaks may be provided on a one-off basis or rotated so that the cared-for person has a specified number of weeks at intervals in the hospital. Different policies appear to be adopted towards older people than towards younger age groups. A recent SSI inspection of local authority support for carers of all age groups in York pointed out that 'unlike the situation for younger people with a physical or mental disability all the respite care for older people was residentially based' (DoH/SSI, 1997d). Similarly a Scottish study, *A Patchwork Service*, examining the use of different types of respite care by users of different age groups reported that older people tended to experience placements in hospitals or care homes mainly for permanent residents (Lindsay *et al.*, 1993). Unlike younger people with a physical or mental disability they rarely experienced family based care or care in facilities solely for respite care. A recent postal survey of 3,000 members of the CNA confirms that co-resident carers are more likely than non-resident carers to obtain a short-term break (Henwood, 1998, Table 3.2). Breaks were also reported to be more likely when carers were supporting a younger person (*Ibid.*, Table 3.3).

(i) The demand for short-term placements is greater than the supply.

In the past, many short-term placements have been made in local authority care homes and in the geriatric and psycho-geriatric wards of NHS hospitals. The closure or transfer to the voluntary sector of many local authority residential homes and the sharp decline in NHS hospital beds has had an impact. Although independent sector residential and nursing homes will provide short-term placements there has been a reluctance to designate beds permanently as short term because continuity of income has not been guaranteed. The two NISW studies of the care of confused older people in three local authority areas described short-term placements as quite sparse and inflexible, with little scope for carer choice (Moriarty and Levin, 1998). Attention was drawn to the difficulty of finding good quality short-term places in residential care homes by participants in the three focus discussion groups run by ACIOG. The situation was perceived to have worsened recently as local authority homes which had been reliable providers in the past were closing. Carers had to scramble for the few places available in the independent sector. An illustration of the problems was one participant reporting desperately needing an immediate week's break to avoid breakdown. Despite approaching all the local care homes in March, the carer was only able to locate a short stay place for the last week in October.

(ii) Inequities in paying for short-term breaks.

Carers may have to pay quite different amounts for a short breaks. The amount depends on the type of placement and the geographical area. A placement in an NHS hospital is free. Care in a residential or nursing home may be means tested or at full cost.

(iii) Difficulties for spouse caregivers wanting a break.

Spouse caregivers are far less likely to place a husband or wife in an institutional setting to get a short break from caring than are other types of carers. This may be because they are less likely to want a break from caring or more likely to feel that such a placement would be unfair. Several studies have drawn attention to the dilemma for spouses in obtaining relief from the burden of care (Nolan and Grant, 1989; Parker, 1993; Twigg and Atkin, 1994).

Other ways of obtaining a short break may be more acceptable to spouses. Crossroads is one of the better known national schemes which will provide paid carers to stay with the cared-for person for a few days to enable a carer to get away from caring responsibilities. One of the husbands in the ACIOG focus groups was delighted at a Crossroads care attendant provided at the local authority's expense allowing him to take a short holiday for a few days (Appendix 1). He would not have been prepared to place his wife who had suffered a major stroke in a care home or hospital.

(iv) Appropriate short-term placements for dementia sufferers.

An important issue, given the incidence of dementia and the difficulties in sustaining a dementia sufferer at home, is the desirability of a removing a person with severe short-term memory problems from the familiar environment of home to the unfamiliar institution. An inspection of services for people with dementia drew attention to the shortcomings of institutional provision for this group (DoH/SSI, 1997a). These included;

- few places in specialist homes for people with dementia;

- a number of homes suffering from design problems for older people with dementia such as long uniform corridors, large central lounge and dining areas;

- uniform colour schemes.

The ADS, in evidence to the Royal Commission, argued that short-stay institutional care is not necessarily the most effective or desirable for those suffering from dementia and that flexible, community-based models, such as family support schemes would extend the range of options available (1998).

(c) Sitter services

Sitter and other types of home care relief schemes are popular with co-resident carers. A sitter service may have modest aims such as providing companionship, limited surveillance and assistance. Other schemes provide a substitute for the carer who will give all the kinds of care normally given by the carer. Many of these schemes are provided by the voluntary sector. Sitters may be volunteers or paid staff. In some areas night sitting services exist (see Annex E, 3B). Payment is normally required for the service. This type of support is not without its problems. As Leat points out volunteers may not easily, or immediately, recognise the needs of carers and just sitting may prove more difficult than performing a practical task (1992). Finding sitters to intervene in certain kinds of caring situations may be problematic. A recent SSI report on services for carers in the London Borough of Merton described a sitting scheme finding it difficult to provide a service for those with challenging behaviour (DoH/SSI, 1998a).

4. Home care

Home care has changed radically in the past decade. An integral part of the service used to be providing assistance with a range of domestic tasks. But part of the 1993 community care reforms was to re-focus the service with an emphasis on giving personal care. Controversially many home care assistants now decline to give a cleaning service. Home care is a crucial form of support for older people with high dependency living alone. The role of home care in a situation of co-resident caring is far less certain. In a re-analysis of the 1985 GHS Arber and Ginn calculated that 85% of domestic tasks for severely disabled older people living with their spouses were undertaken by those spouses (1991). Social Services home care provided only 5% of such help. Over half of co-resident caring for older people is provided by a spouse but that spouse is likely also to be old and possibly also have disabilities. Pragmatically a spouse is likely to help a partner with personal care such as using the toilet or getting out of bed than wait for a home care assistant. As an SSI report on local authority support of carers pointed out the tendency to move home care services away from cleaning towards personal care is not always helpful to carers (DoH/SSI, 1995c, p. 41). It recommended that social services departments should be flexible enough to provide a cleaning service for carers.

Incomprehension at the refusal by home care staff refusing to provide a cleaning service was expressed in all the ACIOG focus group discussions with carers. One of the participants, a wife in her eighties, providing her husband with considerable personal care, recounted returning home from hospital soon after an operation to look after her husband. Even though she was unable to climb stairs to reach the bedroom and had considerable difficulty in even getting out of a chair the home care service refused to do any cleaning or household tasks.

ACCEPTABILITY OF CO-RESIDENT CARE

1. Acceptability of co-resident care to caregivers and those being cared for

It is difficult to know from existing research whether husbands and wives providing care identify themselves as carers and how strongly they feel about their situation. The situation for a daughter or son caring for a parent in the same household is a very different from that of a co-resident spouse. Equally there are quite different scenarios for offspring living with a parent. Some daughters and sons will have never married and will have remained living in a parent's household. Married sons and daughters are likely to have had a parent move into their households or into an attached household, a granny flat. There is insufficient research evidence to discuss the acceptability or otherwise of some of these arrangements. Despite the apparent popularity of this living arrangement in new or extended owner occupied property, the implications for offspring and the older person concerned remain to be explored.

The ACIOG focus group discussions raised some very interesting contrasts between the views of people currently caring and older people who were not currently in a caring role (Appendix 1). Many of the participants in the three carers' focus groups were co-resident with a spouse or a parent. Although they recognised the pros and cons of this arrangement many considered that co-residence solved some of the stresses of the two parties living in separate households. Interestingly the four focus groups of older people not currently in a caring situation were unanimously opposed to the idea of living with a son/daughter. They made the following points:

- older people prefer their independence;

- daughters and daughters-in-law could be too bossy;

- different generations in the same household do not gel;

- their adult children's first responsibility had to be to their own children not to their parents.

2. Acceptability of day care

Day care is generally considered relatively successful in providing company and social contact to dependent older people living alone. In a situation of co-resident caring, day care does not meet the precisely the same needs of the dependent person because a carer would generally be providing company and social contact. Although some of those living with a co-resident carer are likely to enjoy the sociable aspects of day care, others may feel resentment at leaving the familiar home. It has been argued that day care for a dementia sufferer living with a carer is primarily for the benefit of the carer. But there is evidence that day care in a situation of dementia benefits both the sufferer and the carer. The NISW study of respite care for confused older people in three areas reported that the vast majority of carers (92%) considered that day care had brought about some improvement in their own lives (Levin *et al.*, 1994). Many carers (40% of the first NISW study and 30% in second) reported their relatives seemed more happy and relaxed with going to day care (*Ibid.*, Levin *et al.*, 1989). Day care had a beneficial effect on the relationship; Most frequently, the carers described their relatives on their return as seeming pleased to be home and to see them (*Ibid.*, p. 74). A study of the effect of high quality day care on a sample of dementia sufferers drew similar conclusions (Curran, 1996) (see Annex E, 3A). Half a sample of carers interviewed shortly after a dementia sufferer started at a day centre and again three months later concluded that that the cared-for person showed a distinct improvement in mood and behaviour when at home, a change attributed to the day centre.

3. Acceptability of short-term breaks

Although most daughters and sons in a caring role are enthusiastic about short-term breaks, spouses are less likely to be so. As argued earlier in the chapter, they are less likely than co-resident offspring to seek short-term breaks through the cared-for person entering institutional care. When a partner enters an institution they are also likely to visit frequently rather than go away for a holiday. Studies of long-term care report the same phenomenon. A high proportion of husbands and wives visit their partner in a residential care or nursing home on a daily basis (Wright, 1998).

A frequently expressed concern about short stays in hospital or care homes is that the cared-for person will deteriorate. Despite regular respite care being high on carers' agendas, little is really known about the effects of short-term breaks on either the cared-for person or the carer. A study by Homer and Gilleard (1994) (see Annex E, 4A) sought to discover the effect of a break from caring on carers and how the cared-for person's functioning was affected by respite care. Although virtually all the carers thought that respite care was worthwhile, there was no change in their well-being during the cared-for person's stay in respite care. But many of the cared-for people actually improved in their functioning during the short-stay placement. The greatest improvement in functioning was in those people looked after by highly stressed carers.

4. Acceptability of sitting services

One of the issues identified by the SSI inspection of services for carers in the London Borough of Merton was that although many of the carers talked to were enthusiastic about the concept of a sitting service, they lacked knowledge of what was available locally (1998). Carers may be reluctant to use a sitting service where there is a charge. The SSI inspection of services for carers in York commented, for example, on a sitting service for carers run by Age Concern which some carers were reluctant to use for this reason (DoH/SSI, 1997d).

OUTCOMES OF CO-RESIDENT CARE

Much co-resident caring continues within the home until the cared-for person dies or is admitted to a hospital or a hospice for the last few weeks of life. Even dementia sufferers can be cared for successfully at home. Levin and her colleagues, interviewing carers in three areas at yearly intervals, reported that by the end of the second year 35% of the sample of dementia sufferers had died most of them at home (1989).

Some co-resident caring comes to an end and the cared-for person enters residential or nursing home care. Modeling the likelihood of admission to long-term care on the basis of the OPCS survey of disability Opit and Pahl (1993) concluded that key variables were a high degree of dependence, living alone and dementia. Dementia at an advanced stage puts co-resident caring under considerable threat. Current estimates are that about 40% of people with dementia live in institutional care (Gordon and Spicker, 1997).

Common reasons for co-resident caregiving coming to an end

- Carer's own health problems

- Carer's stress

- Sleep deprivation

- Carer unable to cope with incontinence

- Carer unable to cope physically with caregiving tasks

- Hospitalisation of the cared-for person

On the whole, however, married men and women aged 65 or over are far less likely to live in institutional care than those who are not married. Spouse carers may become unable to continue giving care. The 1991 Census indicates that just under 50,000 married older men and women were resident in communal establishments in Great Britain, 52% of them were women and 48% men (OPCS, 1993, Table 3). In effect, this means that approximately one in ten people in long-term care are married. Although some married residents would have a spouse also in a care home most would have a spouse living in the community.

The NISW study of dementia sufferers in three areas concluded that day care made little difference to the outcome (Levin *et al.*, 1989). 'Overall, elderly people with day care were equally as likely to have died or to have entered residential care between interviews as those without it' (*Ibid.*, p. 251). Similarly a study of a psycho-geriatric day hospital concluded that it did little to divert patients from the ultimate destination of in-patient care (Smith and Cantley, 1985).

The question of whether short-stay breaks contribute to co-resident caring continuing or whether such breaks lead finally to a permanent long-term care admission is a complex one. Levin *et al.*'s first study of the care of confused older people in three areas showed that when the cared-for person was using respite care at the first interview there was an increased chance of that person actually being in institutional care by the second interview (1989). Moriarty and Levin argue that users of respite care can be divided into subgroups: those for whom it is a way of helping them to stay at home and others who are offered temporary stays as holding measure while the process of arranging a permanent place is made (1998, p. 135).

Training and support programmes can make a difference to carers continuing to provide care at home. An evaluation of an intervention programme which included individual and family counselling and support group participation for spouse caregivers of dementia sufferers confirmed that spouses could be helped to go on caring at home (Mittelman *et al.*, 1993). A treatment group was compared with a control group whose members did not benefit from any of these interventions. In the first year after intake, spouses in the treatment group were only half the long-term nursing home placements of their partners as spouses in the control group.

Admissions to hospital are as significant in co-resident caring coming to an end as they are when people live alone. A study carried out by one of this report's authors for the JRF on the effect on family caregivers of a cared-for person's admission to a care home found that a high proportion of caring situations whether co-resident or not had come to an end following the cared-for person's admission to hospital (Wright, 1998).

COSTS OF CO-RESIDENT CARE

Co-resident caring involves many different kinds of costs. When there is a high level of dependency the number of hours spent in caring activities are likely to be high. If a carer is below retirement age a high dependency situation is likely to have an impact on employment and income. Carers are less likely than non-carers to be in paid work. If they do work they are likely to have reduced earnings because of shorter hours. Caring has long-term financial consequences which affect carers after caring has ceased because either not being in employment or having part-time employment affects pension contributions (Hancock and Jarvis, 1994).

If a carer has support from social services there are likely to be charges. Although local authorities have to implement a national scheme for charging for residential or nursing home care, they do not have to charge for domiciliary services. Under Section 17 of the Health and Social Services Adjudication and Social Security Adjudication Act 'an authority providing a service may recover such charge (if any) for it as they consider reasonable S.17 (1)'. Most authorities now charge for support services in the community and the level of charges has been rising (Secretary of State for Health, 1996, B.13). The basis of charging varies, with some services (particularly meals-on-wheels) charged for at a flat rate and others at differential rates (related to the level of service provided and the income of the service user). Day care continues to be a service for which the majority of London authorities (54%) make no charge (Pettitt, 1997). This, however, is a considerable change from 1994/95 when 90% of London authorities made no charge. Overall service users meet 10% of the total cost of day and domiciliary services (*Ibid.*, A18).

The evidence is that charging policies have led to greater hardship to carers. A national postal survey of carers carried out for the Carers National Association, concluded that as many as half the carers in the country may be being incorrectly assessed for contributions to service charges because their own income is being assessed or is being inappropriately included in a joint assessment with the service user (Warner, 1995).

SUMMARY

Over half of co-resident care is provided by a spouse and over a fifth by an offspring or daughter/son-in-law. At its best co-resident care gives both the person being cared for and the caregiver a good quality of life in which support is given in the context of a loving relationship. In reality co-resident caregiving often inflicts a heavier care burden on the carer than is the case for a carer living in a separate household. Conversely a co-resident carer is far less likely than a carer living in a separate household from the cared-for person to share the care burden with health or social services.

There are often positive reasons for spouses and offspring wanting to continue caregiving in the community. But there may be considerable difficulties in continuing to care. Spouses in particular themselves usually above retirement age may have serious health problems. A wide literature indicates that it is common for carers to have high stress levels. Living with a dementia sufferer is likely to generate considerable stress.

There have been significant developments in recognising the situation of carers and their needs for support. Two major national organisations, the CNA and the Princess Royal Trust for Carers have established substantial frameworks both to champion the cause of carers at a national and local level and to develop support services. There has been considerable expansion in the network of carer support workers and of carer support groups.

Carers emphasise their need for more information and training and more guaranteed breaks from caring. Day care, in its many forms, remains an appreciated service. Nevertheless the amount of support given is limited and few dependent people have more than one or two days of the week in day care. The demand for short-term breaks far outstrips the supply. Placements may be free to the user if in a hospital but high charges may be made for care in a local authority or independent sector care home. Spouses may find it difficult to get, or be induced to take, a break of some days from caring.

Many spouses and offspring continue to care for a dependent older person to the end, or virtually to the end, of that person's life. It is likely to be particularly difficult to maintain a dementia sufferer in a co-resident caring situation and the cost to the person providing such care may be very high.

Chapter 5

The Models:
Very Sheltered Housing

INTRODUCTION

1. Overview

The essence of sheltered and very sheltered housing is that the person has their own home with their own front door. They may socialise there or in a communal space. Most have one bedroom but a few have two and some still have bedsitters. The people are either owners (private sector) or tenants (social rented sector) with rights and are not residents living a communal life as they would be in residential care.

Sheltered housing is accommodation which is grouped with some communal facilities (a common room and usually also a laundry and guest room), a warden (resident or non-resident) and an alarm system which links the people who live there with a warden. Schemes can be very small, less than twenty units, or large – over 100. Their origins can be found in almshouses and other similar schemes provided by the churches or voluntary bodies. Since the 1960s they have been increasingly provided by LAs and housing associations (HAs) and have attracted housing subsidy. A philosophy underlying them was that there should be a mixture of fit and frail and that the warden would only be a 'good neighbour'. The private sector has increasingly been providing sheltered housing for leasehold purchase.

Although much sheltered housing is popular with tenants some schemes have become obsolescent (Fletcher, 1991; Tinker *et al.*, 1995). In 1994 40% of LAs and 36% of HAs had between 1% and 9% of their sheltered housing stock which was difficult to let but 8% of LAs and 13% of HAs had over half their stock as difficult to let. This was mainly because locations were no longer desirable, the accommodation was too small (e.g. bedsitters), because facilities, such as a lift, were not provided or others, such as bathrooms, were shared. In addition, the expectations of people have increased. More seriously some schemes were inherently unsuitable for very frail people unless large amounts of help were provided from outside. In a survey of private sheltered housing 10% of the older people were thinking of moving and 17% of these gave as the reason the need for increasing care and support (Rolfe *et al.*, 1995, p. 52). Some schemes did enable very frail people to stay there but at the cost of a warden undertaking many tasks for which she was neither qualified nor paid.

Very sheltered housing. In the 1970s very sheltered housing (sometimes called extra care housing or, in the private sector, close care) began to be developed to house older people who had more needs than could be met in sheltered housing. Sometimes this was purpose built while in others sheltered housing was adapted, for example by adding additional communal facilities and providing more care from wardens or other people. Although there is no formal definition of very sheltered housing, its characteristics, in addition to those for sheltered housing, are additional communal facilities (such as baths to allow disabled people to be bathed, a dining room, a sluice room etc.), 24-hour cover by a warden and meals (sometimes two a day but sometimes only one). One LA (Wolverhampton) plans to replace all its residential care homes for physically frail older people and those with dementia with very sheltered housing (see Annex E, 1A). There are usually also extra staff to give help with personal and domestic tasks. A whole scheme may be very sheltered or some extra help/facilities may be provided to a few people in a sheltered scheme. A further complication is that very sheltered schemes may have to be Registered Homes Act 1984 if they provide both personal care and board (not 'pay as you eat').

It is salutary that in 1994 four-fifths of both LAs and HAs had between 1% and 9% of their very sheltered schemes as difficult to let and three LAs (4%) had between 70% and 100% in this situation. As noted above one reason may be the dislike of shared facilities. The DoE national survey showed that 32% of very sheltered housing was not self-contained (McCafferty, 1994). There is also tremendous variation in the range of facilities and help.

2. Research on very sheltered housing

There can be a reasonable degree of confidence about the following findings on LA and HA schemes for older people because they have been subject to two large national surveys with robust data although, of course, changes have occurred and research may not have caught up with them. The national surveys are *An Evaluation of Very Sheltered Housing* in 1986/7 (Tinker, 1989 – although some of the data was updated in the next DoE study some key questions discussed below were not asked) and *Living Independently: A Study of the Housing Needs of Elderly and Disabled People* in 1991/2 (McCafferty, 1994). Both were large national studies of both local authorities and housing associations and they embraced not only the views of users and providers but costs as well. Some of the findings were supported by another national study – *Difficult to Let Sheltered Housing* (Tinker *et al.*, 1995).

Most of the findings of these studies are also supported by smaller ones such as those for specific housing associations or groups including people with dementia (Kitwood *et al.*, 1995). There is also a high degree of unanimity among professional bodies such as the National Housing Federation and providers such as Anchor Trust (previously called Anchor Housing Association) and Housing 21. Anchor Trust has commendably sponsored a good deal of research although much of it is on their own schemes. There is a lack of recent research on local authority schemes except by individual providers. The schemes in Annex E, 1A illustrate some of these.

Although there are many descriptions of schemes in the last 3-4 years there is little evaluation in general or for specific groups such as older people from black and ethnic minorities and virtually nothing on the quality of care. In the private sector there is hardly any research on very sheltered housing apart from a DoE study in the 1980s (Fleiss, 1985) and one on people living in Guardian Housing schemes (Rolfe *et al.*, 1995).

3. Current provision of very sheltered housing

(a) Underprovision? Overall provision of sheltered and very sheltered housing and the balance between the two

There were over half a million (516,524) units of sheltered and very sheltered housing in England in 1997 (Table 5.1).

Table 5.1: The provision of sheltered and very sheltered housing units for elderly people. England, 1997					
	LAs	HAs	Other public sector	Private*	Total
Sheltered housing	282,114	169,586	2,225	44,558	498,483
Very sheltered housing	7,134	9,873	1,034	–	18,041
Total	289,248	179,459	3,259	44,558	516,524

* No distinction is made between sheltered and very sheltered housing.
Source: Extracted from Department of the Environment, Transport and the Regions (DETR), (1997) *Housing Investment Programme Returns*. Laid before the House of Commons.

The majority (56%) of the total units were provided by LAs with the balance mainly managed by HAs (35%). Some LAs have transferred some of their stock to HAs. The private sector had 9%. There are major variations between areas which 'cannot be explained by reference to the number of older people living in the area' (Audit Commission, 1998, p. 25).

In 1997, as Table 5.1 shows, there was very little very sheltered housing (3.5%) compared with conventional sheltered (96.5%). Because the figures for the private sector are not disaggregated it is likely that very sheltered is slightly higher. The DoE national survey showed that in England in 1991 out of a total of 641,494 units of subsidised (social rented) accommodation for older and disabled people 51% was sheltered and only 2% (14,782 units) was very sheltered (McCafferty, 1994, pp. 36-37). Nor was much expansion by LAs and HAs planned in very sheltered. Only 18% of planned increases were in very sheltered. It was, therefore understandable that the DoE study concluded that there was overprovision of sheltered and underprovision of very sheltered. This message seems to have been taken by providers. For example, there has subsequently been major expansion by some housing associations such as Anchor and Hanover although this has not necessarily been new build.

(b) New build

Looking at overall new provision of sheltered housing, and this includes very sheltered, there has been a dramatic decline in new build by LAs and HAs and in the private sector (Table 5.2).

	Sheltered				Other			
	Private sector	Housing associations	Local authorities and New Towns	Total	Private sector	Housing associations*	Local authorities and New Towns	Total
1989	3,242	1,092	2,523	6,857	554	339	1,004	1,897
1993	808	1,442	202	2,452	179	724	57	960
1997**	155	245	2	402	45	113	11	169

Table 5.2: Number of dwellings for elderly people completed 1989-1997, England

* There was a peak in 1993 and then a steady fall.   ** Provisional.
Source: DETR (1998) *Housing and Construction Statistics Part 1*. HMSO: London.

Recent Government advice from DoE and the DoH has not been encouraging (Housing Corporation, 1996b). They jointly stated that 'Specialised developments of very sheltered housing (either conversions of existing stock or purpose built schemes) may have a part to play in addressing the housing needs of older people' (*Ibid.*, p. 4). But also 'Expanding the supply of very sheltered housing is, however, neither the best option for addressing the needs of older people as they become more frail, physically or mentally' (*Ibid.*, p. 2). The Housing Corporation have also been cautious about their funding of housing associations. 'Before approving new specialised housing schemes for older people, we will want to see evidence that housing and care needs have been properly assessed through joint planning mechanisms' (Housing Corporation, 1996b, p. 23). Significant changes to sheltered housing including remodelling schemes to enable them to cope with frailer tenants, a changing role for the warden and greater involvement with health and social services will enhance the potentiality of this kind of housing (see Appendices 2 and 3).

(c) Implications for sheltered housing of changes in very sheltered housing

The potential of very sheltered housing has implications for sheltered. The large amount of provision of the latter is a resource which cannot be wasted. One answer is to turn it into very sheltered and imaginative ways are being developed of remodeling schemes e.g. by Housing 21 (Trotter and Phillips, 1997). HAs are also concerned about a lack of resources to do this. Also, any changes in schemes, whether it is bringing in different kinds of tenants and/or demolishing/closing/ changing schemes needs careful thought because of the effect on existing tenants.

Another change, and the two may go hand in hand, is to use the schemes as resource centres for use by other people in the community. For example special baths can be used by district nurses who can bring in older or younger physically disabled people. However, research on both very sheltered housing and residential care homes shows that there may be considerable resistance on the part of the older people who feel that their communal space is being invaded by 'outsiders' (Tinker, 1989; Wright, 1995). The answer seems to be some degree of separation at least as far as the entrance is concerned. For example if there is a communal dining room where outsiders are allowed to come and have meals they should not have to go through the part of the building where the individual flats are. Anchor Trust is one organisation which has been experimenting with various activities such as a preventive health care clinic and movement to music classes and have produced a Guide to opening up resources to the wider community (Riseborough, 1995, p. 31). They have found that:

- the experience has been largely positive (despite some problems and misgivings by some staff);

- projects have been largely innovative;

- Anchor tenants and community users have made new friends and enjoyed themselves;

- sheltered schemes have developed into lively places.

(d) The effect on provision of a changing and ageing population

Five per cent of people aged 65 and over in Great Britain lived in sheltered or very sheltered housing in 1994 (OPCS, 1996, p.157). A higher proportion are very old compared with nationally. Research on national housing association statistics shows that in 1995 27% of tenants were aged 80 or over compared with 17% nationally (Tinker and Jarvis, in press). There is some evidence of an ageing population in very sheltered housing which is presenting problems for providers. In Anchor Trust 'The largest five-year age group has shifted from 75 to 79 years (representing 30% of respondents in 1984) to 80 to 84 (26% in 1993). Only one respondent in ten was aged 85 and over in 1984 compared with almost one in four in 1993' (Riseborough and Niner, 1994, p. 12). There is also evidence that the average age of people taking up tenancies has gone up (*Ibid.*). This data is similar to that of Hanover Housing Association (summarised in Tinker and McCreadie, 1998, unpublished). The DoE study pointed to the increasing polarisation of tenants in sheltered housing towards the extremes of high and low dependency (McCafferty, 1994, p. 175). Nor must the projected increase in older people from black and ethnic minorities be neglected.

4. Relationship to schemes

Numerous housing associations are now developing very sheltered housing including Hanover, Anchor, Focus, Servite, Coventry Churches and many others. Local authorities are similarly developing schemes, sometimes in their own right and sometimes in partnership with a housing association or independent care provider. The schemes described in Annex E, 1A are illustrations of current developments.

FEASIBILITY OF VERY SHELTERED HOUSING

Very sheltered housing has been running successfully for about 20 years and is provided by all local authorities and all the major housing associations. Very sheltered housing does, however, have some problems which affect their feasibility. Most revolve around:

- its purpose and allocation;

- the role of the warden;

- how care is provided, accessed and paid for;

- difficult to let accommodation;

- specific issues in the private sector.

1. The purpose and allocation of very sheltered housing

Although in theory very sheltered housing is for people who need housing and support over and above that provided in conventional sheltered it is difficult to draw this simple conclusion from looking at the kinds of people housed. One in five recent entrants to very sheltered housing in the DoE study had no physical or mental frailty. In the schemes described in Annex E there were some who did not have high care needs. Questions arise over why these people need very sheltered housing and whether they could either be kept or rehoused in ordinary mainstream housing? If the need is for greater security or social support there may be other ways of giving this. However if schemes only take very frail people, as the National Housing Federation have argued (Fletcher, 1991, p. 28), that too would have implications for provision. Some people enter because they are bereaved and lonely (e.g. Riseborough and Niner, 1994) but there may be little communal life and they may remain lonely. In the private sector people may move to sheltered housing as one way of trading down and releasing equity but amounts generated are usually relatively small (Fleiss, 1985, Rolfe *et al.*, 1995).

Unless providers make clear what the purpose of their schemes is allocation procedures are likely to be haphazard. The main tension seems to be between provision solely for very dependent people (and this is logical if provision is expensive and priorities have to be made) and those who still maintain that it is for a mixture of 'fit and frail'. An agreed assessment process, preferably multi-disciplinary, should take place. The DoE study recommended that the housing aspirations of older people must be taken into account as well as dependency levels (McCafferty, 1994, p. 176). Making part of a sheltered scheme very sheltered is one way of coping with frail tenants.

2. The role of the warden

The shift to housing with care has had major implications for the role of the warden. The feasibility of schemes is partly dependent on someone to provide care and to organise it. There have been endless discussions about what role the warden should play at the same time as they have become more professionalised. In general it seems to be agreed that the warden should be the enabler rather than the provider (except at times of emergencies) of services but should have close links with these other services. The large national surveys showed that older people with a warden receive more services than those of a similar dependency level without someone to act as advocate/organiser (e.g. Tinker, 1989; McCafferty, 1994).

A wide and responsible role is suggested in a campaign supported by 34 housing associations. This suggested that wardens are:

- housing professionals with responsibilities towards building and tenants;

- managers of sheltered housing, not 'hands on' carers;

- there to enable older people to live independently with privacy, dignity, security and fulfilment;

- able to assist with communication solutions due to sensory impairment, language or illness (including dementia);

- trained to encourage older people to ask for support, to respect refusal of offers of help and to give information on the availability of and access to services;

- ideally placed, with tenants' agreement, to contribute to assessments and the monitoring of care packages. (Means, 1998, Appendix 3)

This wider role may be more 'hands on' than the wardens would wish. When a warden is available it may be assumed that a service is provided. This may be particularly likely to be the case if the warden is a nurse. What happens if the services which the warden is supposed to be organising are not there? Do they then have to provide the care? And what are the implications? At the very least there is need for close links between the various key services i.e. housing, health and social services. An additional factor is that some research indicates that tenants would prefer care to come from other professionals and/or their families and not from the warden (Riseborough and Sykes, 1995).

Whether wardens should be part of the Social Services Department or from the Housing Department or Housing Association is another issue. However, one of the prized elements of sheltered and very sheltered housing in the public sector is that people are treated as tenants with rights and not as the clients of a social worker. This points to a strong housing bias.

In addition, it is likely that sheltered housing wardens may be encouraged to take on a wider role to the surrounding community. This was found in early research (e.g. Tinker, 1989) and is now part of an initiative by Anchor Trust (Riseborough, 1995).

Whatever the role there needs to be clarity about it. Useful codes of practice have been developed and these include advice about the rights of older people to take risks and to have privacy and dignity and the right to refuse services (Knight, 1992). A recent publication on changes in the role of the warden gives useful case studies of innovatory practice (Hasler and Page, 1998).

3. How care is provided, accessed and paid for
(See also Chapter 9.)

A key to very sheltered housing is the role of health and social services (see next section on difficult to let housing). As the ACE submission to the Royal Commission has stated there are different models for providing personal and domestic care (ACE, 1998) but there is no research on the feasibility of the different ones. The two main models are:

- providing care services from outside the scheme through social services (mainly the LA model) with the danger that services may not materialise as has been the case (e.g. Kitwood *et al.*, 1995, p. 58);

- providing care from staff in the scheme on site (mainly the HA model) where the provision of care by staff resident in a scheme is likely to be more expensive than if it comes from outside.

(See costs section.)

Anchor Trust has developed an in house care scheme (Anchor Care Alternatives) which provides services both to people in sheltered housing and to people outside. Older people either pay themselves or social services do if they are eligible after assessment. There is some evidence now that more formal relationships are beginning to develop between housing associations and social services. Social services would normally nominate tenants for a certain number of places and agree to meet most of their care costs. This would be after assessment and as an alternative to residential care (Means, 1998, Appendix 3). It is at least possible that the growing involvement of social services is in part because it is cheaper for them to provide home care in a scheme provided by the housing department or housing association than providing their own residential care. In Hanover very sheltered housing the care is provided under a separate agreement from the accommodation and the warden has no involvment with the provision of care. Wardens liaise with members of the care team.

In private schemes owners are as entitled to social and health services as anyone else. Most schemes also provide some services such as domestic and personal care up to a certain level and this is covered by the service charge.

A complicating factor is the difference between housing association and local authority schemes (National Housing Federation memo, 1998). The costs of warden services are included in the service charges of HA schemes. This is not the case for LA schemes because the costs are met directly from LA budgets without a charge to tenants. Some components of service charges are considered part of 'eligible rent' for the purposes of Housing Benefit. Under interim arrangements due to end in October 1999, warden costs (except where wardens are managing or providing care) are treated as part of eligible rent. Where the resident's income and savings are low enough these costs may therefore be met in part or in full by HB. Compared with ordinary sheltered housing schemes, it is easier in very sheltered housing schemes to establish that they are not managing or providing care because these tasks are clearly the responsibility of an on-site team. The National Housing Federation has argued for the retention of warden costs as a component of eligible rent.

A further complicating factor is where HAs (but not LAs) are also registered under the Registered Homes Act 1984. (See definition of very sheltered housing. Whether they are registered or not is a grey area and has important implications for who pays.) The HA might feel 'safer' to be registered for a variety of reasons to do with the finances or professional advice available from the local registration and inspection unit. Similarly the LA might think that it is better to have the involvement of the registration and inspection unit as a means of quality control, rather than do this as part of the usual contract monitoring which happens in non-registered schemes where a part of the care contract has been awarded. Most HAs prefer not to register their very sheltered housing because the ethos of sheltered housing is to maintain independence. Registration greatly reduces tenants rights, in that they have less security of tenure and only receive pocket money to live on rather than having access to benefits that allow them to pay for their rent and service charges.

The availability of Attendance Allowance and Disability Living Allowance can also be crucial. There may be other sources open to providers such as the Housing Corporation Supported Housing Management Grant (previously called the Special Needs Management Allowance) which occasionally pays for a member of staff to give 'floating support' to tenants (i.e. rather than to the property).

4. Difficult to let accommodation

The issues are those mentioned earlier to do with location, bedsitters and amenities. A good deal of remodelling is taking place. As Means points out this is:

> 'often linked to a more general review of where sheltered housing should fit into community care. The remodelling of sheltered housing is not just about redesigning old buildings but it is also about the repositioning of sheltered housing within community care. More and more housing associations stress that such accommodation should be a "home for life" and that tenants should be enabled to "stay put" as their health deteriorates. This requires the bringing in of health and social care services into present accommodation rather than having access to such support through a move into residential or nursing home care.'
> (Means, 1998, Appendix 3)

An issue to do with feasibility is the balance which providers have to make between remodelling, including turning sheltered schemes into very sheltered for existing tenants, and new build. As has been noted there has been very little new build recently and this may in part be due to the pressures of existing tenants and the need to keep them 'at home'. If this is the case it has implications for older people in mainstream housing who might want and need to move into very sheltered. There is need for capital investment in reshaping a proportion of sheltered housing so that it can cater for a much frailer group.

5. Specific issues in the private sector

Although there is little research on the private sector there are some indications of some problems. One is of a shortage of suitable land to build schemes on and the other is problems of getting planning permission. The latter is because it is thought that additional numbers of frail people would cause strain on local health and social services. The level of service charges in some private schemes causes some dissatisfaction (Rolfe *et al.*, 1995).

ACCEPTABILITY OF VERY SHELTERED HOUSING

1. Older people

Overall research on people in very sheltered housing shows that there is widespread satisfaction with schemes. The majority of older people:

- are satisfied or very satisfied with the schemes (about three-quarters were very satisfied, McCafferty, 1994);

- are satisfied or very satisfied with the home/accommodation (about three-quarters were very satisfied, McCafferty, 1994);

- do not want to move (6% thinking of moving again (Tinker, 1989), 2% very/fairly likely to move within 12 months (McCafferty, 1994);

- would advise other elderly friends or relative to live in very sheltered housing (89% said 'yes', but 10% of the most dependent said 'no', Tinker, 1989);

- are particularly appreciative of the safety of the environment (e.g. see Appendix 2).

However about one in five said that they wished they had stayed in their previous home (Tinker, 1989) and in the DoE study one in six of those who had been in the scheme for less than five years thought this (McCafferty, 1994). There is some evidence (e.g. Woolham, 1998) that few tenants feel that alternatives had been discussed with them before moving into very sheltered housing. Subsequent research has discussed the question of whether housing with care contradicts the desire for independence and concluded that this may happen (Riseborough and Sykes, 1995). In this research some tenants were ambivalent about getting personal care from the warden and wardens were ambivalent about providing it (*Ibid.*).

Discussions in the ACIOG focus groups showed some confusion between sheltered housing and residential care. Their views were coloured by the experiences of friends or relatives. This included dissatisfaction with bedsitters and cuts in the hours worked by the warden. What we have no evidence about is the acceptability of very sheltered housing to older people outside schemes and why they do not choose it. Is this from a lack of knowledge? Or lack of provision? Or a distaste for this kind of accommodation and care? However, for those who do wish to move only a minority choose any kind of sheltered housing (Leather and Sykes, 1996). For those asked to consider accommodation if they could not cope independently in their existing home sheltered housing was the most popular choice and only 16% favoured residential care (*Ibid.*, p. 33).

What is difficult to assess is the views of people with dementia but there is some evidence of the success of very sheltered housing for this group (Tinker, 1989, Kitwood *et al.*, 1995). There are other groups for whom there is a strong case for very sheltered housing such as those from black and ethnic minorities but researchers point to the need for both separate provision and ethnically mixed schemes (e.g. Jones, 1994).

2. Carers

Very little research has been done on the views of carers where a relative has gone into very sheltered housing. However, some indication is that research shows that a small proportion of older people move from living with their sons and daughters and about one quarter move at the suggestion of the family/relatives friends. Among black and minority ethnic older people, while family care may be the preferred option, it is not always possible or desired by the family or the older person (Inquilab, 1996). In the focus groups few carers had any personal experience of sheltered or very sheltered housing.

3. Staff

In the national research in 1987 staff, which included both permanent and visiting, on the whole thought that very sheltered housing was a good type of provision and three-quarters said that they would like to move into it in their old age (Tinker, 1989).

The dissatisfactions, which have financial implications, in the main revolved round their own pay and conditions. With a possible shortage of workers in the future, because of demographic pressures, it seems likely that salaries will have to rise. This will increase costs but also possibly the job satisfaction of staff. The increasing professionalism of wardens is also likely to lead to demands for higher salaries. (See also the section on the warden).

OUTCOMES OF LIVING IN VERY SHELTERED HOUSING

There has been little research which overtly includes outcome measures but there are some that could be used. These include:

- ability to keep frail older people in schemes/provide an alternative to institutional care;

- numbers who move on to other accommodation/care i.e. they cannot remain there;

- numbers who have been enabled to move out of institutions into the scheme;

- vacancies in schemes.

1. Ability to keep frail older people in schemes/provide an alternative to institutional care

Evidence from the 1987 study from older people and staff showed that for some care was not adequate (Tinker, 1989). More recently in Anchor Housing Association there is evidence that some wardens have felt that they were having to undertake more 'hands on' care because community services were so patchy and in some cases had been withdrawn (Riseborough and Sykes, 1995). This is well illustrated in research on very sheltered housing in Hampshire where it was found that 'a significant minority of tenants are moving on from enhanced sheltered schemes into Part 111 residential or long-stay hospital accommodation (Lupton, 1990, p. 114). One explanation seemed to be 'the difficulty of getting the right intensity of support at the right time' (*Ibid.*). As already noted Anchor Trust have subsequently provided their own care system. The level of services is key and there is no national data which directly addresses the question of adequacy of levels of care.

The Audit Commission maintain that LAs (but they are not specifically talking about very sheltered) have become 'locked in' to supporting their own council tenants. 'Consequently, sheltered housing is failing to provide an effective alternative to residential care for non-council tenants' (Audit Commission, 1998, p. 27).

2. Numbers who move on to other accommodation/care

In the 1987 study two-thirds of tenants had died while 14% had moved to residential care and 10% to hospital (Tinker, 1989). No equivalent data is available from the later DoE study.

3. Numbers who have been enabled to move out of institutions into the scheme

It appears that a growing number of people are moving from a residential or nursing home into very sheltered housing. Between 1987 and 1992 there was a four-fold increase – from 3% to 11% of new entrants (McCafferty, 1994, p. 112). It is not known if this was due to closure of long-stay insitutions.

4. Vacancies in schemes

As already stated there have been problems with difficult to let schemes.

5. Others

It would have been useful to **assess quality of life, general health, morale and feeling of independence** but there is little evidence to support a view one way or another. Equally it would have been helpful to have evidence that very sheltered housing **helps/substitutes for carers** but again this is not available.

COSTS OF VERY SHELTERED HOUSING

The most recent costings of sheltered and very sheltered housing are those produced by Ernst and Young for DoE (McCafferty, 1994). These costings are up-rated to 1996/97 prices in Netten and Dennett (1997). In Table 5.3 they are further up-rated to 1997/98 prices. The figures quoted are capital and running costs of sheltered and very sheltered housing itself and do not include any of the externally provided services that are specified in Table 7.1 and costed in Annex B of Chapter 8. We have given the housing association costs here because they are more likely than local authorities, on present policies, to be providers of additional stock of sheltered and very sheltered housing.

Table 5.3: Average gross resource costs of housing association sheltered and very sheltered housing	
	(£ p.a. at 1997/98 prices)
Very sheltered housing Sheltered housing	13,778 7,210

Source: Netten and Dennett, 1997 Schemas 1.6 and 1.8 (£135 and £258 per week multiplied by 52 and up-rated to 1997/98 prices)

There are variations in costs around these averages. The research for DoE found that schemes that employed permanent staff had higher revenue costs than those that made more use of visiting domiciliary staff (McCafferty, 1994, p. 174) but that finding does not affect the costings of packages of services in Chapter 8.

RETIREMENT COMMUNITIES

Retirement Communities (sometimes called Continuing Care Communities), where a variety of accommodation and care is provided on the same site, are a relatively new concept of housing in the UK. In the United States and Australia they are more common and tend to be very large with different kinds of housing with varying degrees of support, residential care homes, nursing home and sometimes a hospital all on one site. In theory people can remain on one site but either move from one kind of care to another, or care can be delivered to them. Von Mering and Neff (1993) describe such schemes as a continuum which 'consists of housing where residents live independently and receive certain residential services such as meals, activities, housekeeping and maintenance; *support services* for disabled residents who require assistance with activities of daily living (ADLs); and *health care service* for those who become temporarily ill or who require long-term care' (p. 6). Schemes are popular abroad but there have been problems such as providers going bankrupt and elderly people being turned out when they become too dependent (Weaver and Peace, undated, *Journal of Housing for the Elderly*, vol. 3, Nos. 1/2, 1985). In the UK there are a few experimental schemes, such as one in York, provided by the Joseph Rowntree Memorial Housing Trust, but no evaluation.

The focus group in the main looked on such a concept favourably.

SUMMARY

Only 5% of people over the age of 65 live in sheltered and very sheltered housing. Of the half a million units of sheltered housing in 1997 only 3.5 % is very sheltered. Despite a good deal of satisfaction with both forms of housing, problems are developing particularly with sheltered due to lack of facilities, location and greater choice for people to remain in their own homes. There has been a dramatic fall in provision of all kinds of sheltered housing and in 1997 only 402 units were built in England.

There is a high level of satisfaction with very sheltered housing from tenants but a minority who would have prefered to have remained in their own homes and felt rushed into making decisions. There is little research on the views of carers or of staff. It is difficult to obtain evidence about outcomes of living in very sheltered housing but encouragingly it appears that a growing number of people are moving into it from institutions. The evidence is mixed about the ability of current schemes to provide an alternative to institutions with some evidence of a lack of care services. It is, for most of the situations described in Chapters 7 and 8, more expensive in terms of resource costs to the economy than staying at home options.

Ways of meeting a potential demand for very sheltered housing and of making better use of sheltered include turning the latter into very sheltered, making greater use of communal facilities and enhancing the role of the warden. However there needs to be clear agreement about allocation procedures in the public sector with a likely emphasis on more dependent older people. The different models of providing care i.e. in house or from outside need more research and evaluation and some interesting new ways are being developed.

Very sheltered housing is therefore one of a range of options and not a panacea. However, the dramatic drop in recent provision and the remodelling which is taking place for existing tenants, does suggest that there is a case for some expansion to meet the needs of people who are in mainstream housing.

Chapter 6
The Models:
Assistive Technology

INTRODUCTION

Note: Please note that this section has been a selective look at some technological developments. It draws heavily on a specially commissioned paper from Dr. Donna Cowan and Dr. Alan Turner-Smith and colleagues (Appendix 4).

Assistive technology (AT) is 'an umbrella term for any device or system that allows an individual to perform a task that they would otherwise be unable to do or increases the ease and safety with which the task can be performed' (Cowan and Turner-Smith, 1998, Appendix 4). The aims include allowing people to maintain their dignity and autonomy, to enable them to pursue self-fulfilment and to encourage independence. The use of appropriately chosen aids may allow an individual to function independently for a longer period of time, facilitate the ease with which an activity can be performed or decrease the amount of assistance required from another person (*Ibid.*).

It is unlikely that technology can completely replace care by human beings of old and disabled people on the margins of institutional care. However, technology has already transformed the lives of most people through the design of housing and equipment (e.g. programmable machinery such as washing machines, videos, micro-ovens etc.) and through the development of new methods of communications (e.g. mobile phones and alarm systems). New products are currently being developed which may help older and disabled people to live more independent lives.

The kinds of technology discussed in this section are various types of communications equipment (telephones and alarms), equipment to aid problems of mobility, personal and domestic care, 'smart homes' and telemedicine/telecare. While some, such as telephones and wheelchairs, have been provided for a long time, most are very recent and some still at the design stage. It is therefore, a matter for conjecture how current technical developments will impact on home care in practice.

1. Needs which technology might be able to meet

Before looking as what is currently provided it would be sensible to look at the needs that they are supposed to address. Only by doing this can some evaluation take place.

The main needs causing an older or younger disabled person to seek help (and possibly go into institutional care) are:

- **mobility** (e.g. problems with getting around the home or outside);

- **personal** (e.g. problems with bathing, washing, toileting);

- **domestic** (e.g. problems with taking care of the home such as cleaning, washing clothes);

- **nutrition** (e.g. problems with feeding or drinking unaided);

- **communications.** (e.g. problems with contacting people in an emergency, for information, reassurance, practical or, not the least, for social reasons). Table 6.1 classifies the relevant areas of assistive technology.

Table 6.1: A classification of assistive technology

Communication	Mobility
interpersonal computer access telcommunications multimedia user interfaces environmental control seating and positioning	manual mobility aids powered mobility aids private transportation public transport motor function seating and positioning
Manipulation	**Orientation**

recreational/sports devices
environmental control/adaptation
  of houses
aids for daily living devices
motor function
	orientation and navigation systems
	telecommunications (e.g. video
	  telephones)
	robotics

	Cognition
	time aids planning aids (including reminder devices)

Source: Heart study: Ohlin, P., Fagerberg, G. and Lagerwall, T. (1995)

Another need is for medical help – telemedicine – and it may be helpful to bring this into the home of someone who is disabled. This may be used for:

- diagnosis (e.g. so that a consultant can advise from a distance);

- treatment (so that doses can be measured and administered);

- rehabilitation (so that someone's progress can be monitored).

There is little research on the views of users or costs of telemedicine.

It should also be remembered that carers may be the ones with needs e.g. for help with lifting, feeding, communicating with someone.

2. Current and future provision

There are few items of a technological nature where there is a statutory requirement in the UK for provision by a health or local authority. For example some people are eligible for phones under the Chronically Sick and Disabled Persons Act 1970. Many devices are provided by social services but there is much variation in eligibility and the range available. For example there is variation in provision and eligibility for door openers and intercoms.

Some complex pieces of equipment, such as environmental control systems for people with severe and complex physical disabilities which control a variety of household equipment, can be provided through the NHS after assessment in the home by a medical consultant. It is interesting to note that users of wheelchairs in the UK can add to the basic prescription by paying for customisation or special designs through a voucher scheme (Cowan and Turner-Smith, 1998, Appendix 4).

Some devices fulfil a number of needs. Computers are a form of technology currently used by some disabled people, for example those with motor neuron disease, but now increasingly by older people too. However, for those with disabilities, they may be used to enable the manipulation of objects but also to communicate with others and so greatly enhance quality of life (see AgeNet, 1998 for the role of the Internet). An alarm may be provided both for communication and for security.

(a) Mobility aids

Mobility aids range from the high tech, such as for prosthetic joint replacements, to low tech such as simple sticks and crutches. Wheelchairs may be for inside or outside or both. Stair lifts (to enable people to reach a floor above the ground level) can restore access to a home.

(b) Aids to daily living

There is much equipment for personal care (e.g. long handled brushes and combs), for housework (e.g. adapted mops), for cooking (e.g. bottle openers), for leisure activities (e.g. needle threaders and easy grip scissors) which may help with these problems.

(c) Environmental control systems

Environmental control systems may be operated by the person concerned or be automatic. 'Environmental control systems are devices that allow the user to retain control of their environment within the home despite changing physical disabilities. In general they allow control of any household item which can be operated by a remote control' (Cowan and Turner-Smith, 1998, Appendix 4). Ones which operate automatically such as those that turn off cookers may help reduce the risk of someone who is forgetful or with dementia having an accident.

(d) Communication and security

Taking one of the simplest forms of technology, a telephone can be used for social contact, for contacting someone in an emergency and for business transactions. It is almost universally available. In 1994 93% of households containing someone over the age of 65 in GB had a telephone compared with 61% in 1980 (OPCS, 1996, p. 157). That does not necessarily mean that all could use it. People who are deaf have, on the whole, been well provided for with many different kinds of additional features added. Some alterations, for example for those with visual problems, may be simple such as the large button pad for dialling numbers. People with dementia may find it difficult to use the telephone. Some devices used, for example in Norway where a picture (such as the daughter) of the person to be contacted replaces the number, can be helpful.

The development of alarms has helped both with communications and with the need for people to contact someone in an emergency. They can add to people's feelings of security. They are mainly provided for elderly people but are now being provided for other groups such as those with learning disabilities and women and children at risk of violence in the home (Riseborough, 1997). They were originally mainly provided in sheltered housing but are now increasingly used in the community and are usually called community or dispersed alarms.

Alarms have three main features:

- a means for calling for help (usually a small portable trigger which is carried. When activated it triggers an alarm unit situated by the phone which is programmed to contact a central control point);

- the control centre operator interpreting the call and initiating action (the operator will talk through the problem with the user and if necessary initiate action through contacting whoever is appropriate);

- respondents (if necessary designated people will visit the user and assess the situation/offer help. Sometimes they are employed by the answering service or else designated by the user e.g. family members, neighbours. They may give physical help or simply act as key holder to enable others to enter the home).

A number of variations exist. These include:

- fixed as well as mobile triggers;

- some have no speech link between user and operator;

- some providers use radio based alarm systems;

- the organisation responsible for the service varies (it is most likely to be the housing or social services department or a voluntary body);

- relief call centres may be used outside certain hours or at holiday periods;

- the type of visitor or respondent may vary depending on the time of day the call is received;

- passive alarms e.g. smoke detectors, thermostats, sensors. These are a more recent development and can operate if the person falls or does not take certain action such as flushing the lavatory within a certain specified time.

In 1994, 75% of local authorities in the UK and 21% of the larger housing associations provided community alarms and over 1 million people in sheltered housing and in the community had the use of one (Calling for Help Group, 1994). Research shows that they are safe, most are easy to use but that appreciable numbers do not wear their alarm (40% in one survey – Research Institute for Consumer Affairs (RICA), 1986).

Another type of alarm designed to give security to carers and safety to users is what are sometimes called 'wander' alarms. These devices clip on to the user or may even be implanted, as demonstrated recently *(The Times*, 26.8.98, p. 3) and interact with a radio detector. If a detector within a specified distance does not receive the signal either continuously or at predetermined intervals depending on the system used, an alarm is activated indicating that the wearer has travelled a significant distance. These are particularly used for people with dementia. Costs for these vary between £25 to £6,000 upwards for a residential installation (Cowan and Turner-Smith, 1998, Appendix 4).

Other forms of communication may take place through technology. An Economic and Social Research Council (ESRC) research project is currently examining the use of technology for older people in high rise flats in Glasgow and Edinburgh (McGrail, personal communication). A concierge system has been installed and the concierge can monitor movements in the flats of older people. Cameras in the lift and landings are other devices which have helped stop vandals.

Shopping via Cable television and the Internet is already taking place. The Internet is also proving useful for older and younger disabled people to communicate with others.

(e) Cognition

AT is available for people with learning disabilities e.g. reminder systems, special clocks, diary systems to help them plan their day. This is still rather a small area but some equipment is available and could be used for people who become confused or suffer from a cognitive impairment. For people with a failing memory or impaired reasoning reminder devices can be helpful (Marshall, 1997). It is sometimes thought that people with cognitive impairment cannot manage new technology. These aids demonstrate that this is not the case (Cowan and Turner-Smith, 1998, Appendix 4).

(f) Smart houses

'Smart housing', sometimes called 'intelligent houses', are terms used to describe the electronic and computer controlled integration of many of the devices within the home. It allows the integration of environmental control of a building, either by deliberate control or automatically. This includes door and window openers, heating, lighting, security devices, and telephone and video surveillance. It can include telemedicine so that monitoring can include daily health checks. For example an instrumental toilet/bidet has been developed to measure heart rate, temperature and nutrition.

Some examples of the many test sites for smart home technology include a customer centre which displays many types of housing technology in Japan which is visited by 30,000 visitors a year (Palmer *et al.*, 1998). In Norway, a scheme of eight small flats for people with dementia have been built around a communal area after experiments with three prototypes (Bjorneby, 1998). Technology was proposed as a solution to problems of fire, the residents falling and the danger of them wandering and getting lost. The solutions included a light automatically coming on if the resident gets up at night, staff being alerted if the resident is out of bed for more than 30 minutes at night and the provision of magnet detectors on the exit doors at night.

There is little provision outside demonstration projects. For example, Edinvar Housing Association have developed a demonstration home in Edinburgh (Edinvar, 1998). They say that:

'Wherever possible equipment has been integrated to blend in not just with the physical environment of the home, but also take account of individual needs of end users. As well as assisting occupants with a range of tasks such as opening doors, the equipment Edinvar has installed in their demonstrator flat will help in tracking an occupants movements and identifying potential emergency situations.'
(*Ibid.*, 1998, back page)

The kinds of equipment installed includes: controls for heating, lighting and the bathroom, pressure pad, audible reminders, loop induction amplifier, video entryphone, door opening mechanisms, heat/smoke detectors, curtain motors, fridge/freezer 'defrost' alarms and remote monitoring. Many of these would be useful for everyone.

(g) Telemedicine/telecare

A number of technologies allow health care to be delivered at a distance or remotely (Institute of Health Services Management, 1998; Fisk, 1997; Williams, Spicer and Doughty, 1998). The services which can be given include transmitting images for investigation, community nursing (a nurse can monitor the patient, supervise medication and self injections), advice to patients and carers and the live teleconferencing between a patient, GP or nurse and specialist. Among the potential benefits for people at home are:

- the provision of services locally so cutting down on time, cost and inconvenience for the patient (although people might like the visit);

- access to expert advice from home;

- remote location – allowing services to be provided to people in remote areas;

- better targeted treatments;

- more accurate records.

These may be useful both for people in their own homes and for people who can get to a doctor's surgery or local health centre but not to a more distant hospital.

Similar developments of telemedicine in social care have sometimes been referred to as telecare. For example Williams *et al.* (1998) are developing prompting and monitoring systems to monitor pressure sore preventative care, to support dementia sufferers in the community and other applications.

Thinking about future provision we have to think both about people and AT. In the future people may be fitter, better informed and more articulate in expressing their views. There are lessons here for older people from the Disability Lobbies. As for AT itself the development of technology, especially computing, has been rapid in the last 20 years. It is at least possible that there will be further dramatic advances. But 'It should always be remembered that the opportunities and equalities created by technology, where physical strength or memory does not matter so much, also creates barriers. For example, new interfaces that fully-abled people can enjoy may be unusable by older people with cognitive, vision, hearing, manipulation or other infirmity' (Cowan and Turner-Smith, 1998, Appendix 4).

3. Research on assistive technology

There is very little research on the efficacy in widespread use of technical solutions. A certain amount is known about basic services, such as the extent of telephone coverage, but little on types of provision or evaluation. The Disability Surveys carried out by the OPCS were in the mid 1980s and have not been repeated (Martin *et al.*, 1988). Probably the most extensive national research has been on alarms where RICA has evaluated the technical aspects, ease of use and costs (RICA, 1986; 1997). A recent one on alarms is a survey of 3 local authorities and 1 housing association with interviews with 2,109 older people and 523 staff (Riseborough, 1997) and there have been qualitative studies (Thornton and Mountain, 1992). In addition, most research on sheltered housing includes data on alarms.

Smart homes are only a prototype both in this country (e.g. those by Edinvar Housing Association). There is just a small Norwegian scheme which has been subject to a preliminary evaluation after one year. Prototype smart homes have also been subject to a great deal of professional comment and some by consumers.

FEASIBILITY OF ASSISTIVE TECHNOLOGY

A major issue is that of *cost and production on a large scale*. Economies of scale have not been achieved for many of these examples nor have software systems and network standards converged to the point where large quantities can be sold to reduce the costs. It is probably too early to say whether some very sophisticated technology will become much cheaper if it is mass produced (e.g. as video recorders and mobile homes have) but the problem may be thought to be the limited size of the market in the UK. This is why the interest by the European Union in Technology through their various programmes of research such as European Co-operation in the field of Scientific and Technical research (COST) and Telematics for Elderly and Disabled People (TIDE) programmes are so important. An expanding European market would make it more worthwhile for manufacturers to produce more technological solutions. Some of the devices, such as sensors which detect smoke or intruders, are becoming more widespread among the whole population and may become much cheaper and more readily available.

Another major issue of feasibility is *subsidy and the contribution of the public sector*. There is little indication in the public sector that a technological solution, with the possible exception of alarms, has played much part in packages of care. Whether they would figure highly if people had the money, such as through Direct Payments (currently not available to those aged 65 and over) is unknown and might depend on knowledge of both what is available and their potential.

Assistive technology is provided by the statutory services, however its availability can vary greatly (Cowan and Turner-Smith, in press). Lamb's survey of disabled people reported that they wanted greater independence (Lamb and Layzell, 1994). 64% felt that they would be more independent if better equipped but 75% could not afford to buy suitable equipment (*Ibid.*).

Another problem is the **reliability** of some equipment. It is essential that any equipment provided for an older or disabled person be reliable, relatively simple to operate and have access to quick and regular maintenance and repair. Reliability is very high on consumers' list of requirements for AT (Lane *et al.*, 1997) and is a significant contributory factor in the usage or non-usage of a device (Clemson and Martin, 1996). If equipment is to be accepted and used by older or disabled people, issues such as training (user and carer) and maintenance must be included as part of the service providing the equipment.

Another problem is that the equipment may be both *bulky and expensive*. Videophones, a phone with a video link, are an example.

To be feasible technological models have to be accessible to those who might use them. One of the factors in the uptake of assistive technology is the availability of current and easily accessible information about availability, cost, assessment procedures and funding sources.

ACCEPTABILITY OF ASSISTIVE TECHNOLOGY

Before an aid is considered an individual has to recognise that they have a need and that it could be met. Acceptability will depend in part on the perceptions of the users. For example older people who require aids to daily living may not put themselves in the same category as people who have had a disability since birth or acquired later in life. 'The social model of disability recognises that people may not define themselves as disabled or in need of special equipment so they may not take up a service offered with the best of intentions' (Cowan and Turner-Smith, 1998, Appendix 4). 'To ensure relevant design and uptake of technology, older people have to be given power to influence developments for themselves. This may be through the interested involvement of industrial designers, but most effectively it will be by the financial power older people can exert' (*Ibid.*).

1. Older and disabled people

It is difficult to generalise about acceptability. In some cases it may not be used but there may also be a stigma. 'I am ashamed of the (adapted) bathroom when anybody goes, I feel like oh it's so terrible you know . . . You see I'm not a normal person' (Lebbon and Boess, 1998 quoted in Cowan and Turner-Smith, 1998, Appendix 4). The telephone has no stigma and the mobile phone is looked on by many as a modern attribute. It has also been suggested that some items of AT are accepted readily by most users because they serve both able and disabled users (Cowan and Turner-Smith, 1998, Appendix 4). Reclining chairs and adjustable beds are examples.

Where most of the research in the UK has taken place is over telephones and alarms. In general there is satisfaction with alarms but conflicting evidence on whether there is a stigma attached to them. What is clear is the lack of knowledge by users over their purpose. Riseborough's study found that the alarm was used repeatedly by some older people who were housebound or had high care needs (1997). She found that some of these people used the alarm repeatedly because they needed an advocate and were not sure who to contact over small scale or everyday emergencies. There is some evidence that alarms were seen as poor substitutes for wardens for 24-hour cover (*Ibid.*). Some people who had moved to sheltered housing were angry and fearful about the changes in the warden service.

Some types of technology have been shown not only to be acceptable but also can be a link between able and disabled people – for example the use of the Internet.

There was no discussion in the focus groups about this type of solution.

2. Carers

There is little evidence about the acceptability of technological solutions by carers. It has been suggested that it could release staff for more person-centred activity and might reduce stress but that it should not be used to reduce staffing levels, to compensate for bad design or without thorough debate (Marshall, 1997).

Some research has shown that video conferencing and computer interaction via a television has proved an effective way of forming self-help groups (Cowan and Turner-Smith, 1998, Appendix 4). There is also some evidence from the USA of the use of technology, especially computers, to give information and support to carers (Hunt, 1998; Morris, 1998)

There was no discussion in the focus groups about technology.

3. Service providers

There is little evidence about the views of staff on technology but it is clear that many are not aware of the potential over alarms (e.g. Thornton and Mountain, 1992). It is also evident from research on alarms that there is need for the continued involvement by staff so that the equipment and the users are monitored. For all these groups there are special issues to do with acceptability to the public over passive monitoring especially where people with dementia are concerned and where it is difficult or impossible to get consent. Staff in the Norwegian prototype smart homes were positive about their value especially the night staff who could sleep knowing that they would be alerted if there was an emergency (Bjorneby, 1998).

As Cowan and Turner-Smith point out not all professionals are adequately trained or knowledgeable about what AT can do. There is little in the way of specialised training and education. This is where the European educational programme (Telematic Multidisciplinary Assistive Technology Education – TELEMATE) is important.

OUTCOMES OF ASSISTIVE TECHNOLOGY

There is a lack of research on whether technology can keep people in their own homes. What research there has been on alarms and telephones has shown quite clearly that they are only part of a package of care (e.g. Tinker, 1984; 1989; RICA, 1986).

1. Restoration of mobility

An example of restoration of some mobility is the use of wheelchairs which can be electrically or manually powered. Sometimes technology may encourage a healthy lifestyle rather than compensate for an unhealthy one.

2. Enabling a greater degree of independence

Some technological aids will enable people to be more independent but they will need help when equipment breaks down or is difficult to understand. This, of course applies to people of all ages and levels of ability.

3. Saving lives

There is evidence that telephones and alarms can summon help very quickly but there are also cases highlighted in the press regularly where they have both failed an older or disabled person. However, there has been no systematic study of this.

4. Improving the quality of life

Again there is little systematic research on how some of these devices, including gadgets and aids improve the quality of life although common sense dictates that those that are well designed and user friendly will do so.

5. Ability to be used by older and disabled people

Research by RICA has shown that some aids are little, if ever, used. Bath aids are a classic case. It is also salutary to remember that some devices, such as mobile phones, which would be ideal for disabled people are not able to be used by those who have hearing aids. There are also problems for people because of the complex controls and also the need for dexterity to operate them.

COSTS OF ASSISTIVE TECHNOLOGY

Many items discussed in this report are now available for people privately and not necessarily for people with disabilities. For example devices to open and close curtains. Home-based alarm systems can be bought for (on average) £250 and the cost of renting one from a local authority, together with the services, is approximately £17 per month. The cost of a 'wander' alarm varies from £15 to £6,000. A mat with implanted sensors across a doorway can be bought for about £230. The private sector, including retailers such as Boots and mail order firms, are increasingly providing a range of aids which can be bought by disabled or elderly people or their relatives. As can be seen some of the aids are simple and inexpensive. The Norwegian prototype smart homes found savings compared with the cost of a nursing home place (Bjorneby, 1998).

As already mentioned one of the problems is the lack of a large market which would reduce costs. The market is small and fragmented. Europe, however, is the largest potential market for AT products in the industrialised world. In 1995 about 26 million potential customers of AT products can be expected. Between 1995 and 2020 the estimated number of people who are potential users of AT will increase by more that 25% (Carr, 1993 quoted in Cowan and Turner-Smith, Appendix 4).

Housing grants may be possible for people who are disabled but most of these are not mandatory.

SUMMARY

The assistive technology described in this chapter includes communications equipment, equipment to aid problems of mobility, personal and domestic care, 'smart homes' and telemedicine/telecare. They can answer problems of communications, mobility, manipulation, orientation and cognition. Some will answer more than one problem e.g. an alarm for both communication and security and may greatly enhance the quality of life.

Issues of feasibility are around those of cost and production on a large scale, the degree of subsidy and the contribution of the public sector, the fact that some equipment is bulky and expensive, and the lack of information and advice. On acceptability much depends on the perception of the person – for example mobile phones are very acceptable and do not have a stigma. In general there is satisfaction with some types of AT such as alarms but sometimes a reluctance to use them. There is little evidence about acceptability to carers or service providers. On outcomes one cannot generalise but some have the potentiality to restore mobility, give greater independence and save lives as well as improve the quality of life. There is not a great deal of data on costs but the development of a market in the EU would undoubtedly bring prices down.

Chapter 7
The Vignettes

INTRODUCTION

So far we have summarised the data by using four broad models of alternatives to institutional care. The next stage is to cost these differing approaches, but before doing that it is necessary to consider the missing link: the heterogeneity of the care needs of older people. The kind of support, facilities and services needed by older people on the margins of institutional care will differ depending, for example on whether they are disabled by a physical or a mental health condition, whether they live alone or with a spouse or with another relative/friend, and the kind of housing they occupy. It was not of course possible to cost all major combinations of circumstance; we had to be selective, but there also had to be justification for selecting illustrative situations. This brief chapter therefore describes some of the major types of circumstance of people on the margins of institutional care, and shows how these hypothetical cases were derived. The next chapter shows how these were used to cost different forms of care arrangement.

THE CRITERIA

It was decided that the key variables were age, co-residence and level and type of dependence. Gender was not considered to be a key variable as far as care needs were concerned, though it could clearly have resource implications (and it should be noted that approaching 80% of admissions to institutional care are of women). Genders have therefore been assigned to the hypothetical cases below. The 'type of dependence' variable is perhaps more usefully translated into whether care is required at long, short or critical intervals (Davies *et al.*, 1990).

Rather than select characteristics in an arbitrary way it seemed advisable to select them on the basis of the known distribution of such characteristics in samples of people on the margins of residential care (e.g. those thought by professional staff to be at risk of residential care, or on a waiting list).

The problem was that there were no really adequate data sources for this selection (apart perhaps age). Many of the studies were very out of date, small and drawn from special populations. Added to this was the on-going problem of the complexity of assessing dependency. However, some crude assessments, considered to be sufficient for our purposes, can be made.

1. Age

DoH statistics on **admissions** to residential care by people aged 65 years and over (1995-96, England, long-stay only) showed the age distribution as follows:

65-74 years	10%
75-84 years	39%
85 yrs and over	51%

This distribution was confirmed by other studies such as Allen *et al.,* (1992).

2. Co-residence

Good data on this were hard to find. However, Allen *et al.,* (1992) used two small but relevant samples: (i) 100 elderly people known to Social Service Departments (SSD) and identified by them as at risk of entering residential care, and (ii) 103 elderly people recently admitted to residential care. The residence distribution for these two samples was approximately:

	Sample (i)	Sample (ii)
Lived alone*	67%	74%
Lived with spouse	26%	10%
Lived with younger relative	17%	16%

*although most had some informal care from a non-resident relative or friend and this too is reflected in the vignettes

3. Dependency level/care needs

This was the most difficult variable on which to obtain useful summary data (Sinclair, 1986). For the purposes of this exercise we excluded the small proportion of admissions who seemed to have no dependency problem or a very low level need for care. Summarising existing data Sinclair (1986) suggested that about half of residents appeared to have fairly low levels of need for care, and most (six out of seven) were not totally dependent.

He summarised a number of studies in suggesting the following major characteristics:

serious problem of incontinence	10-20%
serious problem of immobility	10-20%
serious mental health problem	10-20%

He also suggested that proneness to falls was the fourth major problem leading to entry to residential care. We thought we should perhaps also add to this loneliness and fear or anxiety about being able to cope on one's own.

In addition to this Davies *et al.,* (1990) developed a typology relating to whether people need long-interval, short-interval or critical-interval care. Because their own samples did not relate directly to people at the margins of institutional care it was, therefore, hard to assess the distribution of such care needs for our purposes. However, they could be quite easily related to the dependency problems outlined in our vignettes. This has been done to aid costings.

VIGNETTES

On the basis of these variables – and acknowledging the inability to cross-tabulate accurately one with another – we derived six vignettes which would satisfy these criteria. Six was considered the maximum possible number for costing purposes. It also allowed the major types of care need circumstance to be included. People's circumstances are likely to change over time and their needs for support change. The vignettes do not reflect changing needs and only relate to one point in time. They are as follows:

- **Vignette 1.** Man aged 65-74, married and living with a spouse. His dementia is severe enough that he cannot safely be left alone in the house. He is often awake and active at night. During the day he uses the toilet frequently and needs some help and supervision. His wife has arthritis and finds it difficult to get up the stairs. He has short-interval needs (i.e. 'unable to perform one or more domestic tasks which require to be undertaken frequently, that is more often than daily'). He received higher rate Attendance Allowance.

- **Vignette 2.** Woman aged 75-84, recently widowed and living alone. She has a supportive neighbour who is in full-time employment. She has some restrictions on mobility and moderate confusion. She is unwilling to go outside by herself now and is unable to go shopping alone or to collect her pension. She does not receive the Attendance Allowance. She has long-interval needs (i.e. 'unable to perform one or more domestic tasks which require to be undertaken occasionally but less often than daily').

- **Vignette 3.** Woman aged 75-84, living alone, is mentally capable and has become wheelchair-bound after e.g. a stroke. She finds her situation demoralising and needs to be encouraged to socialise and take holidays. She has the lower rate Attendance Allowance. She has critical-interval needs (i.e. 'unable to perform crucial self-care tasks which need to be undertaken frequently and at short notice').

- **Vignette 4.** Woman aged 85+, has moved to live with her married daughter who works part-time. She is mentally capable but has developed diabetes in recent years and now has terminal cancer. She has become doubly incontinent. She has the higher rate Attendance Allowance and her daughter has the Invalid Care Allowance. Her daughter cannot provide her with 24-hour-a-day care but is able to provide care at the weekend. She has critical-interval needs.

- **Vignette 5.** Man aged 85+, living alone. He is prone to falls and is a recent widower, not used to performing any domestic tasks. Cooking, cleaning and doing the laundry are problematic for him. He is lonely. He has short-interval needs. He does not receive Attendance Allowance.

- **Vignette 6.** Woman aged 85+, living alone, and has become anxious and clinically depressed. Physically quite active but needs encouragement to leave the house and to socialise. Needs some support with domestic and self-care tasks. She has long-interval needs. She does not receive Attendance Allowance.

ASSIGNING SERVICES TO THE CASES

The next step in the exercise was to determine, using the framework of the four models of care discussed in the preceding four chapters, the kinds of service which would be needed to keep people in these different types of circumstance at home rather than in an institution. This was done through a pooling of the knowledge of team members, based on research findings from a variety of sources. It has to be emphasised that in many cases our decisions about services had to be speculative because there was no definitive evidence about what would be needed. Although needs for support are likely to change over time, the vignettes relate to only one point in time. Some of the services described are directed primarily at the family caregiver to help that person continue providing care and some at the user to help them remain at home. These (as outlined in Table 7.1) were then used as the basis of the costing exercise as detailed in Chapters 8 and 9.

Table 7.1: Services suggested to maintain at home people in different kinds of care-need circumstances

Vignette/setting	Home environment	Day/night care	Personal care/ household/ shopping/finance	Health care* (excluding bathing)	Respite	Counselling etc.
1a. Ordinary housing with carer	adaptations e.g. downstairs wc, safety devices (value £200)	■ day centre 2 days per week ■ night sitting 1 night per week (48 weeks)	bathing assistance 1 hr per week (48 weeks)	CPN visit once a month (48 weeks)	4 weeks a year	1 hour a month (for carer)
1b. Ordinary housing with carer (alternative support package)	as above	■ day sitting 1 day per week (4 hrs) ■ night sitting 1 night per week (36 weeks)	bathing assistance 1 hr per week (36 weeks)	CPN visit once a month (36 weeks)	16 weeks a year i.e. 2 weeks every 4 weeks.	nil
1c. Very sheltered housing**	*purpose built*	day centre 1 day per week (48 weeks)	bathing assistance 1 hr per week (48 weeks)	CPN visit once a month (48 weeks)	4 weeks a year	nil
2a. Ordinary housing, no carer	nil	day centre 1 day per week (52 weeks)	■ home care 2 hrs per day for 7 days a week ■ bathing assistance 1 hr per week (52 weeks)	nil	nil	nil

Vignette/setting	Home environment	Day/night care	Personal care/household/shopping/finance	Health care* (excluding bathing)	Respite	Counselling etc.
2b. Very sheltered housing**	*purpose built*	nil	■ home care 2 hrs per day for 5 days a week ■ bathing assistance 1 hr per week (52 weeks)	nil	nil	nil
3a. Ordinary housing, no carer	■ alarm ■ adaptations e.g. stair lift, ramps, door widening, downstairs wc, kitchen adaptation, special furniture e.g. bed, battery operated wheelchair	day centre 1 day per week (50 weeks)	■ home care 10 hrs per day 6 days of the week and 2 hrs on the 7th day ■ bathing assistance 1 hr per week (50 weeks)	■ community nurse once per week ■ continence supplies weekly (50 weeks)	2 weeks holiday per year	counselling 1 hr per week (50 weeks)
3b. Smart home – no carer	*purpose built*	day centre 1 day per week (52 weeks)	NOT POSSIBLE TO COST			

Vignette/setting	Home environment	Day/night care	Personal care/household/shopping/finance	Health care* (excluding bathing)	Respite	Counselling etc.
3c. Very sheltered**	*purpose built*	nil	■ home care 6 hrs per day 7 days per week ■ meal per day 7 days of the week ■ bathing assistance 1 hr per week (50 weeks)	■ community nurse once per week ■ continence supplies weekly (52 weeks)	nil	nil
4. Ordinary housing with carer	alarm adaptations e.g. stair lift, downstairs wc	nil	2 hrs home care per day 5 days per week	■ Macmillan nurse 1 hr per week ■ community nurse 1 hr per day 7 days of the week ■ continence supplies (46 weeks)	hospice care 1 week every 2 months (6 weeks)	

Vignette/setting	Home environment	Day/night care	Personal care/ household/ shopping/finance	Health care* (excluding bathing)	Respite	Counselling etc.
5a. **Ordinary housing, no carer**	alarm	■ day centre 1 day per week ■ lunch club 2 days per week (52 weeks)	home care 3 hours per week (52 weeks)	nil	nil	3 times week call from befriender/ advocate/good neighbour/visiting warden) (52 weeks)
5b. **Very sheltered housing****	*purpose built*	nil	■ home care 3 hours per week ■ meal per day 7 days of the week (52 weeks)	nil	nil	nil
6a. **Ordinary housing, no carer**	alarm	■ psychogeriatric day hospital 1 day per week ■ live-in 'lodger' – 'homeshare' (52 weeks)	■ home care 5 hrs per week (including 2 hours week gardening) (52 weeks)	CPN 2 hours per week	nil	

Vignette/setting	Home environment	Day/night care	Personal care/ household/ shopping/finance	Health care* (excluding bathing)	Respite	Counselling etc.
6b. Very sheltered housing**	*purpose built*	as above	■ home care 3 hours per week ■ meal per day 7 days of the week (52 weeks)	as above	nil	nil

* It is assumed that, in addition, all users require a standard package of health care comprising: 2 annual GP visits (a) in their own home, or (b) in the surgery; 1 annual assessment by (a) community nurse or (b) occupational therapist; 4 chiropody sessions; 1 other health/therapy visit (e.g. optician, dentist, physiotherapist); 1 out-patient hospital consultant appointment.

** It is assumed that users in very sheltered housing have one meal per day but in some schemes more meals would be provided. The costs would not be included in the rent.

SUMMARY

In summary, therefore, this short chapter sets out how the alternative models of care were linked to the costing exercise through the development of vignettes (hypothetical cases). These vignettes can also be used to compare the models as far as feasibility, acceptability, and outcome are concerned. This is done in the final chapter.

Chapter 8
Costings of Packages of Care Services for Older People in their Own Homes

SCOPE AND COVERAGE

This chapter provides costings of packages of care services for men and women with characteristics and circumstances depicted in the six 'vignettes' in Chapter 7. For all six vignettes, packages of service were designed for men and women living in ordinary mainstream homes – houses, flats, bungalows etc. – as opposed to sheltered housing. For five of the vignettes, packages were designed as well for people living in very sheltered housing. Full time residential care is not one of the packages of services. But clearly, the costs of packages of services in ordinary homes or very sheltered dwellings must be capable of being compared with full time residential care.

The costings are in terms of resource costs to the economy, which are not always costs to be met in cash by recipients of services or the public purse. Particularly is this so for housing, which is the reason why the value of the home is difficult to treat in cost comparisons between provision of services in ordinary homes (adapted if necessary) and very sheltered housing. This problem is discussed in the fourth section of this chapter.

Three sets of costings are presented:

- costings of packages of services, including dwelling adaptations, for people living in ordinary mainstream homes;

- costings of provision of services in very sheltered housing, including the cost of the housing itself;

- costings for full time residential care.

The scope of the three sets of costings is different. The first set does not include the cost or value of the home, apart from adaptations, whereas the second does include it. The cost of full time residential care includes meals and domestic running costs such as lighting, heating, water supply and furniture which people living in ordinary homes or very sheltered housing pay for from their own income and are not included in the costings in the first two sets. To compare like with like, the value of the home must be added to the cost of services to people living in ordinary homes if a comparison is being made with the cost of care in very sheltered housing. In a comparison of either or both with the cost of full-time residential care, domestic running costs have to be added.

Excluded from the costings are services that would be provided to anyone with the specified characteristics irrespective of the kind of accommodation in which they live. Examples are hospital treatment, GP visits and chiropody. Because they do not vary with accommodation type they do not effect any of the comparisons and so need not be included in the costings.

DEFINITIONS AND SOURCES

The costings presented are averages for England. Within national averages there is considerable diversity, with costs in London, in particular, considerably higher. Ernst and Young (1994) in *The Cost of Specialised Housing* presented cost estimates for London and the rest of England separately and these are summarised in Table 8.4 to give an indication of the cost differential.

Where possible, costs are taken from Ann Netten and Jane Dennett, *Unit Costs of Health and Social Care 1997* (PSSRU, 1997): this work is cited as 'Netten and Dennett 1997', followed by a 'Schema' number or page reference. These costs refer to 1996/97. Also used are costs given by Ernst and Young in *The Cost of Specialised Housing* (1994, p. 63, Table 11). These are shown for London and the rest of England separately and are at January 1992 prices. For comparability with Netten and Dennett 1997, Ernst and Young's figures for London and the rest of England are combined in proportion to population (1:5) and up-rated to 1996/97 prices pro rata to the increase in pay and prices for personal social services between 1991/92 and 1996/97 (Netten and Dennett 1997, p. 85). Many of the costs quoted by Netten and Dennett and in the work by Ernst and Young, are necessarily estimates. Particular problems arise over allowances for overhead costs and in working from an annual salary to costs per hour spent with people receiving services. For details reference should be made to the original sources. The cost figures given by Netten and Dennett and Ernst and Young are considered the best estimates available. But because they are estimates, modest differences between costs of care in ordinary homes, very sheltered housing and full-time residential care cannot be conclusive about which form of care is least costly.

The price basis for this report is 1997/98 prices. In order to show clearly, for purposes of record, how the estimates of costs were made, the detailed working is in terms of 1996/97 prices so that unit costs can be taken directly from Netten and Dennett 1997. Estimates of total costs are then revalued from 1996/97 to 1997/98 prices. For a very heterogeneous array of services, revaluation pro rata to the change in the general price level, usually measured by the Retail Prices Index

(RPI) would be appropriate. Over a run of years social services pay and prices have tended to rise faster than RPI, but not in every individual year. What was the change in personal social services pay and prices between 1996/97 and 1997/98 was not known at the time of writing. So, rather than make an assumption, it seemed better to use the known actual increase in the RPI. Between 1996/97 and 1997/98 mortgage interest has an unusually large effect on the RPI. The whole index, including mortgage interest, rose by 3.3%; but excluding mortgage interest, the increase was 2.7% only. Mortgage interest is not part of the cost of the services included in these costings, so the RPI excluding mortgage interest is used here for revaluing to 1997/98 prices.

UNITS COSTS AND TOTAL COSTS OF SERVICES AND AND ADAPTATIONS IN ORDINARY HOMES

Unit costs of the services are assembled first, and then used to cost the packages of services for the different vignettes. The cost of full time residential care must be mentioned here because it is used in the costing of respite care. It is not the only form of respite care, but normally has to be used if the co-resident carer is ill, for example. Netten and Dennett 1997 quote: £454 as the average cost per week for full-time residential care provided by local authorities and £250 a week for private residential care as a current rate (Schemas 1.2 and 1.3). The figures for local authority and private residential care are not a comparison of like with like. The local authority figure is derived from the cost of a newly built care home with space per resident that conforms to official standards and the charge of £250 a week for private care does not necessarily provide a return on capital that is adequate in the long run quite apart from any differences in standards. Laing estimates that to cover costs, including a reasonable return on capital, for an efficient provider of good quality care for frail elderly people, a charge of about £350 a week would be required outside London, at 1997/98 cost levels (Laing, 1998). A national figure including London would be higher even if scaled back to 1996/97 prices, but it would be well below the £454 a week for local authority accommodation. Where comparisons are made between costs of care in ordinary homes or very sheltered housing and full time residential care, both the local authority figures of £454 a week and a charge based on Laing's figure are used. Cost comparisons may be for the long term, so Laing's estimate of the charge that would cover the cost of good quality care with a reasonable return on capital is more appropriate that a current market average for all standards of care which may not provide a sufficient return on capital for the long term. The figure of £454 a week is used for respite care, which is understood to be more commonly provided by local authority homes than in private establishments.

Not all the unit costs employed in Annex A (costs of services for people in ordinary homes) and Annex B (costs of services for people in very sheltered housing) are shown below. Costs of services included in only one package or two, such as gardening, a lunch club, the services of a Macmillan nurse and a day in a psycho-geriatric day hospital, are estimated in the relevant tables. Costs of services that are more frequent components of packages of services are better discussed at this point, however.

1. Day care

Netten and Dennett 1997 (Schema 1.4) give an average day centre cost of £36 per day. Ernst and Young (1994) quoted average costs of a visit to a day centre, including transport, of £22.06 in London and £19.06 elsewhere. Combined and uprated to 1996/97 prices these figures give £23 per visit. Netten and Dennett 1997 say that the revenue costs included in the figure of £36 refer to a wide variety of types of care. On balance the uprated figure derived from Ernst and Young (£23) seems preferable.

2. Night care (night sitting)

Neither Netten and Dennett 1997 nor Ernst and Young give a figure for night care. An overnight stay in residential care is one possible basis for a figure. But more likely would seem to be a care worker staying overnight in the person's home. Netten and Dennett 1997 (Schema 6.16) give a figure of £8.17 per hour for 'a home care worker providing primarily personal care'. Ten hours can reasonably be assumed for overnight (10 p.m. to 8 a.m. next day), which gives £81.70. 44p was added for travel, which makes £82 per night in round terms. Dividing the weekly figure of £454 for local authority full time residential care by 7 gives £65, to which the cost of transport would have to be added.

3. Respite care

Netten and Dennett 1997 mention respite care only in connection with learning disabilities (p. 43), where they say that there is little information about the cost of homes that specialise in short-term care. For lack of anything better, respite care is costed here at the weekly average cost of full time residential care by local authorities (£454 per week).

4. Adaptations to ordinary dwellings

Adaptations are costed according to their capital cost (Netten and Dennett 1997, Schema 6.18) and the probable length of time that the person for whom they are installed will use them. For there is no presumption that when the person for whom they were installed ceases to live there the home will be relet or sold to someone else who needs the adaptations. The assumptions about the length of time the adaptations will be used has to be based on life expectancy, less a small deduction to allow for the possibility of a later move to residential care. Values for life expectancy are taken from Table 13 of Population Trends No 89 (ONS, 1997). For three of the six 'vignettes', adaptations are included in the package. The durations of use assumed are:

Vignette 1	Man aged 65 – 74	10 years
Vignette 3	Woman aged 75 – 84	7 years
Vignette 4	Woman 85 plus	4 years

With these durations of use, annual equivalents were derived by using an 8% discount rate (for consistency with Netten and Dennett, 1997). Alarms can be dismantled when no longer needed and so a 20-year life is assumed for them. The costs do not include assessments of the type of adaptations needed.

5. Personal care

The cost of providing personal care is taken from Netten and Dennett 1997 (Schema 6.16), i.e. £8.17 per hour plus 44p for transport. See para. 2. The hourly rate of £8.17 is used, plus 44p travel , to calculate costs per day according to the number of hours per day specified in Table 7.1. Where home care is specified in hours per week, one hour per day is assumed. Ernst and Young quote the cost of home help service at £9.32 per hour in London and £6.52 elsewhere. When combined and uprated to 1996/97 prices, these figures give £8.20. This is the same as for the care worker, who is understood to do shopping and similar as part of the care provided.

6. Meals on wheels

No cost is quoted in Netten and Dennett 1997. Ernst and Young (1994) quote £8.15 per meal in London and £6.23 elsewhere. Combining these figures and uprating them to 1996/97 prices gives £6.70 per meal.

7. Continence supplies

What would be required would vary with circumstances. To allow for changes and wear, five new pairs of briefs per month are included and two packs of heavy duty pads (10 per packet) per week. The former are priced at £6.38 (excluding VAT) and the latter at £4.33 in the Boots *Active and Independent* catalogue. At the prices quoted, the briefs would cost £383 a year and the pads £450, £833 in total. These are retail prices for items sold singly. Health authorities would probably be able to buy more cheaply. How much more cheaply is not known, but for present purposes 15% is considered reasonable, which would put the annual cost at £708, £13.60 per week.

8. Alarms

The costing is based on data complied by the Research Institute for Consumer Affairs (RICA, 1997). The average price of the alarms listed was £180. £79 was quoted for a telephone socket for the alarm. £75 a year is quoted for the response service. Alarms can be reused when no longer needed, so a 20 year life is assumed. The same period may be taken for the cost of the telephone socket, as this will remain available for use by subsequent occupiers. The annual equivalent of the capital cost of £259 at an 8% rate of discount is £26. The annual cost of a response service brings the costs to £101 a year. Mention is made of batteries, without costs or prices being cited. An allowance for this would put the total as £110 a year.

9. Community nurse

The costs are taken from Netten and Dennett 1997, Schema 6.9, for a district nurse. Where in Table 7.1 'once per week' is specified, Netten and Dennett's cost per visit is used, £12 plus £1 for travel. Where one hour per day is specified, the figure of £35 per hour on home visits plus £1 travel is used.

10. Community psychiatric nurse

Abbreviated to CPN in Table 7.1. Netten and Dennett 1997, Schema 6.7 gives £52 per hour on home visits, plus £1 for travel. Where the service specified is a visit once a week or once a month, a half hour is assumed plus travel, i.e. £27. Where two hours per week is specified, two visits of one hour are assumed, i.e. each at £52 plus £1 for travel.

11. Counselling

The costs for the service of a community psychiatric nurse are used.

12. Meals for people in very sheltered housing

These are costed on the same basis as meals on wheels. No cost is quoted in Netten and Dennett 1997. Ernst and Young quote £8.15 per meal in London and £5.23 elsewhere. Combining these figures and uprating then to 1996/97 prices gives £6.70 per meal.

13. Care management

Costs of managing the individual services are included with the other service costs, but not managing the care packages as a whole. Netten and Dennett 1997 in Schema 1.9, estimate costs for 'local authority intensive care case management', an experimental scheme where all the clients were elderly and suffering from dementia. The cost is put at £49 per case per week. For want of anything better, this cost is the basis for estimating the cost of care management. It is taken in full for vignettes 1 and 3 where the recipient of the services lives in an ordinary house, with a complex array of services. For other vignettes where the recipient of services lives in an ordinary house one half of the average (i.e. £24.50) is taken. In very sheltered housing, the staff can reasonably be taken to do part of the organising of services, so the care management cost is taken as one quarter of the average.

The persons depicted in vignettes 1 and 4 have co-resident carers (wife and daughter respectively). Caring imposes costs; but they are different in status and kind from the services discussed above and so are not included formally in the costings.

For clarity, the annual costs of care packages, derived from unit costs, are shown in Table 8.1. They are at 1996/97 prices, to match the detail in Annex A. They are shown to the exact pound, again to match the detail, but they cannot be considered anywhere near as precise as that.

Table 8.1: Costs of packages of care for older people living in ordinary homes (£/year)		
	Total cost	**Day, night and respite care**
Vignette 1 alternative (a)	12,229	7,960
Vignette 1 alternative (b)	14,934	11,404
Vignette 2 alternative (a)	9,032	1,196
Vignette 3 alternative (a)	36,073	1,950
Vignette 4 alternative (a)	25,517	7,386
Vignette 5 alternative (a)	6,424	2,990
Vignette 6 alternative (a)	12,343	3,065

Source: Annex A, Tables A.1 to A.7

PROVISION OF CARE PACKAGES IN ORDINARY HOMES: THE COST OR VALUE OF THE DWELLING

A like with like comparison of the cost of provision of services to someone living in an ordinary home (in the sense not being sheltered or very sheltered) with the cost of care in a very sheltered dwelling must include the cost of the home. This is most clearly seen if the home belongs to a local authority or housing association, but the same principle holds if the home is owner-occupied or rented from a private landlord.

For consistency with the way in which the cost of very sheltered housing and local authority residential care is calculated, the cost of ordinary housing occupied by older men and women receiving services should be calculated as the annual equivalent of the capital cost plus necessary costs (upkeep of the dwelling, plus – with rented housing – management costs). Such a calculation of costs provides figures for resource costs in economic terms, which are by no means the same thing as cash costs incurred by public authorities, tenants or owner-occupiers. An owner-occupier who owns their home outright – 'free and clear' – has only the cost of upkeep to pay, in contrast with owner-occupiers with a mortgage.

For reasons discussed in Annex C, it is not possible to calculate the value of the dwellings on a fully consistent basis as between the main tenures – owner-occupied, renting from a local authority or housing association, or renting from a private landlord. Since the costings for provision of services to men and women in very sheltered housing included the cost of very sheltered housing provided by housing associations (see next section), comparability is best achieved by using the cost of ordinary (in the sense of non-sheltered) housing provided by housing associations for the housing component of the cost of provision of services in an ordinary house. Using values of owner-occupied houses can produce anomalous results with very expensive houses.

The cost of the dwelling is taken to be the annual equivalent of the capital cost of a new dwelling plus running costs. There are two reasons for taking the cost of a new dwelling. The first is that if the more older men and women are enabled to continue to live in an ordinary home instead of moving to full time residential care, fewer dwellings are vacated and therefore fewer dwellings available for reletting to new tenants. Correspondingly, more new dwellings are therefore required to make the same impact on housing need. So the housing component of the cost of providing care for older men and women in ordinary housing on this analysis is the cost of a new house or flat. The second is that the costs for very sheltered housing provided by housing associations (see next section) are for recently built dwellings

The estimate of the cost of new housing is based on the cost of new dwellings for housing associations and the Housing Corporation's allowances for the running costs (management and maintenance) of new dwellings. Also included is the recommended annual provision for major repairs not included in the allowance for maintenance, 0.8% of capital cost excluding land. The capital cost taken is the average for England for dwellings designed for two persons, £45,070 in 1996/97.

With major repairs provided for, a 100-year life can be reckoned on for converting the capital cost to an annual sum. The annual cost is therefore:

	1996/97 prices
Capital cost: £45,070, annualised at 8% over 100 years	£3,607
Running costs	£675
Provision for major repairs:	
0.8% of building cost (= 80% of total cost)	£288
Total of above	£4,570

For a comparison between the costs of providing care for older people in ordinary homes with the cost of providing care in very sheltered housing, the annual resource cost of ordinary housing, £4,570 on the assumption specified, has to be added to the total costs of services in Table 8.1.

PROVISION OF CARE PACKAGES: COST OF CARE FOR PEOPLE IN VERY SHELTERED HOUSING AND COMPARISON WITH ORDINARY HOUSING

Netten and Dennett 1997 in Schema 1.8 quote £258 a week as the cost (capital cost and running costs) of very sheltered housing provided by housing associations. Its basis is the costings by Ernst and Young *(The Cost of Specialised Housing*, report to the Department of the Environment, 1994), up valued to 1996/97 prices. This weekly average rent has to be taken to apply to all of the vignettes where very sheltered housing is one of the forms of provision of services. In Table 7.1, packages of services are specified for people living in very sheltered housing that are different from those specified for people living in ordinary housing. No adaptations are required in very sheltered housing and requirements for day centres and night sitting are less owing to the services provided by the staff in very sheltered housing. Costs of services for older people in very sheltered housing are in Annex B. The basis of the cost estimates there is the same as in Annex A for people in ordinary housing. Costs of care in ordinary housing and very sheltered housing are compared in Table 8.2, which is arranged to show how the difference in the cost of externally provided services (i.e., not included in the cost of very sheltered housing) compares with the difference between the value of ordinary houses occupied by older people receiving services and the cost of very sheltered housing. This difference is the same for all vignettes (£13,416 – £4,570 = £8,846). Vignette 4 is omitted because very sheltered housing for this vignette is not included in Table 7.1.

Table 8.2: Cost comparisons between services in ordinary homes and in very sheltered housing (£/year) 1996/97 prices					
	Vignette no				
	1	2	3	5	6
Services other than housing					
Ordinary homes	12,229 or 14,934	9,032	36,073	6,424	12,343
Very sheltered housing	4,294	5,452	22,925	4,418	12,995
Difference	**+7,935 or 10,640**	**+3,580**	**+13,148**	**+2,006**	**−652**
Housing					
Difference	−8,846	−8,846	−8,846	−8,846	−8,846
Difference in totals	**−1,011 or +1,794**	**−5,266**	**+4,302**	**−6,840**	**−9,498**

Source: Table 8.1 and Annex B Tables B.1 to B.5

The cost of the externally provided services is higher for people living in ordinary homes than in very sheltered housing in all but one instance, as would be expected. The exception, Vignette 6, is explained by the cost of services for people in very sheltered housing including a meal every day, which for the person living in ordinary housing is assumed to be provided by the rent free lodger. The differences for vignette 1 are within the margin of uncertainty that arises from (among other things) the way care management is costed. For vignettes 2, 5 and 6 the resource costs of care in very sheltered housing appear higher than in suitably adapted ordinary houses; for vignette 3 the opposite is the case.

The figures in Tables 8.1 and 8.2 are at 1996/97 prices. Totals (including housing) revalued to 1997/98 prices are in Table 8.3.

Table 8.3: Annual costs of services (including house values and costs) in ordinary homes and very sheltered housing revalued to 1997/98 prices (£/year)						
	Vignette no					
	1	2	3	4	5	6
Ordinary homes	17,253 or 20,031	13,969	41,740	26,206	11,291	17,370
Very sheltered housing	18,188	19,377	37,322	–	18,316	27,124

The costings in Tables 8.1, 8.2 and 8.3 are national averages. Within the national average, costs in London are higher than elsewhere. Evidence of the magnitude of the difference is provided by unit costs published by Ernst and Young and summarised in Table 8.4. With two exceptions, they show a difference of 20-30%.

Table 8.4: Average unit costs of health and social care services in London and the rest of England 1992			
	Unit cost London (£)	Unit cost rest of England (£)	London as percent of rest of England
Health visitor (per visit)	20.20	16.71	121
District/Community nurse (per visit)	10.87	9.11	119
Home help (per visit)	9.32	6.52	143
Meals on wheels (per meal)	8.15	5.23	156
Chiropodist (per visit)	23.46	19.38	121
Social worker (per visit)	40.68	31.50	129
Day centre and transport (per visit)	22.64	19.06	119
Occupational therapist (per visit)	23.00	19.10	120
Physiotherapist (per visit)	23.53	19.54	120

Source: Ernst and Young, 1994, The Cost of Specialised Housing, p. 63

COMPARISON WITH COSTS OF FULL-TIME RESIDENTIAL CARE

Comparison between costs of services and adaptations for someone living in an ordinary house or in very sheltered housing with the cost of full-time residential care is difficult and uncertain. The first reason has already been alluded to, the large difference between reported costs for local authority residential care homes and fees charged by privately owned homes (see Netten and Dennett 1997, Schemas 1.2 and 1.3 and Laing (1998)). The average weekly cost for local authority homes was used for costing respite care (see p. 69, Netten and Dennett 1997), so for consistency it has to be used for comparison with services in ordinary housing and very sheltered housing. The second reason is uncertainty about how much to allow for people living in ordinary houses or very sheltered housing having to pay for goods and services (food, heating, lighting, water etc.) which are provided to residents in care homes and included in the weekly cost or charge.

The difference between the estimated weekly resource cost of accommodation in a new or recently built residential care home and private sector charges were referred to above. In many instances like is not being compared with like. Laing's figure of £350 per week is for nursing homes (Laing, 1998). At least some of the people depicted in the vignettes would be likely to need the kind of care provided by nursing homes. To represent the private sector the figure of £350 per week is scaled up to include London and scaled for 1996/97 prices to £365 per week, £18,980 a year. Comparisons are made both with this cost and with the LA cost of £454 per week, £23,608 a year.

Domestic running costs and living expenses are usually brought to account by reference to Income Support scale rates. For residents in care homes, the scale rate in 1996/97 was £13.75 a week. For people living in a house or flat (including very sheltered housing) the scale rate varied through pensioner premiums, at one of three rates according to age: under 75; 75-79 and 80 or over. The persons represented by vignette 1 would receive a premium at the under 75 rate; vignettes 2 and 3 at either the 75-79 or 80 and over rate and Vignettes 4, 5 and 6 at the 80 and over rate. The 1996/97 scale rates were:

	Personal allowance	Premium	Total
Vignette 1	£47.90	£19.15	£67.05
Vignette 2	£47.90	£21.30	£69.20
Vignette 3	£47.90	£21.30	£69.20
Vignette 4	£47.90	£25.90	£73.80
Vignette 5	£47.90	£25.90	£73.80
Vignette 6	£47.90	£25.90	£73.80

As well as Income Support at these rates, the man depicted by vignette 1 and the woman by vignette 4 would qualify for higher rate Attendance Allowance (£48.50 in 1996/97) and the woman depicted by vignette 3 would qualify for lower rate Attendance Allowance (£32.40). Attendance Allowance is not means tested and so would be payable in addition to the Income Support scale rates. The allowance is, however, intended to help with the extra costs incurred as a consequence of disabilities and so is not treated as an addition to domestic running costs and living expenses. The woman depicted by vignette 3 would also qualify for the Severe Disability Premium (£36.60 a week) and hence also the highest rate of pensions premium (£25.90). The daughter of the woman depicted by vignette 4 might also qualify for Invalid Care Allowance (£36.40). This likewise is treated as a contribution to living expenses and not as an addition to domestic running costs and living expenses.

In a comparison between the resource costs of care in older people's own homes (ordinary homes or very sheltered housing) and full time residential care, domestic costs could be brought to account in one of three ways:

(i)   add the scale rates of Income Support to the costs of care (including the house value or cost) in people's own homes and add the allowance of £13.75 per week to the cost of residential care;

(ii) add the difference between the scale rate and £13.75 to the cost of care in people's own homes; or

(iii) subtract the difference between the cost of care in people's own homes and £13.75 from the cost of residential care.

The third is the most convenient, as the costs for care in older people's own homes (Table 8.3) can be used without change. The cost of full time residential care calculated on this basis is shown in Table 8.5.

Table 8.5: Cost of residential care adjusted for difference in living expenses (£/year)

	Vignette no					
	1	2	3	4	5	6
Local authority cost						
Cost of residential care	23,608	23,608	23,608	23,608	23,608	23,608
Living cost adjustment	–2,772	–2,883	–5,026	–3,123	–3,123	–3,123
Adjusted cost of residential care (1996/97 prices)	**20,836**	**20,725**	**18,582**	**20,485**	**20,485**	**20,485**
Adjusted cost of residential care (1997/98 prices)	**21,399**	**21,285**	**19,084**	**21,038**	**21,038**	**21,038**
Private sector						
Cost of residential care	18,980	18,980	18,980	18,980	18,980	18,980
Living cost adjustment	–2,772	–2,883	–5,026	–3,123	–3,123	–3,123
Adjusted cost of residential care (1996/97 prices)	**16,208**	**16,097**	**13,954**	**15,857**	**15,857**	**15,857**
Adjusted cost of residential care (1997/98 prices)	**16,646**	**16,532**	**14,331**	**16,285**	**16,285**	**16,285**

SUMMARY

The costings of packages of services for men and women depicted in the six vignettes (provide some comparisons of the cost of care in ordinary homes and in very sheltered housing. Both can be compared with costs and charges for full time residential care. As this Chapter has explained, some parts of the calculations depended on assumptions about the staff time involved in, for example, managing packages of care, and others on incomplete information about how much of the time of (for example) community nurses spent with those who receive their services. The average costs quoted are therefore approximate estimates. Defensible alternative assumptions could sometimes result in different figures for costs, Differences of a few hundred pounds a year cannot in consequence demonstrate a material cost advantage or disadvantage.

A comparison is made in Table 8.6 between the cost of full time residential care as estimated in Table 8.5 and care in older people's own homes (Table 8.3). Whether like is being compared exactly with like especially in terms of quality is not certain, so the comparison must be interpreted with caution.

	Vignette no					
	1	**2**	**3**	**4**	**5**	**6**
Care in people's own homes Ordinary houses	17,253 or 20,031	13,969	41,740	26,206	11,291	17,370
Very sheltered housing	18,188	19,377	37,322	–	18,316	27,124
Full time residential care Local authority basis	21,399	21,285	21,285	21,038	21,038	21,038
Private sector basis	16,646	16,532	16,532	16,285	16,285	16,285

Table 8.6: Summary of costs of different structures of care (£/year) 1997/98 prices

Subject to the provisos, the costings summarised in Table 8.6 show that there is no general rule for all the vignettes about whether care in ordinary housing, adapted if necessary, costs more or less than care in very sheltered housing. Nor is there a general rule about either being less costly than full-time residential care. It depends on how many hours home care, including day and night sitting, are needed and on how far such care is provided by the staff of very sheltered housing. For vignettes 2, 5 and 6 care in an ordinary home is cheaper than care in very sheltered housing. But for vignette 3 the opposite is true. The person depicted in this vignette require large amounts of home care; in an ordinary home it has to be provided by a home carer one to one but in very sheltered housing it can be provided partly by the staff who need not be in a one to one ratio with the residents. For the same reason full-time residential care is substantially cheaper than either care in an ordinary home or in very sheltered housing for the woman depicted in vignette 4.

Each of the vignettes is now considered in detail in relation to each of the models, in order to show the particular strengths and weaknesses of the models in different care-need circumstances.

Vignette 1. Man with severe dementia, who cannot be left alone in the house, living with his wife. Co-resident care appears feasible and acceptable, although respite care to support the wife might be problematic for the husband. It is also not an inexpensive arrangement because the spouse bears the cost of care. Very sheltered housing might be a suitable option for this couple if they were willing to move and could find the kind of housing they liked. The assistive technology model is unlikely to be appropriate for the husband who would have great difficulty in understanding its use but passive monitoring could help his wife.

Vignette 2. Recently bereaved woman living alone but with a supportive neighbour. She has some mobility restriction, moderate confusion, and is unwilling to go out by herself. If this woman has no prospect of a co-resident carer (although she might be a candidate for a home share arrangement – see Annex E), only three of the models are appropriate. Intensive home support appears feasible and to have reasonable cost implications, though there may be problems in accessing appropriate services, providing her with relevant knowledge, and eliciting the woman's own preferences. Such services may also not be acceptable to her because her awareness of need may be limited. The very sheltered housing option also appears feasible but more expensive and its acceptability may be questionable. Assistive technology is probably not the answer for this woman as she is in need of social contact.

Vignette 3. A highly dependent wheel-chair-bound woman living alone, with no cognitive impairment. Again, if there is no prospect of a co-resident carer the second model is not feasible. Given her critical-interval needs, intensive home support may also not be feasible, though it could well be the most acceptable option to her and can work as is evidenced by schemes in Annex E. However, it is clearly very expensive. Very sheltered housing may also be impossible with the woman's level of care need. Extensive assistive technology could provide a feasible care arrangement, but again would be extremely expensive. It is possible that any home care arrangement would break down after some time. She may be a candidate for a nursing home.

Vignette 4. A woman with diabetes and terminal cancer who is living with a married daughter who works part-time. The mother is doubly incontinent and has critical interval needs. This woman has a co-resident but not full-time carer. Her care therefore poses problems for her daughter. Respite care might be feasible and acceptable, though it would be most appropriately offered in a hospice, and there might be a problem of availability. Any such support services would also be expensive. With such a high level of need the co-resident care arrangement might break down. Neither very sheltered housing nor assistive technology would be likely to be able to cater for this woman's care needs. Residential care is the cheaper option.

Vignette 5. A man living alone who is prone to falls and is not used to performing any domestic tasks. If there is no prospect of a co-resident carer any of the other models might be appropriate (and also home share). Intensive home support would probably be acceptable to him (and is the cheapest option), and the services he needs would probably be available; the same is true of very sheltered housing and possibly of assistive technology.

Vignette 6. An anxious and clinically depressed woman living alone. She is physically active but needs encouragement to leave the house and to socialise. The two reasonable options are intensive home support and very sheltered housing. Because the externally provided services are nearly the same, the total cost of home support is much lower. There could, however, be problems. For instance there may be a lack of community based services in her area for people with depression. Assistive technology does not appear to be appropriate because this woman has a need for social contacts.

Annex A: Details of Costings of Services in Ordinary Homes

Table A.1: Vignette 1, Alternative (a)	
	£/year
Home environment	
Downstairs WC (Netten and Dennett 1997, Schema 6.18) £983 annualised	146
Shower downstairs (Netten 1997, Schema 6.18) £1,153 annualised	172
Safety devices £200 annualised	30
Sub total	**348**
Day and night care	
Day centre 2 days per week, 48 weeks: 48 x 2 x £23	2,208
Night sitting, 1 night per week, 48 weeks: 48 x £82	3,936
Sub total	**6,144**
Personal care/household/shopping/finance	
Bathing assistance 1 hour per week, 48 weeks: 48 x £8.60	**413**
Health care	
Visit by community psychiatric nurse once a month: 12 x £27	**324**
Respite care	
4 weeks a year: 4 x £454	**1,816**
Counselling	
1 hour per month: 12 x £53	**636**
Care management	
52 weeks: 52 x £49	**2,548**
TOTAL (of which day care, night care and respite care)	**12,229** (7,960)

Table A.2: Vignette 1, Alternative (1b)	
	£/year
Home environment As in Table A.1	348
Day and night care Day sitting, 1 day per week, 4 hours, 36 weeks: 36 x £33 Night sitting, 1 night per week, 36 weeks: 36 x £82 Sub total	1,188 2,952 4,140
Personal care/household/shopping/finance Bathing assistance 1 hour per week, 36 weeks: 36 x £8.60	310
Health care As in Table A.1	324
Respite care 16 weeks a year: 16 x £454	7,264
Care management As in Table A.1	2,548
TOTAL (of which day care, night care and respite care)	**14,934** (11,404)

Table A.3: Vignette 2, Alternative (a)	
	£/year
Home environment None	nil
Day and night care Day centre, 1 day per week, 52 weeks: 52 x £23	1,196
Personal care/household/shopping/finance Home care, 2 hours per day, 7 days a week, 52 weeks: 7 x 52 x £16.80 Bathing assistance, 1 hour per week, 52 weeks: 52 x £8.60 Sub total	6,115 447 6,562
Health care, respite care, counselling None	nil
Care management 52 weeks at £24.50	1,274
TOTAL (of which day care, night care and respite care)	**9,032** (1,196)

Table A.4: Vignette 3, Alternative (a)

	£/Capital cost		£/year
Home environment			
Alarm – capital and running cost			110
Adaptions (costs from Netten and Dennett 1997, Schema 6.18)			
Stair lift	1,876	annualised over 7yrs:	360
Ramps	219	annualised over 7yrs:	42
Door widening	343	annualised over 7yrs:	66
Downstairs wc	983	annualised over 7yrs:	189
Kitchen	2,250	annualised over 7yrs:	432
Battery operated wheelchair (from Netten and Dennett, 1997, Schema 6.17)	334		
Special bed	1,000	annualised over 7yrs:	192
Sub total			**1,725**
Day and night care			
Day centre, 1 day per week for 50 weeks: 50 x £23			1,150
Personal care/household/ shopping/finance			
Home care, 10 hour per day, 6 days per week, 50 weeks: 6 x 50 x £82			24,600
Home care, 2 hours per day, 1 day per week: 50 x £16.80			840
Bathing assistance, 1 hour per week, 50 weeks: 50 x £8.60			430
Sub total			**25,870**
Health care			
Community nurse, Netten and Dennett 1997 Schema 6.9 gives £12 per visit plus £1 transport: 50 x £13			650
Continence supplies: 50 x £13.60			680
Sub total			**1,330**
Respite care			
2 weeks holiday (say)			800
Counselling			
1 hour per week: 50 x £53			2,650
Care management			
52 weeks at £49 per week			2,548
TOTAL			**36,073**
(of which day care, night care and respite care)			(1,950)

Table A.5: Vignette 4, Alternative (a)		
	£/Capital cost	**£/year**
Home environment		
Alarm – capital and running cost		110
Stair lift	1,876 annualised over 4yrs:	566
Downstairs wc	983 annualised over 4yrs:	297
Sub total		**973**
Personal care/household/shopping/finance		
Day care, 2 hours per day, 5 days per week, 46 weeks: 5 x 46 x £16.80		3,864
Health care		
Macmillan nurse 1 hour per week She is a specialist so costed at same rate as community psychiatric nurse, i.e. £52 per hour plus £1 for transport: 46 x £53		2,392
Community nurse 1 hour per day, 7 days per week From Netten and Dennett 1997, Schema 6.9: £35 per hour, on home visits plus £1 transport: 7 x 46 x £36		11,592
Continence supplies at £13.60 per week		626
Sub total		**14,610**
Respite care		
Hospice care 1 week every 2 months, i.e. 6 weeks per year No figure for hospice care so take mid point of hospital cost for elderly (Netten and Dennett 1997, Schema 7.1 give £117.64 per day. i.e £823 and Laing (1997)'s figure of £350 per week for a private nursing home, i.e. £587) 6 x £587		3,522
Counselling		
1 hour per week: 50 x £53		2,650
Care management		
52 weeks at £49 per week		2,548
TOTAL (of which day care, night care and respite care)		**25,517** (3,522)

Table A.6: Vignette 5, Alternative (a)

	£/year
Home environment	
Alarm – capital and running cost	110
Day and night care	
Day centre, 1 day per week, 52 weeks: 52 x £23	1,196
Lunch club 2 days per week. No cost figure available but assume three quarters of day centre cost since meal and transport provided: 2 x 52 x £17.25	1,794
Sub total	**2,990**
Personal care/household/shopping/finance	
Home care, 3 hours per week: 52 x 3 3£8.60	1,342
Counselling etc	
Call three times a week from befriender, advocate, good neighbour, visiting warden. No specific cost available. Assume half hour at care worker rate, £4.10 plus 44p transport 52 x 3 x £4.54	708
Health care, respite care, counselling	
None	nil
Care management	
52 weeks at £24.50 per week	1,274
TOTAL	**6,424**
(of which day care, night care and respite care)	(2,990)

Table A.7: Vignette 6, Alternative (a)	
	£/year
Home environment	
Alarm – capital and running cost	110
Day and night care	
Psycho-geriatric day hospital 1 day per week, Netten and Dennett 1997, Schema 7.1 give £58.94 per day hospital attendance for elderly people with mental health problems: 52 x £58.94	3,065
Live in lodger/home share. No cost known but assume lodger remunerated by free accommodation	nil
Sub total	**3,065**
Personal care/household/shopping/finance	
Home care, 3 hours per week excluding gardening: 52 x 3 x £8.60	1,342
Gardening: no figure to hand but say £10 per hour 52 x 2 x £10 including transport	1,040
Sub total	**2,382**
Health care	
Community psychiatric nurse, 2 hours per week at £52 per hour plus £1 travel: 2 x 52 x £53	5,512
Care management	
52 weeks at £24.50 per week	1,274
TOTAL	**12,343**
(of which day care, night care and respite care)	(3,065)

Annex B: Details of Costings of Externally Provided Services in Very Sheltered Housing

'Externally provided services' are provided from outside of very sheltered housing. The cost of sheltered housing is not shown here. There are therefore no entries that correspond to 'home environment' in Table A.1 to A.7 in Annex A.

Table B.1: Vignette 1, Alternative (c)	
	£/year
Day and night care Day centre 1 day per week, 48 weeks: 48 x £23	1,104
Personal care/household/shopping/finance Bathing assistance, 1 hour per week, 48 weeks: 48 x £8.60	413
Health care Visit by community psychiatric nurse once a month: 12 x £27	324
Respite care 4 weeks a year: 4 x £454	1,816
Care management 52 weeks: 52 x £12.25	637
TOTAL (of which day care, night care and respite care)	**4,294** (2,920)

Table B.2: Vignette 2, Alternative (b)	
	£/year
Personal care/household/shopping/finance Home care, 2 hours per day, 5 days per week, 52 weeks: 5 x 52 x £16.80 Bathing assistance, 1 hour per week, 52 weeks: 52 x £8.60 **Sub total**	4,368 447 **4,815**
Day and night care, health care, repite care, counselling None	nil
Care management 52 weeks: 52 x £12.25	637
TOTAL (of which day care, night care and respite care)	**5,452** (nil)

Table B.3: Vignette 3, Alternative (b)	
	£/year
Personal care/household/shopping/finance	
Home care, 6 hours per day, 7 days per week: 7 x 52 x £49.50	18,018
1 meal per day, 7 days per week: 7 x 52 x £6.70	2,439
Bathing assistance, 1 hour per week, 52 weeks: 52 x £8.60	447
Sub total	**20,904**
Health care	
Community nurse, once per week: 52 x £13	676
Continence supplies: 52 x £13.60	708
Sub total	**1,384**
Day and night care, respite care, counselling	
None	nil
Care management	
52 weeks: 52 x £12.25	637
TOTAL	**22,925**
(of which day care, night care and respite care)	(nil)

Table B.4 : Vignette 5, Alternative (b)	
	£/year
Personal care/household/shopping/finance	
Home care, 3 hours per week: 3 x 52 x £8.60	1,343
1 meal per day, 7 days per week: 7 x 52 x £6.70	2,439
Sub total	**3,781**
Day and night care, health care, respite care, counselling	
None	nil
Care management	
52 weeks: 52 x £12.25	637
TOTAL	**4,418**
(of which day care, night care and respite care)	(nil)

Table B.5: Vignette 6, Alternative (b)	
	£/year
Day and night care	
Psycho-geriatric day hospital 1 day per week (see Table A.7)	3,065
Live in lodger/home share (see Table A.7)	nil
Sub total	**3,065**
Personal care/household/shopping/finance	
Home care, 3 hours per week: 3 x 52 x £8.60	1,342
1 meal per day, 7 days per week: 7 x 52 x £6.70	2,439
Sub total	**3,781**
Health care	
Community psychiatric nurse, 2 hours per week (see Table A.7)	5,512
Respite care and counselling etc	
None	nil
Care management	
52 weeks: 52 x £12.25	637
TOTAL	**12,995**
(of which day care, night care and respite care)	(3,065)

Annex C: Costs of Ordinary Housing

Calculating the resource cost of the house on an exactly comparable basis for all four of the relevant tenures – owner-occupied, rented from a private landlord, rented from a local authority, rented from a housing association – is not possible for both conceptual and practical reasons. Market values can be estimated for owner-occupied dwellings belonging to older men and women (Hancock, 1997). But the market values of dwellings rented from private landlords by elderly people are likely to be influenced by many being let on regulated tenancies, which restrict the rent and provide security of tenure. In principle, capital values could be assessed with hypothetical vacant possession, but data limitations prevent this at the present time, notably allowing for condition of the dwellings, as the characteristics that are straightforward to specify, such as the number of rooms and whether the house is detached, semi-detached or terraced. For local authority and housing association dwellings, replacement cost is one possibility, but that does not equal to capital value.

In view of all the difficulties, a compromise is necessary, with differing bases for the different tenures.

(a) *Owner-occupied dwellings*. Hancock (1997, Table 6) gives estimates of £76.400 as the mean value and £62,530 as the median for owner-occupiers aged 65-79 and £81,390 as the mean and £63,250 as the median for owner-occupiers aged 80 and over. The median is the more suitable than the mean for present purposes as it is less affected by extreme values. The medians for ages 65-79 and 80 and over are sufficiently close for a single value to represent both age groups and therefore to apply to all 'vignettes'. This value is taken to be £62,900 (the mid point between the two medians rounded to the nearest hundred). The figure refers to 1995. Scaling up pro rata to DETR's mix adjusted index of house prices, gives an increase of 13.3% between 1995 and 1997, to £83,500. The annual equivalent at 8% over a 60-year life (conventional, but at 8%, the exact duration makes very little difference if the life is beyond 40 years) is £6,747. For expenditure on upkeep, the nearest approximation immediately available is average expenditure by outright owners. £974 a week according to the Family Expenditure Survey. A 1997/98 equivalent would be £10 a week. This has to be shaded down because older home owners generally spend less, so £9 is taken, to which insurance (at about £3 a week) is added to give £12 a week, £840 a year. The total annual resource cost of owner-occupied houses for all six 'vignettes' is therefore put at **£7,590** (rounded).

(b) *Private sector tenants*. The average rent paid by tenants above retiring age in 1995/96 (the most recent year for which the required detail is available) was £42 a week. This figure cannot be taken as representing resource costs, owing to many of the rents being set at 'fair rent' levels, which are well below market rent levels as expressed in the rents for dwellings let on assured shortholds. The best that can be done with the data currently available to estimate a market rent for private sector tenants above retirement age, is to work out what would be their average rent of for each type of dwelling (detached house, semi-detached, terrace, purpose built flat, converted flat) the average rent was the same as for all tenants. This calculation gives £79 a week. The Survey of English Housing shows an increase of 3% in assured shorthold rents between

1995/96 and 1996/97. A figure for 1997/98 is not yet available, but a similar increase can reasonably be assumed, to give £84 a week, **£4,370** a year. This could well not be wholly comparable with the figure for owner-occupiers if the estimated market rent gave less than an 8% return in real terms (excluding capital appreciation).

(c) *Social sector tenants.* Here the most meaningful resource cost is probably that for a new housing association dwelling. The rationale is that because the need for social sector tenancies is increasing, fewer departures to live in residential care mean correspondingly fewer dwellings vacated and available for reletting to new tenants; hence to make the same impact on housing need, an equivalent increase in the number of new social rented sector dwellings is required. The resource cost estimated is the annual equivalent of the capital cost plus the Housing Corporation's allowance for running costs (management and maintenance) and the recommended allowance for major repairs not included in the allowance for maintenance (0.8% of capital costs excluding land). For 1996/97, the average capital cost for dwellings designed for two persons was £45,070. The annual equivalent at 8% with a 100-year life (because major repairs are provided for in the costing) would be £3,607; the running cost allowance £675 and the provision for major repairs £288, £4,570 in total. Building cost rose by about 3% between 1996 and 1997 and repair work by a similar amount, so a 3% increase overall is taken between 1996/97 and 1997/98 to give **£4,710** in 1997/98.

Chapter 9
Paying for Care and Support

INTRODUCTION

The previous chapter identified the gross resource costs associated with each of the vignettes, distinguishing care, accommodation and living costs. This facilitates comparison of the costs of providing care in ordinary homes, very sheltered housing (where some of the care costs are included in the rent the tenant pays) and residential care (where the total cost includes care, accommodation and other living expenses).

In this chapter we examine who meets these costs: the individual or the tax payer; and if the latter, from which part of the public expenditure budget. For each vignette a detailed example is given under a base set of assumptions. The effects of varying some of those assumptions is shown for a selection of vignettes. All tables and charts are contained in the annex to this chapter (Annex D).

In the main it is assumed that the packages of care are arranged by a Local Authority (LA) and that the older person has been assessed by the LA as needing such care. People are, of course free to arrange and purchase care privately, without the involvement of the LA, when they would generally have to pay the full market price of that care. Alternatively, some of the care could be provided by a voluntary organisation so that some of the cost could fall on the voluntary sector.

OUTLINE OF THE METHOD

The starting point for each vignette is a base scenario:

1. Accommodation and internally-provided care in very sheltered housing

(a) Ordinary housing corresponds to a new housing association dwelling whose annual capital and running cost is £4,690 in 1997-8 prices[1], but the Housing Association is able to subsidise their tenants, charging them only £2,850 in 1997-8 prices. The rationale for this is that new building by housing associations is partly funded by capital grants which average about 50% of the capital cost. In weekly terms:

- resource cost = £90.26 p.w.

- rent payable by tenant = £54.81 p.w.

(b) The pure accommodation cost for very sheltered housing is taken to be the same as above and subsidised to the same extent. However the rent also includes an element to cover internally-provided care services. It is assumed that this element equals the resource cost of those care services. The latter is taken to be the difference between the resource cost of very sheltered housing and the resource cost at (a). This difference is £8,846 per annum in 1996-7 prices, taken to be £9,085 in 1997-8 prices. In weekly terms:

- resource cost of care element in very sheltered housing = £174.71 p.w.;

- care element of rent in very sheltered housing = £174.71 p.w.;

- resource cost of accommodation and corresponding rent as at (a) above.

Potential contributors to these costs are:

- the Housing Association (or its funding source) to the extent that the total rent, (including any element for care services) is below the total resource cost;

- the Department of Social Security (DSS) through Housing Benefit (HB) may pay all or some of the accommodation component of the rent and may also contribute to the cost of internally provided care services if all or part of the care element is treated as 'eligible rent' for HB;

- the user (tenant) contributes the difference between the rent (including care element) and that part paid through HB.

2. Health care

The costs of health services provided as part of the packages of care (community nursing, continence supplies, attendances at psychogeriatric day hospital) are met in full from the Health budget.

3. Externally provided social care

(iii) All other externally provided care services except gardening and befriending[2] are assumed to be arranged by a LA.

Potential contributions to these costs are:

■ User charges paid from private resources. For this purpose private resources are taken to mean savings and income from private sources together with any state pension and other income from state benefits except Income Support (IS) and Attendance Allowance (AA).

■ DSS through AA, unless the allowance is disregarded by the LA's charging regime.

The rest is assumed to be a charge on the LA budget.

4. Living expenses

Non-housing living expenses correspond to the relevant IS allowances and premiums. In this context the relevant IS allowance for vignette 1 is the couple's rate. (This differs from the approach used in Chapter 8 since the purpose here is to calculate entitlement to IS for the couple living together in the community rather than to make comparisons with the residential care costs of meeting the care needs of just one of them). In the case of vignette 3, as in the previous chapter, the relevant IS allowance includes the Severe Disability Premium which in turn implies entitlement to the higher pensioner premium.

Where the person has capital and income below the IS thresholds, DSS contributes the difference between that income and the IS level towards living expenses and the user contributes the rest. Where the person is not entitled to IS, the whole of these living expenses are met by the individual.

DETERMINING ENTITLEMENTS TO INCOME SUPPORT AND HOUSING BENEFIT AND LIABILITY FOR LOCAL AUTHORITY CHARGES

Given assumptions on income, capital and the accommodation component of rent, entitlements to IS and HB in respect of the latter can be calculated according to national rules. (In practice this also involves calculating liability for income tax since IS and HB are assessed on net-of-tax income). The extent to which the care component of rent is considered as eligible rent for HB purposes is less clear cut (Oldman *et al.*, 1996; Audit Commission 1998). The rules in this area are currently under review. At present eligible rent can include charges for services such as cleaning rooms, if tenants are unable to clean them themselves, and the cost of alarms installed in accommodation specially designed or adapted for older people or those with disabilities (West, 1997). It is apparent that many supported housing schemes rely on the availability of HB to help with such costs (see also Chapter 5).

In the case of LA charges for externally provided services an issue concerns how Authorities determine what to charge someone will be required to pay the full charge. It is not always the case that the full charge equals the true resource cost of the services. Even those who do pay full charges may be subsidised by the LA to some extent.

Once the full charge has been set for each of the packages of care, the next step is to determine the older person's liability to meet that charge from private resources. This depends on:

- the means-testing regime used by the LA;

- the income and savings of the older people themselves.

Unlike the IS-based statutory structure which applies to residential care charges there is no national framework for domiciliary care charges. Section 17 of the 1983 Health and Social Services and Social Security Adjudication Act gives LAs discretionary power to charge adult users for domiciliary care services to recover such costs for them as seems reasonable (Baldwin and Lunt, 1996). No definition of 'reasonable' is given although the wording of the legislation implies that the user's ability to pay should be taken into account. In practice charging systems vary considerably (National Consumer Council, 1995; Baldwin and Lunt 1996; Bennett, 1996; Phelps, 1997). Some involve separate charging arrangements for each service, others make a single combined charge. Increasingly some kind of means-testing is being used but the services to which it applies and the form it takes vary. The means test may involve capital only or include income. Capital thresholds used to determine liability for charges vary. Some LAs use an upper threshold of £8,000 which corresponds to that used for assessing IS entitlement for people living in the community. Others have adopted the £16,000 threshold which applies for people living in residential care and also for HB. We do not try to replicate any specific systems known to be in operation but examine a number of variations from a base charging regime. In many cases the main implications of other sorts of charging arrangements can be deduced from what is presented. To keep the analysis and its presentation manageable, it is assumed that in all cases a single combined charge is calculated covering all the externally provided non-health care services, rather than a series of charges for each service.

In the base scenario it is assumed that:

- The total rent (accommodation and care component) is 'eligible rent' for HB purposes. (This is subsequently varied.);

- The full LA charge for externally provided services is equal to the resource cost of those services (excluding health services).

The charging regime is:

- anyone with savings over £8,000 pays this full charge;

- for others, the charge is the lower of the full charge and 'available income'. (This is subsequently varied.).

Available income is defined as:

- net income – rent + HB – relevant IS allowance.

It includes any AA. Available income is calculated for the benefit unit as a whole.

Detailed examples of the incidence of resource costs under these assumptions is given in Tables D.1 to D.12 in Annex D for the alternative care packages for each vignette. In each case a single gross income level (before tax and any entitlement to IS) is shown, consisting of the basic state pension plus some second-tier pension (which could be from the State Earnings Related Pension (SERPS), an occupational or personal pension). It is assumed that the older person or couple has savings below £3,000 so that they are disregarded in full for IS and do not generate appreciable interest income. In the case of vignette 1 it is assumed that the husband has second-tier pension of £70 a week in 1997-8 terms. £70 is a little below the 1995-6 average of £82 of occupational pension income for pensioner couples where the head is aged under 75 years. The corresponding 1995-6 figure for single pensioners aged over 75 is £27.60 (Department of Social Security 1998, Tables 3 and 4). For vignettes 2-6 a figure of £20 a week in second tier pension is used. In Tables D.1 to D.12 the components of resource costs have been grouped as follows:

(a) non-health care costs including the costs of externally provided care but not the care element of rent for very sheltered housing;

(b) the cost of the care element of rent for very sheltered housing;

(c) health care costs;

(d) accommodation costs;

(e) non-housing living expenses;

and sub-totalled as:

- total health and care costs (a+b+c);

- total health, care and accommodation costs (a+b+c+d);

- total health, care, accommodation and living costs (a+b+c+d).

Contributions from each of the following sources are identified:

- the individual from private resources (distinguishing the LA charge, that part of the rent not met by HB, and that part of daily living expenses not met by IS (in this example there is no contribution from IS));

- DSS (distinguishing the contributions through AA to care costs, through HB to rent and the care element of rent in very sheltered housing, and to living expenses through IS);

- the LA;

- the NHS;

■ the Housing Association providing the accommodation;

■ state sources in total (DSS, LA, NHS and the Housing Association).

The contribution required by the individual is the same in absolute terms for each package of care. This is a result of the assumed LA charging regime which requires people to put all available income towards the non-health care costs. It is only when available income exceeds these costs that the contribution required by the individual is affected by their size. For every vignette the relative contributions of the state and the individual to care costs and to care plus accommodation costs do not vary greatly with the care package. At the income levels illustrated, the state meets the majority of the costs: between 90 and 100%. However, the apportionment of the state's share among the statutory bodies varies significantly. Crucially important is the significance of health costs since these are met in full from the NHS in all cases. Also very important is whether care needs are partly met through internally-provided services in sheltered housing. Under the baseline assumptions and the income levels illustrated, all of this cost is met by DSS through HB. The proportionate contributions of the state and the individual to total care, accommodation and living costs vary more across packages of care. This is due to the variations in the absolute size of the care costs.

In each of the care packages the individual or couple is left with the same amount of income to devote to daily living expenses after paying their contribution to rent and care. This is the relevant IS level. In no case is available income large enough to meet the full LA charge so the LA is assumed to take all of available income towards the cost.

Thus under the baseline assumptions the relative contributions to care costs do not vary greatly among the care packages, the outcome for the older person in terms of money left over to devote to non-care and housing expenses is the same in all cases. Yet the burden on the budgets of each statutory authority can vary significantly.

ALTERNATIVE ASSUMPTIONS

1. Different income levels
Figures D.1 to D.7 in Annex D illustrate for vignettes 1, 3 and 6 how the division of health and care costs varies, under the baseline assumptions, as the older person (or couple's) gross income before tax and IS is increased. This is best thought of as adding amounts of second-tier pensions to the older person's (husband's) income. The lowest income level corresponds to just the basic state pension. In the charts the absolute (£s p.w.) contributions of the various sources of contribution have been stacked so that the level of the top horizontal line represents the total health and care cost – for example £241.52 for vignette 1, care package (a). The charts can be viewed as containing two – or in the case of very sheltered housing three – stacked rectangles, corresponding to the care element of the cost of sheltered housing (if relevant), the cost of care services arranged by the LA and the cost of health services. As income is increased the proportion of the first met through HB falls, and the proportion met by the individual rises. Likewise the proportion of the cost of LA arranged care services met by the LA

falls and that met by the individual rises with income. Under the assumed charging regime the contribution to these costs from AA, if any, does not generally vary with income. The NHS meets the total cost of health services irrespective of income.

To take the example of vignette 1, where the couple live in an ordinary home with care package (a), the LA is no longer bearing any of the cost at an income of about £430 a week and the individual meets all of the LA charge from his pension income, apart from that covered by his AA. £430 a week is well above average pension levels (Department of Social Security 1998). With the more expensive care package (b), the LA continues to meet some of the cost well beyond £450 a week. If the couple live in sheltered housing, the LA ceases to bear any of the cost at about £240 a week. The assumption that the whole of the rent for very sheltered housing is eligible rent for HB is crucial.

Superimposed on the charts as a dashed line is the weekly income that the individual or couple would have left after meeting accommodation and care costs, as their income rises. Often the effect of the charging regime is such that over a wide range of gross income, this level is constant. It is only if the cost of care is low in relation to income that the older person would feel much benefit from, for example, having earned a higher pension.

2. A different charging regime

Some LAs base their charges on a proportion of available income rather than requiring people to put all of their available income towards the costs of their care. This is similar in some respects to the 'taper' in HB. Figures D.8 to D.14 correspond to figures D.1 to D.7 for a charging system where the LA limits the user charge to 65% of available income. The choice of 65% is somewhat arbitrary but happens to be the same as the HB taper. Naturally at all income levels more of the cost of LA arranged non-health care services is borne by the LA and less by the individual, and the individual retains more of the benefits of increasing income. In some cases, the contribution sought from the user is less than any AA, so that the DSS contribution through this route is less. In effect, some of the AA is available to the individual to spend as he or she chooses.

3. The treatment of the care component of rent in very sheltered housing

To investigate the effect of restricting the extent to which the care component of the rent in very sheltered housing is counted as 'eligible rent' for HB purposes, we assume that only half is judged eligible. However we continue to assume that all of it is taken into account in calculating available income. The consequences for vignettes 1,3 and 6 in sheltered housing are shown in figures D.15 to D.17 where we revert to the original LA charging system. The older person now has to make a substantial contribution to this component of the rent and so has much less left to pay the LA charges. For vignette 1 it is only at the highest income levels that the LA requires any contribution; for vignettes 2 and 3 there is no requirement at any of the income levels shown. Moreover, for vignette 6 in very sheltered housing, at the lowest income levels, even though the LA bears all the cost of externally provided care services, the rent is not affordable as income after meeting housing costs is negative. The effect of allowing only 50% of the care component of rent as eligible rent and taking only 65% of available income in charges is shown for vignettes 1 and 3 in figures D.18 and D.19. The corresponding figure for vignette 6 is identical to figure D.17 because available income is zero.

4. Alternative savings assumptions

Table D.13 in the annex shows some of the effects of varying the baseline assumptions by assuming that the older person has savings of £10,000. This means that the LA would charge them the full cost of the externally provided non-health services and they would also be precluded from IS. However, there could still be some entitlement to HB, possibly reduced by the 'tariff income' on the excess of savings over £3,000. The table shows the charge the user would be liable to meet from private sources, the contribution if any from AA, the contributions from HB to accommodation costs and the care component of rent in very sheltered housing. It also shows how long it would be before the older person's savings had fallen to below £8,000 and to below £3,000. This is on the assumption that the older person puts all of any AA towards the charge the LA makes and then draws on capital to pay the rest and if necessary the care component of the rent in very sheltered housing not covered by HB. The results show some of the curious consequences. In theory vignette 3 in ordinary housing would have to pay £634 plus her AA to the LA but after 3 weeks her savings would have fallen below £8,000 and after 12 weeks to below £3,000.

5. Alternative tenure assumptions

Annex C of Chapter 8 discussed some of the issues involved in estimating the resource costs of alternative tenures and the hence the implications of assuming alternative tenures for the care packages which involve older people living in ordinary housing. For the purposes of this chapter, the main consideration for alternative forms of renting is the extent to which rents in the private or LA rented sector differ from those in the HA sector for similar properties. In both cases they are also likely to be less that the full resource cost due to e.g. rent regulation in the private sector and some continued subsidies in the LA sector. The main findings of this chapter are unlikely to be very different for these other forms of renting.

Where the older person is an owner-occupier (and it is reasonable to assume that they own outright or with only a small mortgage) there are two considerations. First they will not be eligible for HB or state help with regular outgoings which are normally covered by rents in the rented sector, such as repairs and maintenance. In principle, if the LA is basing charges on available income as defined above it should make some allowance for these costs. A second consideration is the scope for housing wealth to be used to help meet the costs of care. At present LAs are not able to take the value of an older person's home into account in assessing domiciliary charges, although in most cases it can for residential care. But the older person could use an equity release scheme to generate extra income to help meet the cost of care. Under present rules such income would reduce any entitlement to IS (and Council Tax Benefit) and the LA could take it into account in assessing liability for charges. Some illustrative calculations were performed for all vignettes except vignette 4 (where it is assumed that if the property were owner-occupied it would belong to the daughter). It was assumed that for each of the packages of care in ordinary housing, the property had a 1997-8 market value of £46,300 (for comparability with the housing association tenure) and 75% of it would be used for equity release. The potential extra income which might be generated through a traditional mortgage-annuity type of equity release scheme was calculated using 1997-8 interest and annuity rates. To do this it was necessary to assume exact ages for the vignettes and these were taken to be 70 years for the husband and 65 years for the wife in vignette 1, 79 years in vignettes 2 and 3 and 87 in vignettes 5 and 6. It was also assumed that the LA allowed a notional £10 a week in housing costs in calculating the available income against which it could make a charge but that it would add the extra income generated by the scheme (after allowing for any extra tax liability and the interest due on the mortgage) to available income. The extra income was also assumed to be taken into account when assessing entitlement to IS. Under baseline assumptions and income levels as in tables D.1 to D.12, the main findings from this exercise, compared with the housing association tenants were:

- the couple in vignette 1 are currently too young to benefit from equity release but because they would have no rent to pay they would have to pay £51.40 a week from their private resources for care packages (a) and (b) compared with £21.49 for the housing association tenants;

- vignette 2 could generate an extra £42 a week from equity release, but she would have to pay the LA £44 in charges so she would have no incentive to take out such a scheme. Without equity release, she would have to pay £1.45 in charges compared with £4.01 for the housing association tenant. The reason is that the housing association tenant would have all but about £7 a week of her rent met through HB leaving her with less than the £10 a week allowed by the LA for the owner-occupier's housing costs;

- vignette 3 could also generate about £42 a week through equity release but this would eliminate her IS entitlement of £30.40, leaving her just £11 a week better off before paying any care charges. She would have to pay the LA £1.98 in charges as well as handing over her AA. If she did not take out an equity release scheme she would be entitled to the same IS as the housing association tenant and not be liable to any LA charge apart from her AA;

- vignette 5 could generate £123 through equity release but would be liable for £112.89 in charges. If he did not take out an equity release scheme he would not have any LA charges to pay, compared with £2.36 which the corresponding housing association tenant would have to pay. As for vignette 2, this last difference is due to the availability of HB to help meet rent but not owner-occupiers' housing costs;

- vignette 6 could generate about £90 a week via equity release and but would then be liable for £53.84 in LA charges. Without equity release there would be no LA charge compared with £2.36 for the equivalent housing association tenant.

If the LA takes full account of any extra income generated through equity release, this therefore substantially reduces the incentive for these older people to use such schemes. Under a charging regime in which only a proportion of available income was required to be put towards charges there would be more incentive although those on IS would still stand to gain little. Owner-occupiers are not eligible for HB. If the LA makes an allowance for the net housing costs of owners and tenants, then at income levels where HB is payable to tenants, the LA may be able to charge tenants more than it can charge owners.

COMPARISONS WITH THE INCIDENCE OF THE COSTS OF RESIDENTIAL CARE

If comparisons with the incidence of the costs of residential care are made there are a number of points to bear in mind. These include:

- the different means-testing arrangements for private and voluntary homes compared with LA homes;

- in arriving at the gross costs of residential care the accommodation costs have not been separately identified but are included in the residential care costs adjusted for living expenses. In the case of a resident in a private or voluntary home who is entitled to IS, DSS meets part of these accommodation costs through the payment of a residential allowance. Tenants with income just above the IS level could be eligible for HB to help meet the cost of their rent when living in the community but would not be eligible for the IS residential care allowance. For a resident in a LA home the IS contribution depends on whether and how much the person's income is below the basic state pension level;

- AA can be received by people living in private or voluntary residential and nursing homes who have to meet the homes fees in full themselves. For those who get some help with their fees or live in LA homes, AA will stop four weeks after admission. This provides some incentive for LAs to provide services to people in the community rather than in residential care because AA is then available to be put towards their care costs;

- although the value of the home of an owner-occupier is not taken into account in assessing liability for non-residential care charges, it can be for residential care. This provides a strong incentive for LAs to place people in residential care rather than in ordinary or supported housing in the community;

- vignette 1 consists of a couple. If the husband were to move into residential care this would have implications for both their incomes. LAs must now disregard a half of any private pension income of the spouse who enters care if it is passed to the spouse remaining in the community but also may require the spouse remaining at home to contribute to the costs of residential care. Although the wife would now be living alone, she would remain entitled to only the married woman's rate of basic state pension (unless she had earned a full pension in her own right). Unless her share of her husband's private pension was quite substantial, she would become eligible for IS.

  (These rules relate to people who enter residential care after 1 April 1993. Different rules apply to people already resident on that date.)

All these points need to be taken into account if the comparisons are to be made between the apportioning of the gross costs of residential and non-residential care.

SUMMARY AND CONCLUSIONS

In this chapter we have examined who meets the resource costs identified in the previous chapter for the alternative care packages for each of the vignettes described in Chapter 7.

1. The method

The method involves a base scenario and variations from it:

- in the base scenario both ordinary and very sheltered housing is provided by a Housing Association. The implications of ordinary housing being owner-occupied and the consequent possibility for drawing on housing wealth are also examined;

- the whole of the care element in very sheltered housing is treated as 'eligible rent' for Housing Benefit purposes in the base scenario but a variant in which only half is eligible is also examined;

- the LA sets a full charge equal to the resource cost of externally provided non-health care services and assesses users' contributions to that charge on the basis of the net income they have in excess of their net housing costs and the relevant Income Support threshold ('available' income) and savings. Under the base scenario the whole of any available income is required to be put towards the LA charge. A variant in which the LA takes only 65% of available income is also examined;

- health services are assumed to be free to all users and a charge on the NHS budget;

- the following contributions to components and sub-totals of resource costs are then identified: the individual from private sources; DSS through Attendance Allowance, Housing Benefit and for living expenses, Income Support; the Local Authority; the NHS, the Housing Association providing the accommodation;

- detailed examples are presented in Tables D.1 to D.12 of Annex D for each of the vignettes and care packages on the basis of a modest income level and savings below £3,000. For selected vignettes the effect of varying income, alternative charging regimes and treatment of the care component of rent in very sheltered housing are shown in figures D.1 to D.19. The implications of assuming savings of £10,000 are shown in Table D.13.

2. The findings

Under the baseline assumptions the relative contributions of the state and the individual to health and care resource costs do not vary very much, with the state incurring between 90 and 100%. At the modest income levels assumed, the outcome for the older person concerned in terms of how much income is left after meeting housing and care costs is virtually the same under each care package. Yet the burden on the budgets of each statutory authority varies considerably.

Allowing only 50% of the care component of rent in sheltered housing to be considered eligible rent for Housing Benefit purposes considerably reduces the cost borne by the DSS. Through the calculation of available income it increases the cost borne by LAs to some extent. It also makes very sheltered housing unaffordable to older people on low incomes.

A LA charging system which takes only a proportion of available income in charges obviously places more cost on LA budgets but allows those who have earned higher retirement incomes to retain some of the benefits.

Assuming that the older people having savings of £10,000 reduces the cost borne by the state but where LA charges are high, this saving is short-lived. For one vignette, the extreme case, it would be only 3 weeks before her capital fell below the £8,000 threshold and 12 weeks before it fell below £3,000.

Unlike tenants, low income owner-occupiers are not eligible for help with their housing costs through Housing Benefit. The net housing costs of older owner-occupiers can therefore be higher than those of tenants. If the LA makes an allowance for this in calculating available income, it may find itself able to charge owners less than it charges tenants for care services.

Owner-occupiers have the possibility of using housing wealth to pay for care by taking out an equity release scheme. However, the extra income generated is taken into account in assessing Income Support entitlement. If LAs also include it in available income, calculations show that there is little incentive for those on low incomes to release equity in this way.

It is not uncommon for means testing to produce apparently anomalous results. However, the mixture of nationally specified rules governing Housing Benefit and Income Support, ambiguity over the eligibility of the care component of rent in sheltered housing for HB, discretion and variability in LA charging for care services, the sometimes arbitrary distinction between health (free at the point of delivery to all) and social care services seems to be an extreme case. It embodies incentives for costs to be shunted from one budget to another. It produces different apportionment of care costs depending on whether that care is provided in ordinary homes, very sheltered housing or residential settings.

Most of the issues highlighted by our calculations are already known and some are currently under review (e.g. concerning Housing Benefit). Any reforms risk replacing one set of anomalies with another. Calculations such as those presented in Chapter 9 can help avoid that.

Cost-shunting remains a key issue in paying for care and support for older people. Debate over the division of costs between the state and the individual sector is in danger of missing key issues in relation to the incidence of costs within the public sector.

Some consistency in the charging policies of LAs is surely necessary. This need not rule out local discretion to take account of individual circumstances, but it must be possible to establish some general, publicly-stated principles. If these principles imply means-testing, then the regime must take due account of interaction with means-testing in the social security system without the haphazard adoption of isolated features of Income Support or Housing Benefit.

The current arrangements are complex and opaque, which must place an extra burden on the shoulders of some of the most vulnerable older people and their families. Some complexity is probably unavoidable but a system with more logic might be easier to understand.

Prospects for the growth of private care insurance are not independent of developments in public sector charging. The challenge, as always, is to try to avoid penalising those who have chosen to make private provision while giving security to those unable to do so.

The treatment of housing wealth is likely to remain a contentious area. It too could benefit from a review from first principles, paying attention to fairness between owner occupiers and those who rent their homes.

Most of these issues are wider than paying for long-term care in isolation and therefore raise issues which may be beyond the Commission's terms of reference. But the consequences of isolated policy developments are apparent in the anomalies in existing arrangements.

Footnotes

1 This is lower than the £4,710 given in Annex C of Chapter 8, where the 1996-7 cost was increased by 3%. For consistency with the total costs in 1997-8 terms shown in Chapter 8, the 1996-7 figure for accommodation costs has here been increased by only 2.7%.

2 It is assumed that gardening and befriending are not provided through the statutory authorities and so fall outside any charging regime. Their costs are likely to fall either on the individual who receives the service or perhaps on the charitable sector. They are not very significant parts of the costs and so for simplicity have been excluded.

Annex D: Detailed Examples of Incidence of Resource Costs (Tables) and the Effects of Increasing Income on Contributions to Total Health and Care Costs (Figures)

Table D.1: Detailed example of incidence of resource costs, vignette 1 in ordinary housing, care package (a)

Weekly income details (1997-8 prices and benefit rates):
Husband: full basic state pension (£62.45), second-tier pension (£70), higher rate AA (£49.50)
Wife: married woman's basic state pension (£37.35)
Total gross income: £219.30; income tax: £1.60; net income: £217.70
Savings less than £3,000
Rent on ordinary housing: £54.81

£s p.w (% of total resource cost)

	externally-provided non-health care services (a)	care element of cost of v. sheltered housing (b)	health care (c)	accomm. cost (d)	non-housing daily living expenses (e)	total health and care costs (a+b+c)	total health, care and accomm. costs (a+b+c+d)	total health, care accomm and living costs (a+b+c+d+e)
Resource cost	222.56	–	18.96	90.26	106.80	241.52	331.78	438.58
met by:								
individual (LA charge)	21.49 (10)	–	–	–	–	21.49 (9)	61.40† (19)	168.20† (38)
individual (rent)	–	–	–	39.91 (44)	–	–	–	–
individual (living expenses)	–	–	–	–	106.80 (100)	–	–	–
DSS (AA)	49.50 (22)	–	–	–	–	49.50 (20)	49.50‡ (15)	49.50‡ (11)
DSS (HB)	–	–	–	–	–	–	–	–
care element accomm.	–	–	–	14.90 (17)	–	–	14.90 (4)	14.90 (3)
DSS (IS)	–	–	–	–	–	–	–	–
Local Auth.	151.57 (68)	–	–	–	–	151.57 (63)	151.57 (46)	151.57 (35)
Housing Assoc.	–	–	–	35.45 (39)	–	–	35.45 (11)	35.45 (8)
NHS	–	–	18.96 (100)	–	–	18.96 (8)	18.96 (6)	18.96 (4)
All state sources	201.07 (90)	–	18.96 (100)	50.35 (56)	106.80(100)	220.03 (91)	270.38 (81)	270.38 (62)

Note: Components may not add to totals due to rounding. For assumptions underlying calculations see text
†Cumulative contribution from individual; ‡ cumulative contribution from HB

Table D.2: Detailed example of incidence of resource costs, vignette 1 in ordinary housing, care package (b)

Weekly income details (1997-8 prices and benefit rates):
Husband: full basic state pension (£62.45), second-tier pension (£70), higher rate AA (£49.50)
Wife: married woman's basic state pension (£37.35)
Total gross income: £219.30; income tax: £1.60; net income: £217.70
Savings less than £3,000
Rent on ordinary housing: £54.81

£s p.w (% of total resource cost)

	externally-provided non-health care services (a)	care element of cost of v. sheltered housing (b)	health care (c)	accomm. cost (d)	non-housing daily living expenses (e)	total health and care costs (a+b+c)	total health, care and accomm. costs (a+b+c+d)	total health, care accomm and living costs (a+b+c+d+e)
Resource cost	288.55	–	6.40	90.26	106.80	294.95	385.21	492.00
met by:								
individual								
(LA charge)	21.49 (7)	–	–	–	–	21.49 (7)	61.40† (16)	
individual (rent)	–	–	–	39.91 (44)	–			
individual (living expenses)	–	–	–	–	106.80 (100)			168.20† (34)
DSS (AA)	49.50 (17)	–	–	–	–	49.50 (17)	49.50 (13)	49.50‡ (10)
DSS (HB)	–	–	–	–	–			
care element	–	–	–	–	–			
accomm.	–	–	–	14.90 (17)	–	–	14.90 (4)	14.90 (3)
DSS (IS)	–	–	–	–	–			–
Local Auth.	217.56 (75)	–	–	–	–	217.56 (74)	217.56 (56)	217.56 (44)
Housing Assoc.	–	–	–	35.45 (39)	–	35.45 (9)	35.45 (9)	35.45 (7)
NHS	–	–	6.40 (100)	–	–	6.40 (2)	6.40 (2)	6.40 (1)
All state sources	267.06 (93)	–	6.40 (100)	50.35 (56)	–	273.46 (93)	323.81 (84)	323.81 (66)

Note: Components may not add to totals due to rounding. For assumptions underlying calculations see text
†Cumulative contribution from individual; ‡ cumulative contribution from HB

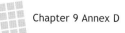
Table D.3: Detailed example of incidence of resource costs, vignette 1 in very sheltered housing

Weekly income details (1997-8 prices and benefit rates):
Husband: full basic state pension (£62.45), second-tier pension (£70), higher rate AA (£49.50)
Wife: married woman's basic state pension (£37.35)
Total gross income: £219.30; income tax: £1.60; net income: £217.70
Savings less than £3,000
Rent on sheltered housing: £229.52 of which £174.71 is in respect of internally provided care services
and £54.81 in respect of accommodation costs

£s p.w (% of total resource cost)

Resource cost met by:	externally-provided non-health care services (a)	care element of cost of v. sheltered housing (b)	health care (c)	accomm. cost of v. sheltered housing (d)	non-housing daily living expenses (e)	total health and care costs (a+b+c)	total health, care and accomm. costs (a+b+c+d)	total health, care accomm and living costs (a+b+c+d+e)
Resource cost	78.41	174.71	6.40	90.26	106.80	259.52	349.78	456.58
individual								
(LA charge)	21.49 (27)	–	–	–	–	21.49 (8)		
individual (rent)	–	–	–	39.91 (44)	–		61.40† (18)	
individual (living expenses)	–	–	–	–	106.80 (100)			168.20† (37)
DSS (AA)	49.50 (63)	–	–	–	–	49.50 (19)	49.50 (14)	49.50 (11)
DSS (HB)	–	–	–	–	–			
care element	–	174.71 (100)	–	–	–	174.71 (67)	189.61‡ (54)	189.61‡ (42)
accomm.	–	–	–	14.90 (17)	–			
DSS (IS)	–	–	–	–	–	–	–	–
Local Auth.	7.42 (9)	–	–	–	–	7.42 (3)	7.42 (2)	7.42 (2)
Housing Assoc.	–	–	–	35.45 (39)	–	–	35.45 (10)	35.45 (8)
NHS	–	–	6.40 (100)	–	–	6.40 (2)	6.40 (2)	6.40 (1)
All state sources	56.92 (73)	174.71 (100)	6.40 (100)	50.35 (56)	–	238.03 (92)	288.38 (82)	288.38 (63)

Note   Components may not add to totals due to rounding. For assumptions underlying calculations see text
†Cumulative contribution from individual; ‡ cumulative contribution from HB

Table D.4: Detailed example of incidence of resource costs, vignette 2 in ordinary housing

Weekly income details (1997-8 prices and benefit rates):
Full basic state pension (£62.45), second-tier pension (£20)
Total gross income: £82.45; income tax: 0; net income: £82.45
Savings less than £3,000
Rent on housing: £54.81

£s p.w (% of total resource cost)

	externally-provided non-health care services (a)	care element of cost of v. sheltered housing (b)	health care (c)	accomm. cost (d)	non-housing daily living expenses (e)	total health and care costs (a+b+c)	total health, care and accomm. costs (a+b+c+d)	total health, care accomm and living costs (a+b+c+d+e)
Resource cost	178.38	–	–	90.26	71.00	178.38	268.64	339.64
met by:								
individual (LA charge)	4.01 (2)	–	–	–	–	4.01 (2)		
individual (rent)	–	–	–	7.44 (8)	–	–	11.45†(4)	
individual (living expenses)	–	–	–	–	71.00 (100)			82.45†(24)
DSS (AA)	–	–	–	–	–	–		
DSS (HB)	–	–	–	–	–	–	–	–
care element	–	–	–	–	–	–		
accomm.	–	–	–	47.37 (52)	–	–	47.37‡ (18)	47.37‡(14)
DSS (IS)	–	–	–	–	–	–		
Local Auth.	174.37 (98)	–	–	–	–	174.37 (98)	174.37 (65)	174.37 (51)
Housing Assoc.	–	–	–	35.45 (39)	–	–	35.45 (13)	35.45 (10)
NHS	–	–	–	–	–	–		
All state sources	174.37 (98)	–	–	82.82 (92)	–	174.37 (98)	257.19 (96)	257.19 (76)

Note: Components may not add to totals due to rounding. For assumptions underlying calculations see text
†Cumulative contribution from individual; ‡cumulative contribution from HB

Table D.5: Detailed example of incidence of resource costs, vignette 2 in very sheltered housing

Weekly income details (1997-8 prices and benefit rates):
Full basic state pension (£62.45), second-tier pension (£20)
Total gross income: £82.45; income tax: 0; net income: £82.45
Savings less than £3,000
Rent on sheltered housing: £229.52 of which £174.71 is in respect of internally provided care services
and £54.81 in respect of accommodation costs

£s p.w (% of total resource cost)

	externally-provided non-health care services (a)	care element of cost of v. sheltered housing (b)	health care (c)	accomm. cost of v. sheltered housing (d)	non-housing daily living expenses (e)	total health and care costs (a+b+c)	total health, care and accomm. costs (a+b+c+d)	total health, care accomm and living costs (a+b+c+d+e)
Resource cost	107.68	174.71	–	90.26	71.00	282.39	372.64	443.64
met by:								
individual (LA charge)	4.01 (4)	–	–	–	–	4.01 (1)		
individual (rent)	–	–	–	7.44 (8)	–		11.45†(3)	
individual (living expenses)	–	–	–	–	71.00 (100)	–	–	82.45†(19)
DSS (AA)	–	–	–	–	–	–	–	–
DSS (HB)	–	–	–	–	–	–	–	–
care element	–	174.71(100)	–	–	–	174.71 (62)		
accomm.	–	–	–	47.37 (52)	–	–	222.08‡ (60)	222.08‡(50)
DSS (IS)	–	–	–	–	–	–	–	–
Local Auth.	103.67 (96)	–	–	–	–	103.67 (37)	103.67 (28)	103.67 (23)
Housing Assoc.	–	–	–	35.45 (39)	–	–	35.45 (10)	35.45 (8)
NHS	–	–	–	–	–	–	–	–
All state sources	103.67 (96)	174.71(100)	–	82.82 (92)	–	278.38 (99)	361.20 (97)	361.20 (81)

Note: Components may not add to totals due to rounding. For assumptions underlying calculations see text
†Cumulative contribution from individual; ‡ cumulative contribution from HB

Table D.6: Detailed example of incidence of resource costs, vignette 3 in ordinary housing

Weekly income details (1997-8 prices and benefit rates):
Full basic state pension (£62.45), second-tier pension (£20), lower rate AA (33.10)
Total gross income: £82.45; income tax: 0; net income: £115.55
Savings less than £3,000
Rent on housing: £54.81

£s p.w (% of total resource cost)

	externally-provided non-health care services (a)	care element of cost of v. sheltered housing (b)	health care (c)	accomm. cost (d)	non-housing daily living expenses (e)	total health and care costs (a+b+c)	total health, care and accomm. costs (a+b+c+d)	total health, care accomm and living costs (a+b+c+d+e)
Resource cost	633.85	–	78.61	90.26	112.85	712.44	802.70	915.55
met by:								
individual (LA charge)	–	–	–	–	–	–	–	
individual (rent)	–	–	–	–	–	–	–	
individual (living expenses)	–	–	–	–	82.45 (73)	–	–	82.45†(9)
DSS (AA)	33.10 (5)	–	–	–	–	33.10 (5)	33.10 (4)	33.10 (4)
DSS (HB)								
care element	–	–	–	–	–			
accomm.	–	–	–	54.81 (61)	–	–	54.81‡(7)	54.81‡(6)
DSS (IS)	–	–	–	–	30.40 (27)	–	–	30.40 (3)
Local Auth.	600.74 (95)	–	–	–	–	600.74 (84)	600.74 (75)	600.74 (66)
Housing Assoc.	–	–	–	35.45 (39)	–	–	35.45 (4)	35.45 (4)
NHS	–	–	78.61 (100)	–	–	78.61 (11)	78.61 (11)	78.61 (9)
All state sources	633.85 (100)	–	78.61 (100)	90.26 (100)	30.40 (27)	712.44 (100)	802.70 (100)	833.10 (91)

Note: Components may not add to totals due to rounding. For assumptions underlying calculations see text
†Cumulative contribution from individual; ‡ cumulative contribution from HB

Table D.7: Detailed example of incidence of resource costs, vignette 3 in very sheltered housing

Weekly income details (1997-8 prices and benefit rates):
Full basic state pension (£62.45), second-tier pension (£20), lower rate AA (£33.10)
Total gross income: £82.45; income tax: 0; net income: £115.55
Savings less than £3,000
Rent on sheltered housing: £229.52 of which £174.71 is in respect of internally provided care services
and £54.81 in respect of accommodation costs

£s p.w (% of total resource cost)

	externally-provided non-health care services (a)	care element of cost of v. sheltered housing (b)	health care (c)	accomm. cost of v. sheltered housing (d)	non-housing daily living expenses (e)	total health and care costs (a+b+c)	total health, care and accomm. costs (a+b+c+d)	total health, care accomm and living costs (a+b+c+d+e)
Resource cost	425.43	174.71	27.33	90.26	112.85	627.48	717.74	830.59
met by:								
individual								
(LA charge)	–	–	–	–	–	–		
individual (rent)	–	–	–	–	–	–	–	
individual								
(living expenses)	–	–	–	–	82.45 (73)	–	–	82.45† (10)
DSS (AA)	33.10 (8)	–	–	–	–	33.10 (5)	33.10 (5)	33.10
DSS (HB)								
care element	–	174.71 (100)	–	–	–	174.71 (28)		
accomm.	–	–	–	54.81 (61)	–		229.52‡ (32)	229.52‡ (28)
DSS (IS)	–	–	–	–	30.40 (27)		30.40 (4)	30.40 (4)
Local Auth.	392.33 (92)	–	–	–	–	392.33 (63)	392.33 (55)	392.33 (47)
Housing Assoc.	–	–	–	35.45 (39)	–	–	35.45 (5)	35.45 (4)
NHS	–	–	27.33 (100)	–	–	27.33 (4)	27.33 (4)	27.33 (3)
All state sources	425.43 (100)	174.71 (100)	27.33 (100)	90.26 (100)	30.40 (27)	627.48 (100)	717.74 (100)	748.14 (90)

Note: Components may not add to totals due to rounding. For assumptions underlying calculations see text
†Cumulative contribution from individual; ‡ cumulative contribution from HB

Table D.8: Detailed example of incidence of resource costs, vignette 4 in ordinary housing

Weekly income details (1997-8 prices and benefit rates):
Full basic state pension (£62.45), second-tier pension (£20), higher rate AA (£49.50)
Total gross income: £82.45; income tax: 0; net income: £131.95
Savings less than £3,000
Rent on housing: £54.81

£s p.w (% of total resource cost)

	externally-provided non-health care services (a)	care element of cost of v. sheltered housing (b)	health care (c)	accomm. cost (d)	non-housing daily living expenses (e)	total health and care costs (a+b+c)	total health, care and accomm. costs (a+b+c+d)	total health, care accomm and living costs (a+b+c+d+e)
Resource cost	215.41	–	288.55	*	75.70	503.96	*	579.66
met by:								
individual								
(LA charge)	6.75 (3)	–	–			6.75 (1)	*	*
individual (rent)	–	–	–	*	–	–	*	
individual (living expenses)	–	–	–	*	75.70 (100)	–	*	82.45† (14)
DSS (AA)	49.50 (23)	–	–	*	–	49.50 (10)	*	49.50 (9)
DSS (HB)	–	–	–	*	–	–	*	
care element	–	–	–	*	–	–		
accomm.	–	–	–	*	–	–	*	
DSS (IS)	–	–	–	*	–	–	*	–
Local Auth.	159.16 (74)	–	–	*	–	159.16 (32)	*	159.16 (27)
Housing Assoc.	*	*	*	*	*	*	*	*
NHS	–	–	288.55 (100)	*	–	288.55 (57)	*	288.55 (50)
All state sources	208.66 (97)	–	288.55 (100)	*	–	497.21 (99)	*	497.21 (86)

Note   Components may not add to totals due to rounding. For assumptions underlying calculations see text
†Cumulative contribution from individual; * accommodation costs are not included for this vignette since for HB it would be assumed that the daughter was liable for the rent. The accommodation costs would be shared among the Housing Association, the daughter and, if the daughter's income were low enough, Housing Benefit.

Table D.9: Detailed example of incidence of resource costs, vignette 5 in ordinary housing

Weekly income details (1997-8 prices and benefit rates):
Full basic state pension (£62.45), second-tier pension (£20),
Total gross income: £82.45; income tax: 0; net income: £82.45
Savings less than £3,000
Rent on housing: £54.81

£s p.w (% of total resource cost)

	externally-provided non-health care services (a)	care element of cost of v. sheltered housing (b)	health care (c)	accomm. cost (d)	non-housing daily living expenses (e)	total health and care costs (a+b+c)	total health, care and accomm. costs (a+b+c+d)	total health, care accomm and living costs (a+b+c+d+e)
Resource cost	112.89	–	–	90.26	75.70	112.89	203.15	278.85
met by:								
individual								
(LA charge)	2.36 (2)	–	–	4.39 (5)	–	2.36 (2)	6.75† (3)	
individual (rent)	–	–	–	–	–	–	–	–
individual (living expenses)	–	–	–	–	75.70 (100)	–	–	82.45† (30)
DSS (AA)	–	–	–	–	–	–	–	–
DSS (HB)	–	–	–	–	–	–	–	–
care element	–	–	–	–	–	–	–	–
accomm.	–	–	–	50.42 (56)	–	–	50.42 (25)	50.42 (18)
DSS (IS)	–	–	–	–	–	–	–	–
Local Auth.	110.53 (98)	–	–	–	–	110.53 (98)	110.53 (98)	110.53 (40)
Housing Assoc.	–	–	–	35.45 (39)	–	–	35.45 (17)	35.45 (13)
NHS	–	–	–	–	–	–	–	–
All state sources	110.53 (98)	–	–	85.87 (95)	–	110.53 (98)	196.40 (97)	196.40 (70)

Note: Components may not add to totals due to rounding. For assumptions underlying calculations see text.
†Cumulative contribution from individual; ‡ cumulative contribution from HB

Weekly income details (1997-8 prices and benefit rates):
Full basic state pension (£62.45), second-tier pension (£20),
Total gross income: £82.45; income tax: 0; net income: £82.45
Savings less than £3,000
Rent on sheltered housing: £229.52 of which £174.71 is in respect of internally provided care services
and £54.81 in respect of accommodation costs

Table D.10: Detailed example of incidence of resource costs, vignette 5 in very sheltered housing

£s p.w (% of total resource cost)

	externally-provided non-health care services (a)	care element of cost of v. sheltered housing (b)	health care (c)	accomm. cost of v. sheltered housing (d)	non-housing daily living expenses (e)	total health and care costs (a+b+c)	total health, care and accomm. costs (a+b+c+d)	total health, care accomm and living costs (a+b+c+d+e)
Resource cost	87.28	174.71	–	90.26	75.70	261.98	352.24	427.94
met by:								
individual (LA charge)	2.36 (3)	–	–	–	–	2.36 (1)	–	–
individual (rent)	–	–	–	4.39 (5)	–	–	6.75† (2)	–
individual (living expenses)	–	–	–	–	75.70 (100)	–	–	82.45† (19)
DSS (AA)	–	–	–	–	–	–	–	–
DSS (HB) care element	–	174.71 (100)	–	–	–	174.71 (67)	–	–
accomm.	–	–	–	50.42 (56)	–	–	225.13‡ (64)	225.13‡ (53)
DSS (IS)	–	–	–	–	–	–	–	–
Local Auth.	84.91 (97)	–	–	–	–	84.91 (32)	84.91 (24)	84.91 (20)
Housing Assoc.	–	–	–	35.45 (39)	–	–	35.45 (10)	35.45 (8)
NHS	–	–	–	–	–	–	–	–
All state sources	84.91 (97)	174.71 (100)	–	85.87 (95)	–	259.62 (99)	345.49 (98)	345.49 (81)

Note: Components may not add to totals due to rounding. For assumptions underlying calculations see text.
†Cumulative contribution from individual; ‡ cumulative contribution from HB

Table D.11: Detailed example of incidence of resource costs, vignette 6 in ordinary housing

Weekly income details (1997-8 prices and benefit rates):
Full basic state pension (£62.45), second-tier pension (£20),
Total gross income: £82.45; income tax: 0; net income: £82.45
Savings less than £3,000
Rent on housing: £54.81

£s p.w (% of total resource cost)

	externally-provided non-health care services (a)	care element of cost of v. sheltered housing (b)	health care (c)	accomm. cost (d)	non-housing daily living expenses (e)	total health and care costs (a+b+c)	total health, care and accomm. costs (a+b+c+d)	total health, care accomm and living costs (a+b+c+d+e)
Resource cost	53.84	–	169.40	90.26	75.70	223.23	313.49	389.19
met by:								
individual (LA charge)	2.36 (4)	–	–	–	–	2.36 (1)	6.75† (2)	–
individual (rent)	–	–	–	4.39 (5)	–	–	–	–
individual (living expenses)	–	–	–	–	75.70 (100)	–	–	82.45†(21)
DSS (AA)	–	–	–	–	–	–	–	–
DSS (HB)	–	–	–	–	–	–	–	–
care element	–	–	–	–	–	–	–	–
accomm.	–	–	–	50.42 (56)	–	–	50.42 (16)	50.42 (13)
DSS (IS)	–	–	–	–	–	–	–	–
Local Auth.	51.48 (96)	–	–	–	–	51.48 (23)	51.48 (16)	51.48 (13)
Housing Assoc.	–	–	–	35.45 (39)	–	–	35.45 (11)	35.45 (9)
NHS	–	–	169.40 (100)	–	–	169.40 (76)	169.40 (54)	169.40 (44)
All state sources	51.48(96)	–	169.40 (100)	85.87 (95)	–	220.88 (99)	306.75 (98)	306.75 (79)

Note: Components may not add to totals due to rounding. For assumptions underlying calculations see text
†Cumulative contribution from individual; ‡ cumulative contribution from HB

Table D.12: Detailed example of incidence of resource costs, vignette 6 in very sheltered housing

Weekly income details (1997-8 prices and benefit rates):
Full basic state pension (£62.45), second-tier pension (£20),
Total gross income: £82.45; income tax: 0; net income: £82.45
Savings less than £3,000
Rent on sheltered housing: £229.52 of which £174.71 is in respect of internally provided care services
and £54.81 in respect of accommodation costs

£s p.w (% of total resource cost)

	externally-provided non-health care services (a)	care element of cost of v. sheltered housing (b)	health care (c)	accomm. cost of v. sheltered housing (d)	non-housing daily living expenses (e)	total health and care costs (a+b+c)	total health, care and accomm. costs (a+b+c+d)	total health, care accomm and living costs (a+b+c+d+e)
Resource cost	87.26	174.71	169.40	90.26	75.70	431.36	521.62	597.32
met by:								
individual (LA charge)	2.36(3)	–	–	–	–	2.36 (1)		
individual (rent)	–	–	–	4.39 (5)	–		6.75† (1)	
individual (living expenses)	–	–	–	–	75.70 (100)			82.45† (14)
DSS (AA)	–	–	–	–	–	–	–	–
DSS (HB)	–	–	–	–	–	–	–	–
care element	–	174.71 (100)	–	–	–	174.71 (41)		
accomm.	–	–	–	50.42 (56)	–	–	225.13‡ (43)	225.43‡ (38)
DSS (IS)	–	–	–	–	–	–	–	–
Local Auth.	84.89(97)	–	–	–	–	84.89 (20)	84.89 (16)	84.89 (14)
Housing Assoc.	–	–	–	35.45 (39)	–	–	35.45 (7)	35.45 (16)
NHS	–	–	169.4 (100)	–	–	169.40 (39)	169.40 (32)	169.40 (28)
All state sources	84.89(97)	174.71 (100)	169.40 (100)	85.85 (95)	–	429.00 (99)	514.87 (99)	514.87 (86)

Note: Components may not add to totals due to rounding. For assumptions underlying calculations see text
†Cumulative contribution from individual; ‡ cumulative contribution from HB

Table D.13: Effect of assuming older person has £10,000 of capital

All other income, rent, accommodation, and care costs as in relevant table above

		user charge £pw	DSS contribn through AA £pw	DSS contribn to rent £pw	DSS contribn to care element of rent in very sheltered housing £pw	Capital reduced to £8,000 after... (weeks)	Capital reduced to £3,000 after... (weeks)
Vignette 1,	ordinary housing, care package (a)	173.06	49.50	–	–	12	40
	ordinary housing, care package (b)	239.05	49.50	–	–	8	29
	very sheltered housing	28.91	49.50	–	171.2	63	219
Vignette 2,	ordinary housing	178.38	–	29.17	–	11	39
	very sheltered housing	107.68	–	29.17	174.71	19	65
Vignette 3,	ordinary housing	633.84	33.10	54.81	–	3	12
	very sheltered housing	392.33	33.10	54.81	174.71	5	18
Vignette 4,	ordinary housing	165.91	49.50	n.a	–	12	42
Vignette 5,	ordinary housing	112.89	–	–	–	18	62
Vignette 5,	sheltered housing	87.28	–	32.22	174.71	23	80
Vignette 6,	ordinary housing	53.84	–	32.22	–	37	130
Vignette 6,	very sheltered housing	87.26	–	32.22	174.71	23	80

Note: n.a: not applicable, accommodation belongs to daughter.

Fig D.1: Effects of increasing income on contributions to total health and care costs
vignette 1 in ordinary housing, care package (a), base scenario and charging assumptions

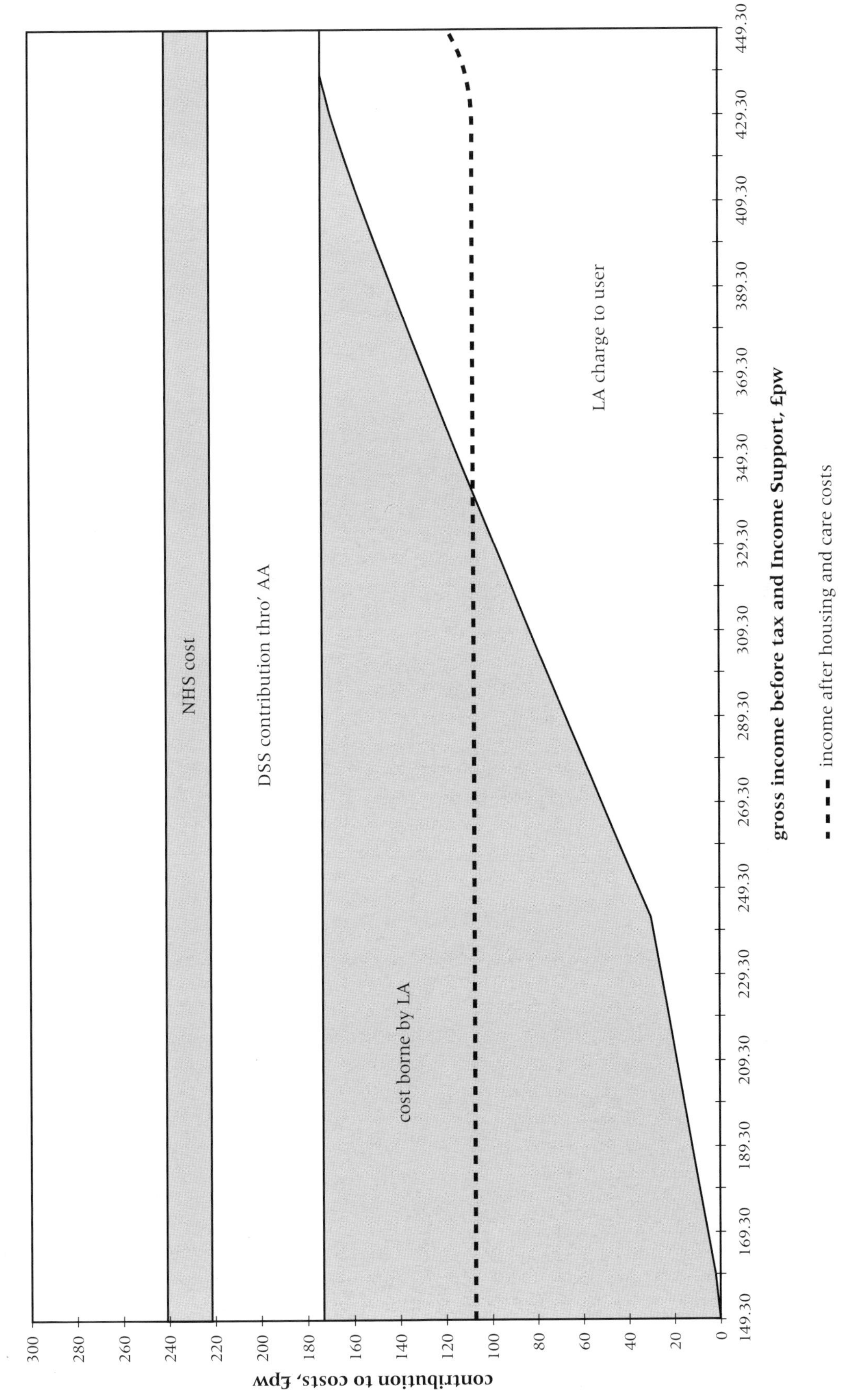

NHS cost

DSS contribution thro' AA

cost borne by LA

LA charge to user

gross income before tax and Income Support, £pw

- - - income after housing and care costs

contribution to costs, £pw

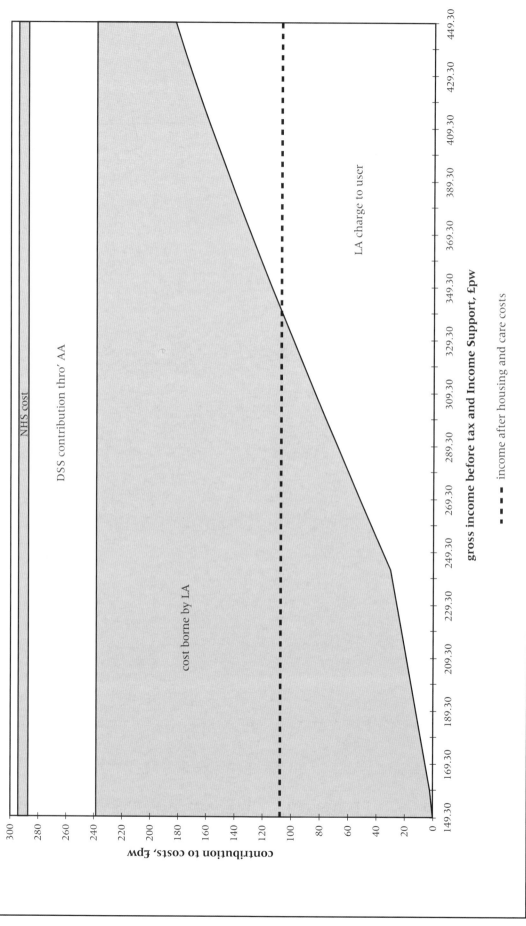

Fig D.2: Effects of increasing income on contributions to total health and care costs vignette 1 in ordinary housing, care package (b), base scenario and charging assumptions

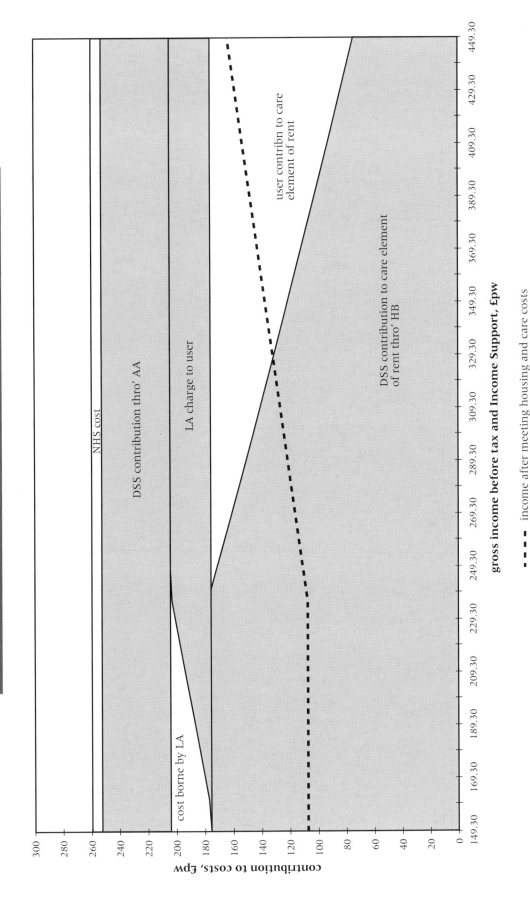

Fig D.3: Effects of increasing income on contributions to total health and care costs vignette 1 in very sheltered housing, base scenario and charging assumptions

NHS cost

DSS contribution thro' AA

LA charge to user

cost borne by LA

user contribn to care element of rent

DSS contribution to care element of rent thro' HB

gross income before tax and Income Support, £pw

- - - - income after meeting housing and care costs

contribution to costs, £pw

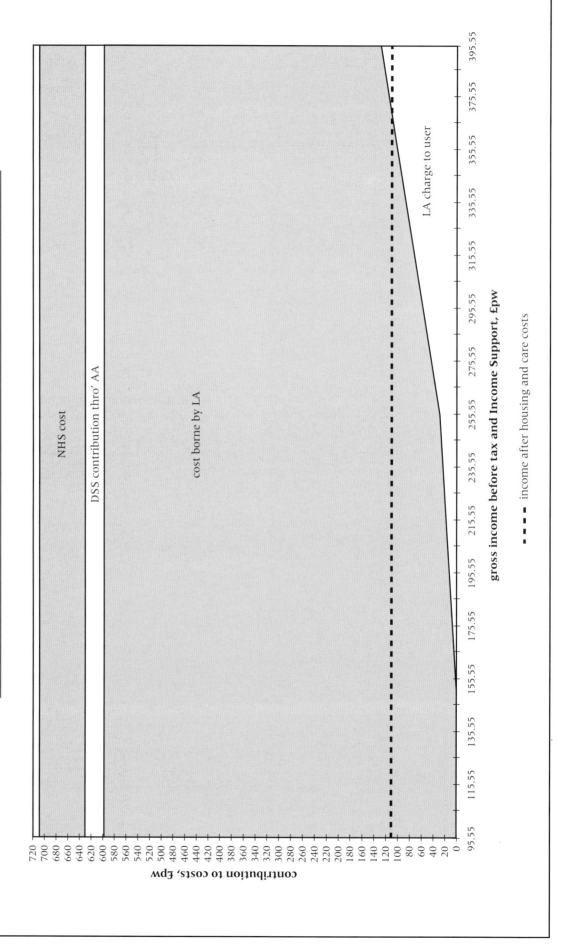

Fig D.4: Effects of increasing income on contributions to total health and care costs vignette 3 in ordinary housing base scenario and charging assumptions

NHS cost

DSS contribution thro' AA

cost borne by LA

LA charge to user

gross income before tax and Income Support, £pw

- - - - income after housing and care costs

contribution to costs, £pw

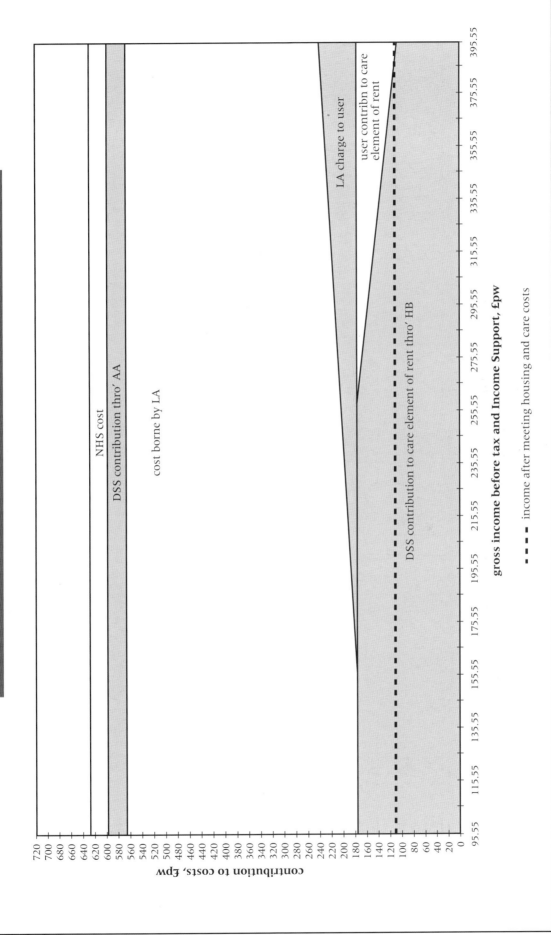

Fig D.5: Effects of increasing income on contributions to total health and care costs vignette 3 in very sheltered housing, base scenario and charging assumptions

Fig D.6: Effects of increasing income on contributions to total health and care costs vignette 6 in ordinary housing base scenario and charging assumptions

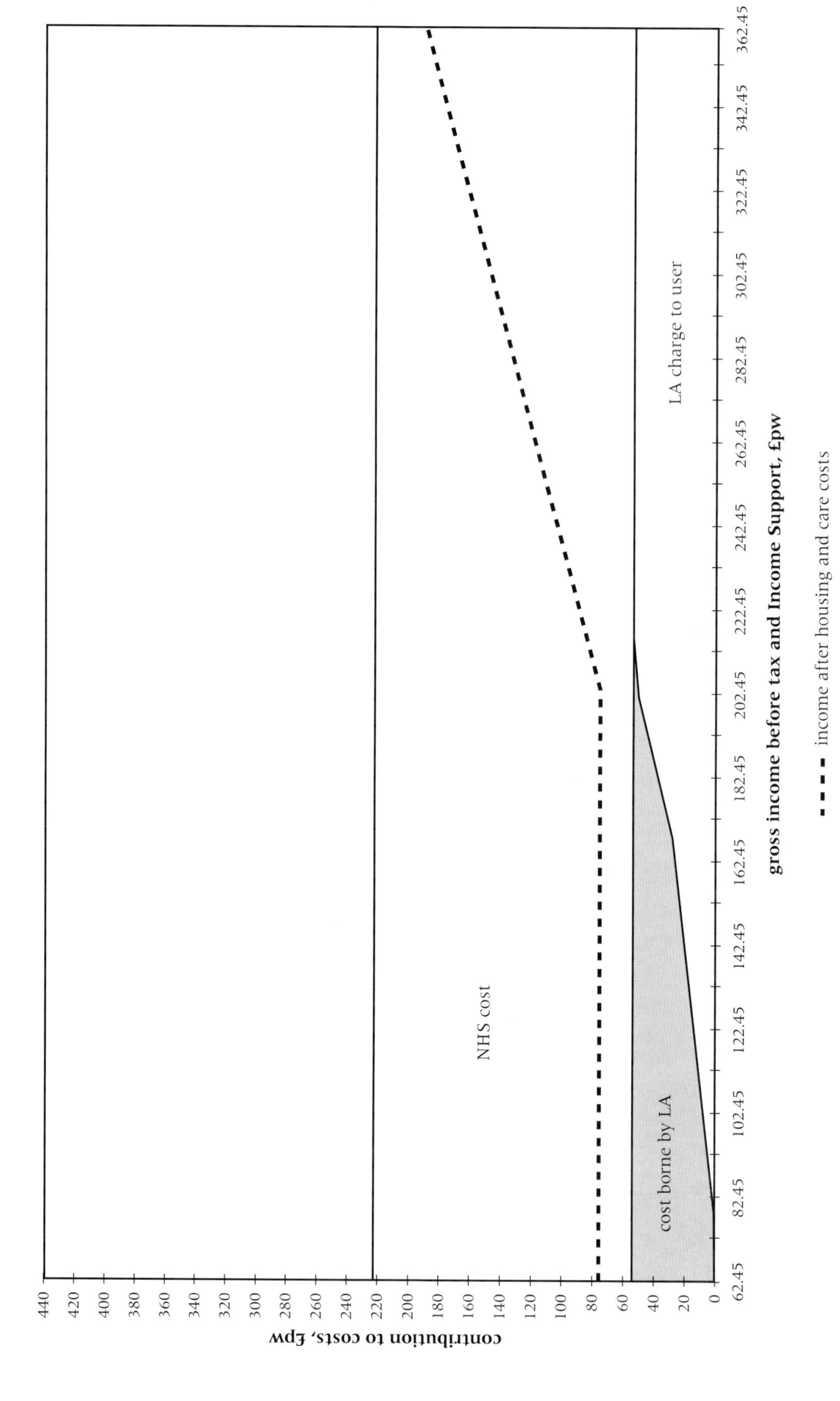

NHS cost

LA charge to user

cost borne by LA

gross income before tax and Income Support, £pw

- - - - income after housing and care costs

contribution to costs, £pw

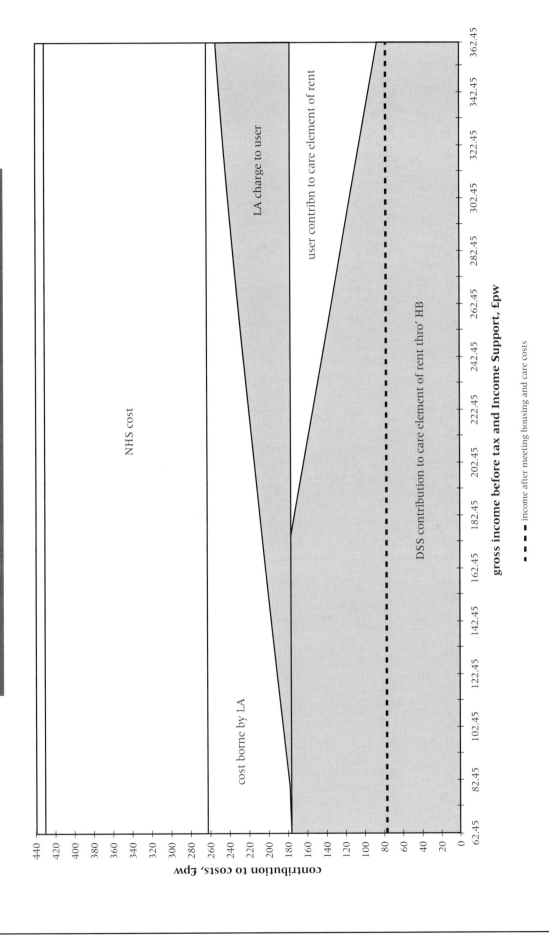

Fig D.7: Effects of increasing income on contributions to total health and care costs vignette 6 in very sheltered housing, base scenario and charging assumptions

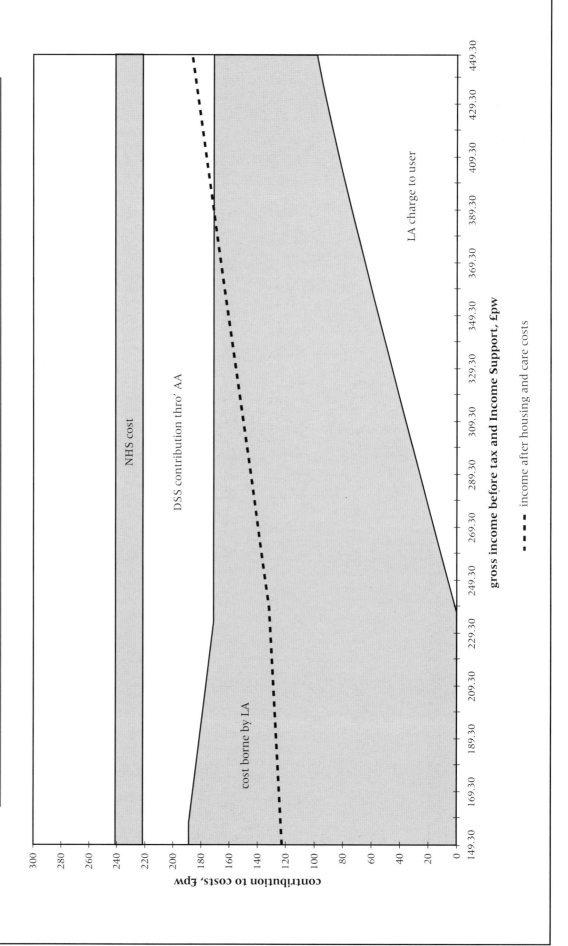

Fig D.8: Effects of increasing income on contributions to total health and care costs
vignette 1 in ordinary housing, care package (a), base scenario, LA charge to user limited to 65% of disposable income

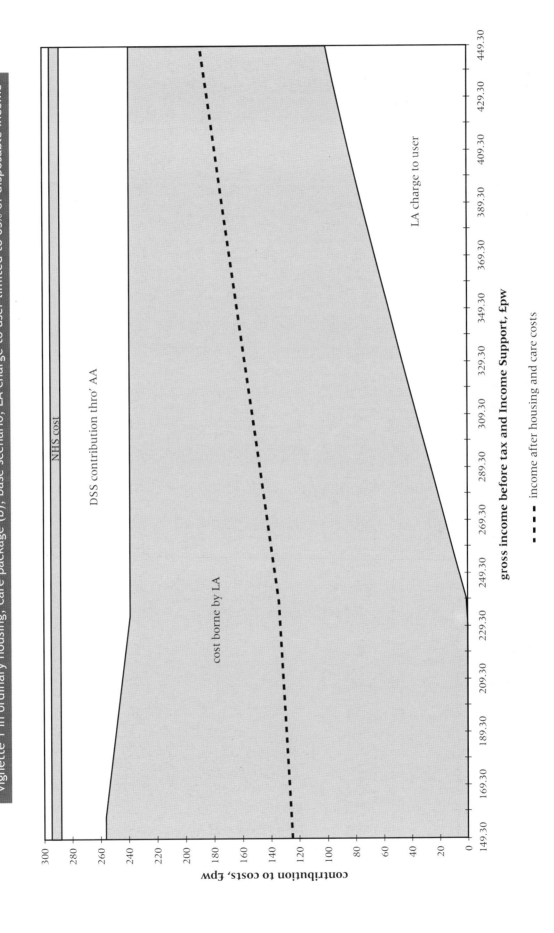

Fig D.9: Effects of increasing income on contributions to total health and care costs
vignette 1 in ordinary housing, care package (b), base scenario, LA charge to user limited to 65% of disposable income

NHS cost

DSS contribution thro' AA

cost borne by LA

LA charge to user

gross income before tax and Income Support, £pw

contribution to costs, £pw

- - - income after housing and care costs

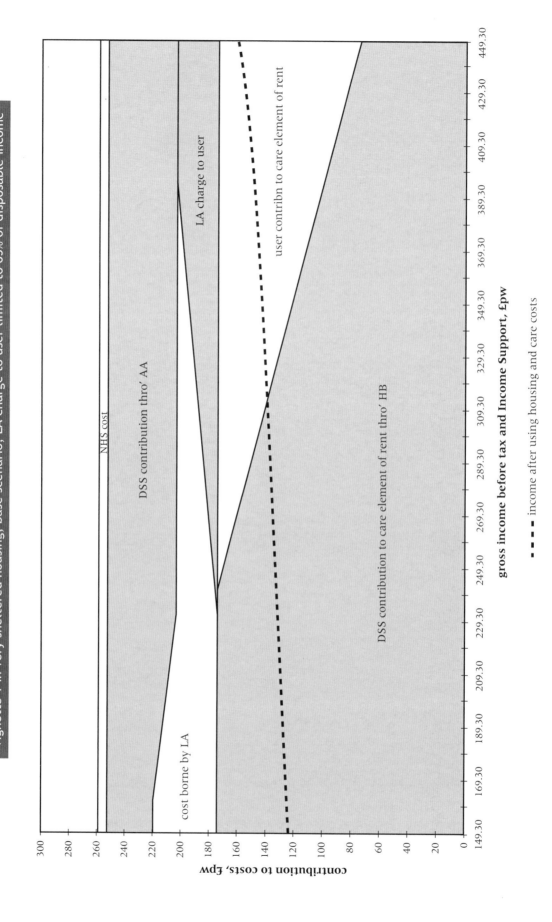

Fig D.10: Effects of increasing income on contributions to total health and care costs
vignette 1 in very sheltered housing, base scenario, LA charge to user limited to 65% of disposable income

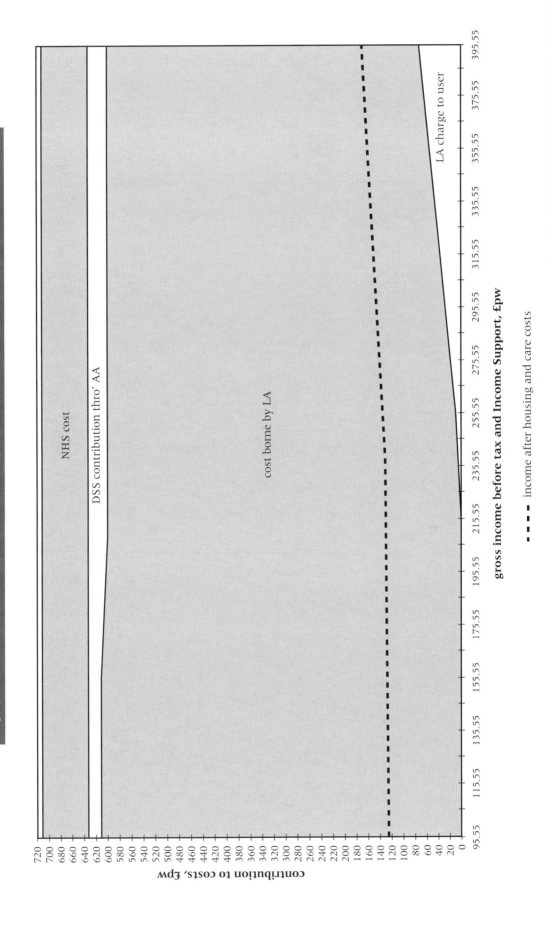

Fig D.11: Effects of increasing income on contributions to total health and care costs vignette 3 in ordinary housing base scenario, LA charge to user limited to 65% of disposable income

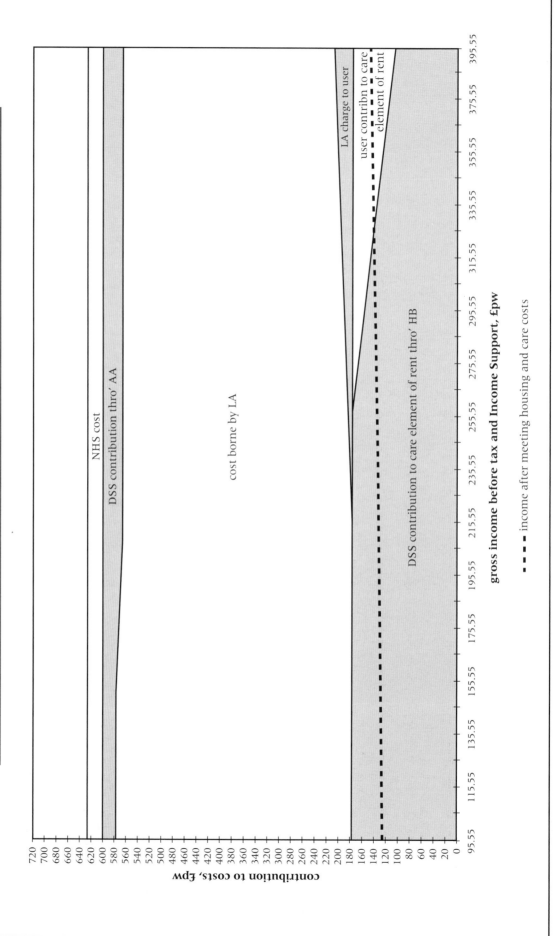

Fig D.12: Effects of increasing income on contributions to total health and care costs vignette 3 in very sheltered housing, base scenario, LA charge to user limited to 65% of disposable income

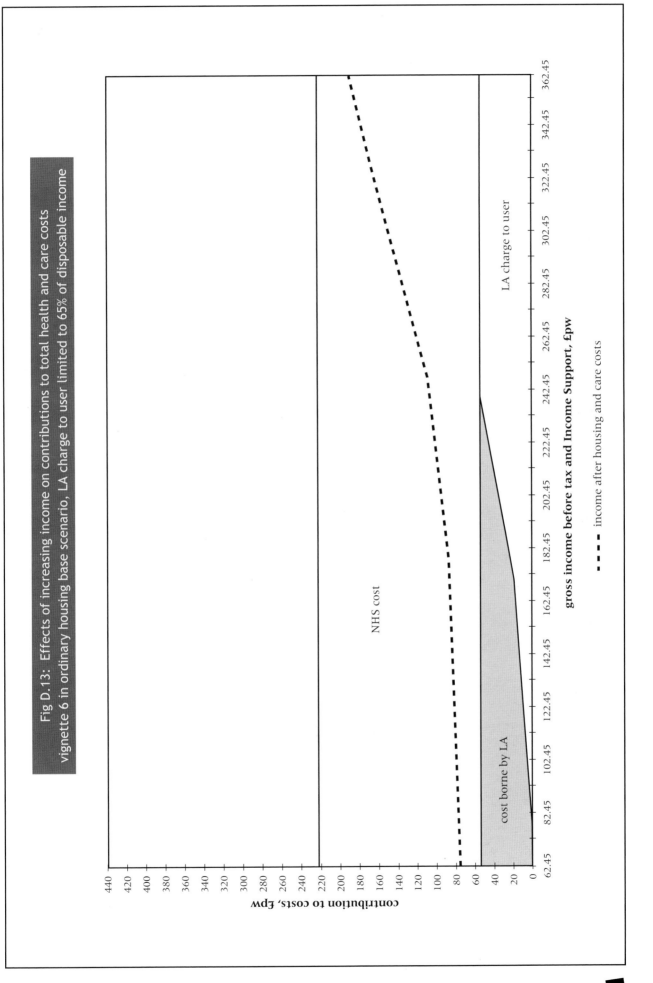

Fig D.13: Effects of increasing income on contributions to total health and care costs vignette 6 in ordinary housing base scenario, LA charge to user limited to 65% of disposable income

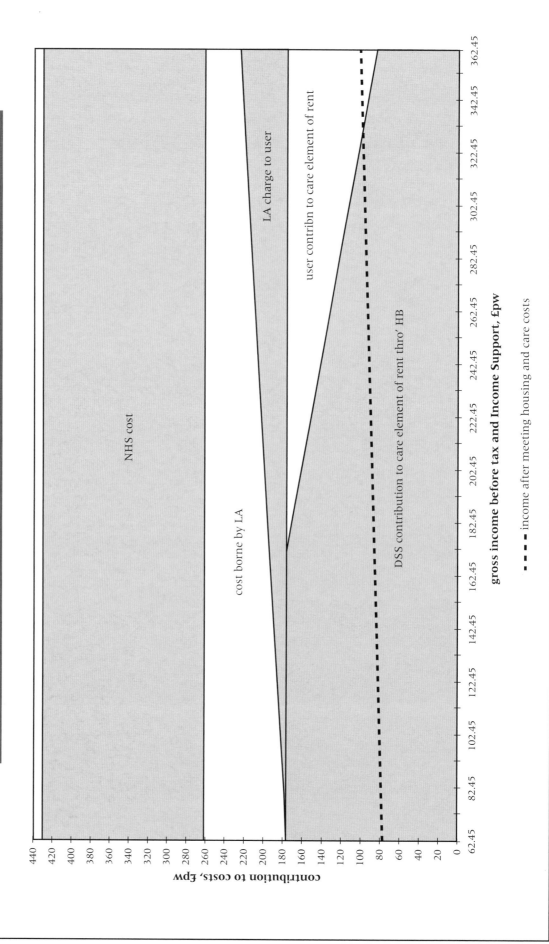

Fig D.14: Effects of increasing income on contributions to total health and care costs vignette 6 in very sheltered housing base scenario, LA charge to user limited to 65% of disposable income

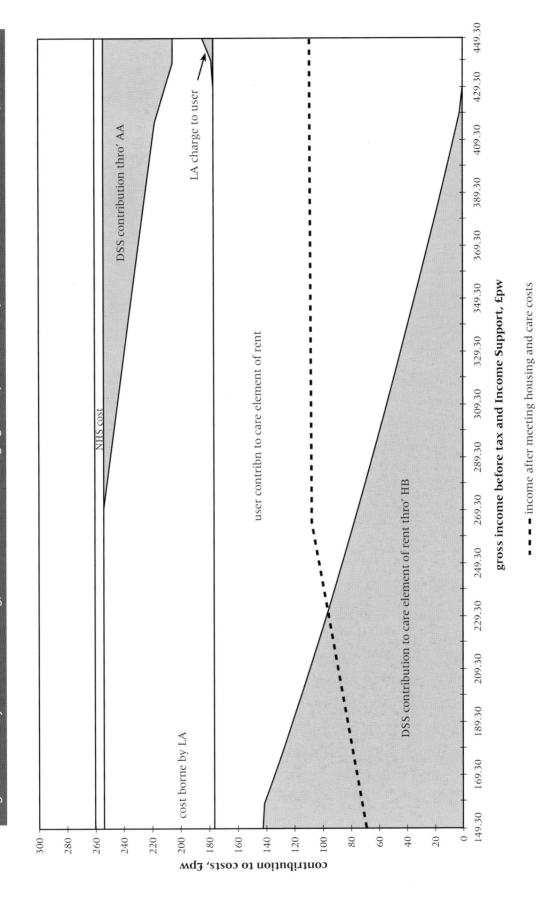

Fig D.15: Effects of increasing income on contributions to total health and care costs
vignette 1 in very sheltered housing, base scenario and charging assumptions but only 50% of care element of rent eligible for HB

DSS contribution thro' AA

NHS cost

LA charge to user

cost borne by LA

user contribn to care element of rent

DSS contribution to care element of rent thro' HB

- - - income after meeting housing and care costs

gross income before tax and Income Support, £pw

contribution to costs, £pw

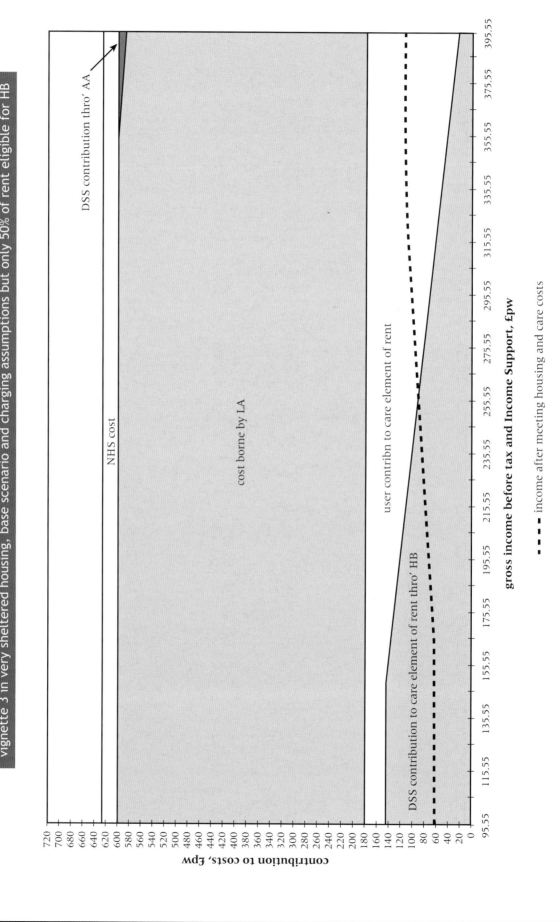

Fig D.16: Effects of increasing income on contributions to total health and care costs vignette 3 in very sheltered housing, base scenario and charging assumptions but only 50% of rent eligible for HB

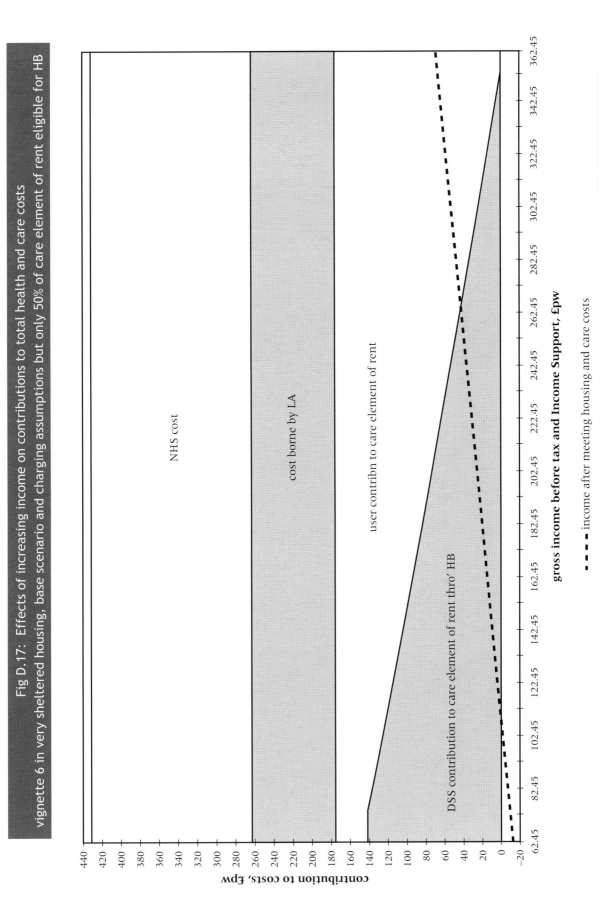

Fig D.17: Effects of increasing income on contributions to total health and care costs vignette 6 in very sheltered housing, base scenario and charging assumptions but only 50% of care element of rent eligible for HB

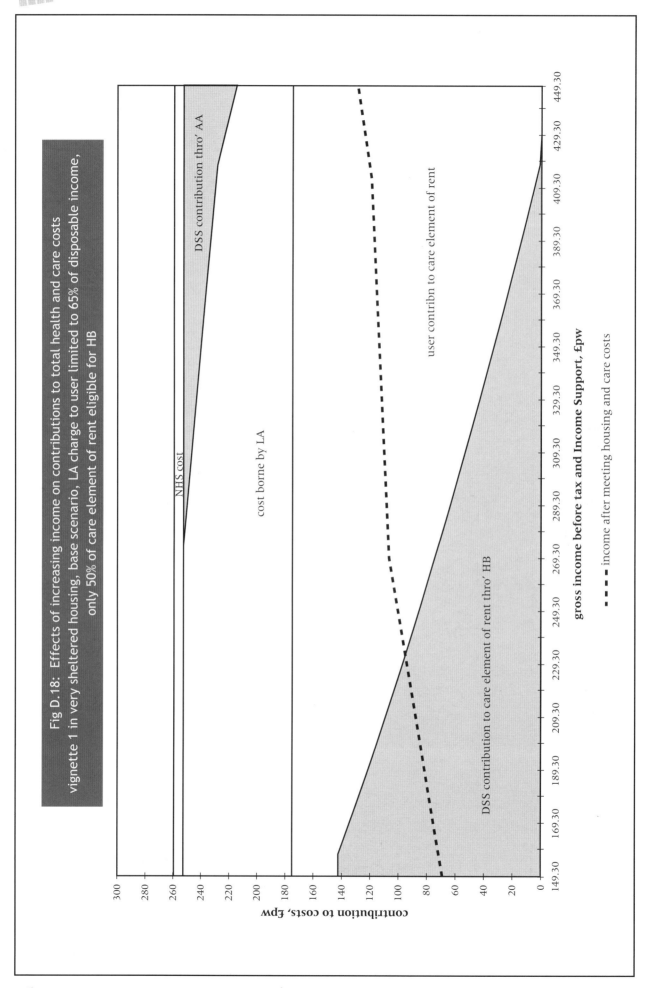

Fig D.18: Effects of increasing income on contributions to total health and care costs vignette 1 in very sheltered housing, base scenario, LA charge to user limited to 65% of disposable income, only 50% of care element of rent eligible for HB

Fig D.19: Effects of increasing income on contributions to total health and care costs vignette 3 in very sheltered housing, base scenario, LA charge to user limited to 65% of disposable income, only 50% of care element of rent eligible for HB

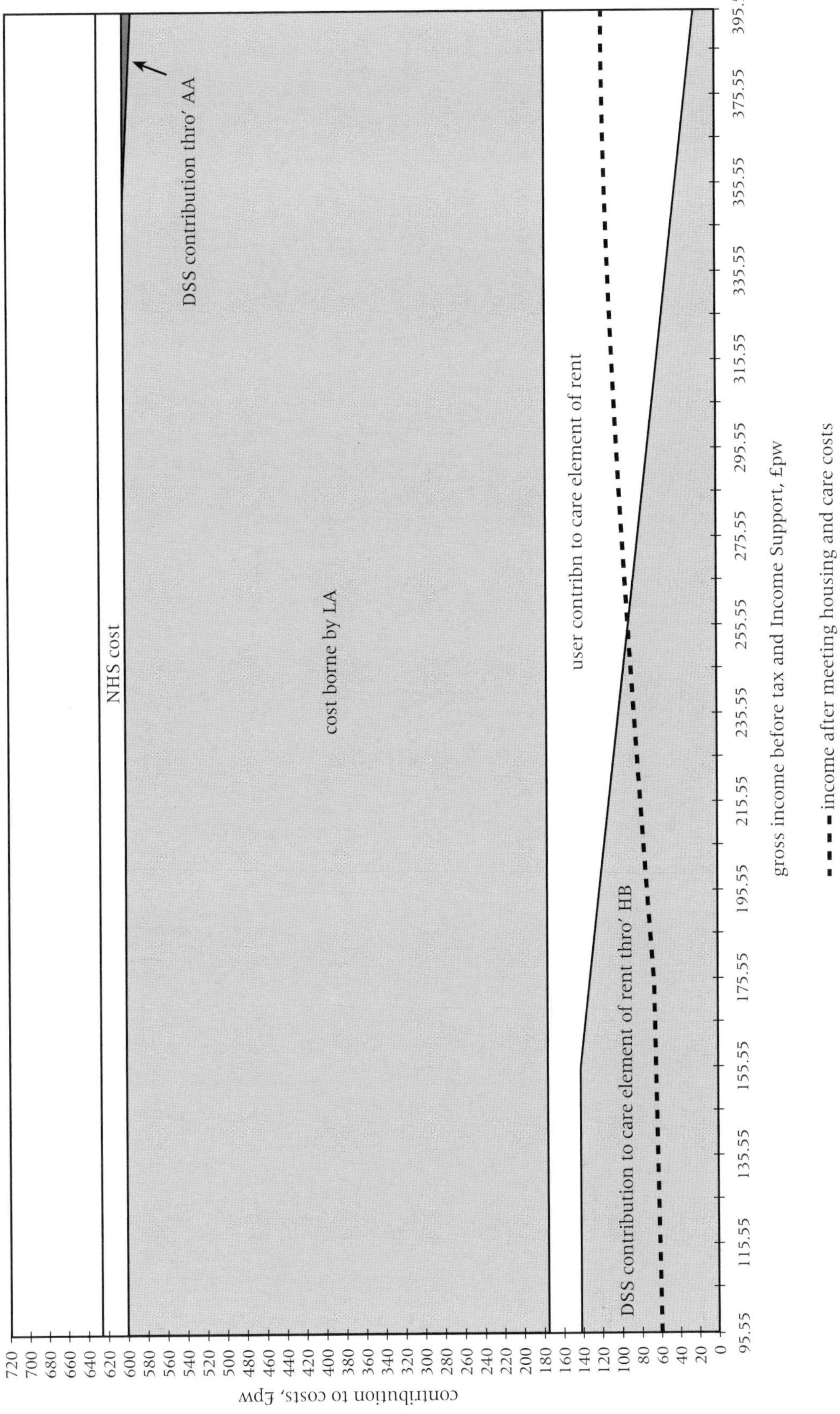

DSS contribution thro' AA

NHS cost

cost borne by LA

user contribn to care element of rent

DSS contribution to care element of rent thro' HB

contribution to costs, £pw

720 700 680 660 640 620 600 580 560 540 520 500 480 460 440 420 400 380 360 340 320 300 280 260 240 220 200 180 160 140 120 100 80 60 40 20 0

95.55 115.55 135.55 155.55 175.55 195.55 215.55 235.55 255.55 275.55 295.55 315.55 335.55 355.55 375.55 395.55

gross income before tax and Income Support, £pw

- - - - income after meeting housing and care costs

Chapter 10
Findings and Issues

INTRODUCTION

We were asked by the Royal Commission to review models of care for older people which were alternatives to institutional care, to cost these and to indicate how they would be paid for. Within time constraints of less than six months, we were unable to undertake much empirical research, but our report is more than a summary of the literature. We investigated a substantial number and variety of schemes that are currently in operation. These are detailed in Annex E. We examined in detail four models of care: intensive home support; co-resident care; very sheltered housing; and assistive technology. In reality these models may overlap as people require different combinations of support. Each model was assessed in terms of its feasibility (the practical issues to be addressed if it is to work), acceptability (to users – older people and carers – and staff), outcomes and economic costs.

To help with the last of these, we devised six vignettes – hypothetical cases – of frail older people living in the community but on the margins of institutional care. They were chosen with reference to what is known about the age, gender and living circumstances of people who enter institutional care. But six examples cannot represent the full range of relevant characteristics of people who are in this situation. They are simply illustrative. Each vignette was assigned to one or more settings (i.e. own home, with or without a co-resident carer, or very sheltered housing) with an appropriate package of care. The combinations and volume of different forms of care allocated to the vignettes were those which research and practice suggested were likely to be sufficient to keep people out of institutions. However, systematic evidence about the precise level of service or facility necessary to keep someone out of an institution is not available. The packages of care are therefore no more than rough estimates of what is likely to be needed to keep people out of institutions, but do not address the issue of comparisons of quality of life in the different settings.

The value of the economic resources used in meeting the care services provided in each vignette was then estimated. These costs were subsequently apportioned between the individual and the different public bodies involved, under alternative assumptions about how the individual's contribution to care costs is determined. An important caveat is that the cost of informal care has *not* been included.

This chapter brings together the key findings and issues which arise from the separate review of each model of care and the vignette-based analysis of costs and where these costs fall. It also draws on focus groups held with older people and carers to explore their views about alternative models of care in old age (Appendix 1), two papers which are concerned with housing issues (Appendices 2 and 3) and one on assistive technology (Appendix 4). To set the findings in context we begin with a recapitulation of important background issues.

In *Chapter 2*, we outlined *the context in which community based services are provided*. We stressed that ageing is not a static process for individuals measured in chronological terms. Particular attention was given to the views of older people and the extent of their stated preferences for remaining in their own homes, to their heterogeneity, to the importance of household relationships and support, and to the infrastructure of primary and secondary health services. Drawing on the two Appendices (2 and 3) we stressed the key role of the provision of warm, safe housing which does not necessarily have to be specialised. Adaptations and simple aids together with the provision of a downstairs lavatory are likely to be cost effective. We identify the key role of Home Improvement Agencies and the role of grants. There is also need for more units of small housing.

We suggested that the *key principles* underlying judgements about community based services should concern the extent to which they:

- promote independence for the older person

- promote 'normal' – as opposed to a stigmatised – life-style

- guarantee rights to safety and freedom from exploitation

- respond to the individual's preferences and choices

- do not 'worsen' an individual's living situation.

FINDINGS

In *Chapter 3*, in the review of *the intensive home support model*, attention was drawn to the well-known differences between health and social care provision and funding, since these affect in a fundamental way what services are received and by whom. A number of schemes (Annex E) illustrated how the intensive home support model can work in practice – to meet both short-term (such as on discharge from hospital) and long-term needs. It was suggested that, at its best, intensive home support can deliver care to the standard of the 'best relatives' and enables people, if they so wish, to continue to live as normal a life as possible in their own home. However, the overall conclusion was that, for intensive home support to work as a national norm, a great many pieces have to fall into place – the adequacy of the person's home, information, comprehensive assessments, access to a wide range of services, availability, affordability and the appropriateness of services. Above all the reliability, continuity and quality of support are identified as crucial. These appear as strenuous requirements when viewed against service divisions, resource constraints, funding differentials and local diversity of standards and social conditions.

In *Chapter 3* we also emphasised that research is consistent in its stress on the powerful influence of personal relationships and support networks on both people's capacity and preference for remaining in their own homes. In *Chapter 4* we examine this model of *co-resident carers* as a most important illustration of the significance of relationships and networks. Attention was drawn (Tables 4.1 and 4.2) to the fact that – contrary to many common assumptions – it is spouses who provide the bulk of co-resident care and hence of intensive support. Married dependent people are far less likely to enter institutional care than those who are widowed or never married. The importance of providing services to carers in their own right – many of whom are themselves above retirement age cannot be over-stated. Co-resident caring by an offspring is the next most likely form of co-resident care. High rates of divorce and increasing levels of women's employment may further hasten the decline of two-generation households.

Chapter 4 shows clearly the vulnerability of co-resident carers in terms of physical and mental stress. It also shows that they are much less likely to have help, such as respite care, from social services than non-resident carers. Sometimes practical help, such as with basic housework, is not available or may be the wrong kind. A service such as respite care for the dependent person in a care home may be unacceptable but a care assistant coming into the home may be more acceptable to carers. Sometimes the problem for carers is the growing tendency of local authorities to charge for community services. Practical support, such as showing how to cope with a dementia sufferers behavioural problems may encourage caregivers to continue caring (see Annex E).

Although the majority of older people, including those on the margins of institutional care, are in mainstream housing and can be supported by intensive home support and/or co-resident carers, a move to specialised housing may be more appropriate. In *Chapter 5* we discuss the model of *very sheltered housing*. This kind of housing with the availability of 24-hour care, together with some extra communal facilities (e.g. special baths) and some meals means that an older person can remain either as an owner or tenant with all the security of tenure that this brings. They are not 'clients' of an institution. Research shows that there is little very sheltered housing (3.5% compared with 96.5% of ordinary sheltered) and that there is underprovision. One way forward described in both this Chapter, in Annex E and in Appendices 2 and 3 is to remodel sheltered housing, some of which is out of date and 'difficult to let', and to change the role of the warden. Although this form of housing is popular with older people and, at its best, to provide a substitute for institutional care there is a dearth of evidence about outcomes.

For all kinds of setting the role of *Assistive Technology* (AT), which is the focus of *Chapter 6* and Appendix 4 (see also Appendix 2), may be helpful. AT includes various types of communication equipment (telephones and alarms), equipment to aid problems of mobility, personal and domestic care, 'smart homes' and telemedicine/telecare. Research is lacking on many aspects of the widespread use of such technical solutions and on whether they can keep people longer in their own home. However problems such as cost and production on a large scale may be solved by a wider market as a result of increased demand. Technical problems are still prevalent but are being overcome. It should not be assumed that older people will not use technology but neither should it be assumed that it will take the place of social interaction. It is likely that a new generation of older people who are used to devices such as computers will use them to a greater extent.

Running through these chapters and the four types of scheme is the particular problem of *older people with dementia*. Dementia, more than physical incapacity, can present both family members and services with particular difficulties and extreme demands. Chapters 3 and 4 both drew attention to this. Some of the innovative schemes discussed in Annex E highlight projects which have tried to address the needs of severe dementia sufferers and their carers both in their own home and in settings which are 'half-way' between one's own home and an institution. In Chapter 5 the success of very sheltered housing for people with dementia was noted. The role of Assistive Technology for this group is mixed. On the one hand passive devices may enable carers to know that the sufferer is being monitored while more active devices may not be able to be used because of cognitive impairment. Because of the likely increase in numbers of older people with dementia this group is likely to provide one of the greatest challenges for families and service providers.

Our illustrative examples (*vignettes*), in *Chapters 7, 8* and *9*, show clearly the wide range of packages of care that are possible and *their costs*. They underline the importance of distinguishing between the economic costs of care and those which fall on the public sector. Although caution is necessary because it is not always possible to compare like with like (see Chapter 8 for other provisos) the costings summarised in Table 8.6 show that there is no general rule about whether care in ordinary housing, adapted if necessary, costs more or less than care in very sheltered housing. Nor is there a general rule about either being less costly than full-time residential care. It depends on the numbers of hours of home care, including day and night sitting, and on how far such care is provided by the staff of very sheltered housing.

For three of our vignettes (2, 5 and 6) care in an ordinary home is cheaper than in very sheltered housing. But for one of our vignettes (3) the opposite is true. The person depicted in this vignette requires large amounts of home care; in an ordinary home it has to be provided partly by a home carer one to one but in very sheltered housing it can be provided partly by staff who need not be in a one to one ratio with the tenants. For the same reason full time residential care is substantially cheaper than either care in an ordinary home or in very sheltered housing for the woman depicted in vignette 4.

Who bears the costs of care in community settings varies in illogical ways. If it is health rather than social care, the costs are borne by the NHS regardless of the users' financial resources. If it is care included with accommodation costs in very sheltered housing it may be met in part or in full by DSS through Housing Benefit depending on the income or savings of the older person concerned but this is under review. The role of Attendance Allowance may also be crucial in helping with costs. If it is social care provided via a Local Authority, the older person may make a contribution depending on his or her financial resources and on the charging system used by the Local Authority. There is no national framework for such charges. For older people with modest financial resources, it is not the division between private and public costs which varies most. It is the apportionment of public costs between the NHS, Local Authorities and DSS. It should be remembered, however, that a cost has not been put on informal care. Had that been possible, those situations where much of the care was provided by a co-resident carer would have shown more of the costs being borne by the private sector.

The problems of costs and who pays for care are illustrated by very sheltered housing (see Chapter 5). Such developments, particularly for housing associations, depend heavily on a combination of housing finance and social security benefits for their viability and exemplify first the importance of financial mechanisms in driving policy in a particular direction and second the distinction between public expenditure and economic costs. The illustrative vignettes indicate that, for a given level of need, the costs of care in very sheltered housing (Table 8.2) are, for four of the five relevant examples, less than they are in ordinary housing. This is a direct consequence of assuming that a lower input of services, including adaptations to the home, would be needed in very sheltered housing. However, when housing costs are taken into account, costs are lower in suitably adapted homes for three out of our five examples, very little different in one, and only higher in one instance (Table 8.3). The comparison of the apportionment of these costs depends critically on the extent to which any services included in the rent of very sheltered housing are eligible for Housing Benefit, in which case much of the cost may fall on DSS. So too does the affordability of very sheltered housing from the point of view of older people themselves.

ISSUES

This review has raised a host of different issues. It is necessary to distinguish them. The most important seem to us to be the following:

(a) The views of people on the margins of institutional care and their carers

- although the evidence is clear that *most older people want to remain in a home of their own* these findings are based on the current generation of older people and current forms of institutions. In the future more older people may not have families to turn to (e.g. because they have no children), or they may choose to live in an institution because circumstances change (e.g. areas may be perceived as dangerous). *Much depends on what choice is being offered*. The Wagner report (1988) pointed to the need for a 'Positive Choice' and institutional settings may become more like hotels which offer choice and comfort;

- potential *conflicts* between older people and their carers when, for example the older person wants to remain at home and the carer would prefer them to move;

■ how services can best be provided for ***older people with dementia*** and their carers.

(b) Information

■ how older people, their carers and professionals obtain ***information about service availability*** (both statutory and independent) and ***access to help*** and social security entitlements;

■ how professionals not only obtain information but are able and willing to communicate it.

(c) Assessment

■ how needs should be assessed *(**preferably a common assessment** for the different kinds of housing and care) and their separation from the costs of meeting those needs, the ability to pay on the one hand, and the ability to provide the service on the other;

■ the need for ***assessment*** before discharge from hospital (a precipitous discharge to an institution without an examination of all the options – both long and short term – may mean that the person never returns home);

■ the value of ***reassessment*** (e.g. after admission to a residential care home where needs may have changed).

(d) Services and how they are provided and organised

■ the ***availability and appropriateness of care services*** as currently constituted; how very dependent older people can be maintained in homes of their own ***without their homes becoming like institutions***;

■ the ***role of different services and professionals*** and how they ***collaborate***;

■ the way ***services are organised, particularly primary care*** and its potential role in bringing together health and social care;

■ the ***neglect of housing*** and its role in community care at a national, local and individual level;

■ the need for ***effective rehabilitation*** services following an episode of ill health including the role of convalescent facilities;

■ the importance of ***planning not just for older people but for everyone*** (such as by good design of housing and the environment);

■ ways in which ***quality*** (including the reliability) of services, or at least a standard below which services may not fall, can be guaranteed to older people whether they are in their own homes or a communal setting;

■ ***targeting*** services for frail older people ***versus the need for preventive services*** for other older people;

- the *failure to follow good practice* when this is well known (e.g. over hospital discharge);

- there are specific *issues to do with sheltered and very sheltered housing*: e.g. people may go in because of emotional/psychological problems such as depression. Their health may improve. Is this a positive or negative outcome? Should they then remain there if they have no 'need'?

(e) How services are funded

- *current financial mechanisms* drive services apart rather than together;

- the extent to which policy should focus on making *cash payments to individuals* and encourage them to make their own care arrangements, with the consequent need both for determining entitlement to such cash payments and for regulation of private suppliers.

(f) Lack of knowledge

- the *limits which current knowledge* still places on the extent to which it is possible to identify the circumstances in which providing services in a community setting, even when it is more costly than in a residential setting, is more *cost effective* bearing in mind

    – the quality of life each delivers and

    – that for community services, the variation in costs over time for one individual and between individuals is likely to be very much greater in the community than it is in residential settings;

- the *lack of evaluation* of innovatory schemes which are thought to be 'good' but where evidence is lacking;

- *problems in assessing outcomes* of services and interventions. While it is relatively easy to obtain measures which are service based 'and deal with the nature, number and intensity of the components of care packages' it is more difficult to focus 'on the impact of such packages on individuals themselves' (Petch *et al.*, 1996, p. 137). As Baldock has pointed out: 'There are many ways of measuring the benefits of interventions, all of them imperfect; do they prevent entry into institutional care, do they affect the expressed satisfaction of users and carers, do they reduce the chance of falling and other accidents and problems, do they affect measures of depression and anxiety, do they slow the increase in disabilities, and, ultimately, do they extend life?' (Baldock, 1997, p. 87). DoH are currently sponsoring a significant research initiative in this difficult area (DoH, OSCA, 1998).

IN CONCLUSION

In this review we have reported on ways in which older people on the margins of institutional care may be enabled to remain in a home of their own. While we have tended to focus, because of our brief, on community services we must not ignore the important advances that have been made in geriatric medicine, the hospice movement and drug therapy. Nor must we ignore the role of acute hospital care. The most difficult task is 'to get the bureaucratic mechanisms attuned to support comprehensive care' (Glennerster, 1996, p. 10). Fundamental to this is getting the financial mechanisms right. Whatever these are it is essential that they should promote, encourage and facilitate the integration of comprehensive care. As the recent Discussion Document *Partnership in Action* states 'There is no single, simple solution' (DoH September 1998, p. 6). The document puts forward a number of proposals including pooled budgets.

There are also changes outside the specific focus of long term care which have to be taken into account. Many professions, such as nursing (see UK Central Council for Nursing, Midwifery and Health Visiting, 1997), are undergoing radical changes and there is need to ensure that others such as home care and occupational therapy together provide a service which is what older people need. At the same time the structure of service delivery is changing with new arrangements for the provision of primary health care and expected changes in the organisation of social services. For some organisations rethinking has gone beyond structures right to the heart of provision. For example the Association of Directors of Social Services, in their submission to the Royal Commission, have argued that residential care for older people is arguably outdated and is unlikely to survive long into the next century.

The review has shown the complexities of provision and funding and the many anomalies that exist. Clear coherent strategies would help but we would also stress that many older people and their carers have modest requests which would make all the difference in their ability to remain at home. We cite small adaptations to the home, help with house cleaning and good practice in hospital discharge as examples.

We would also emphasise that for some people the kinds of housing and care we have examined may be needed for a short time only. Older people in receipt of very intensive levels of support may not live for very long, or may not need them for many years. In this respect the long-term costs of disability are rather different from the long-term cost of ageing.

The needs of older people on the margins of institutional care are complex and depend on many different factors. They need advice and support and those who help them make decisions need to be both sensitive and knowledgeable not only about the services available but also about their costs. We hope that this report will contribute to the Royal Commission's deliberations.

Annex E: Illustrations of Care Schemes

This Annex focuses on examples of individual schemes that give support to older people and their carers in the community. The focus is on schemes that have recently been evaluated by their providers, or commissioners, or as part of academic research.

1. HOUSING RELATED SERVICES (see pp. 184-195)

A: Very sheltered housing/housing with extra care
- Somerville Very Sheltered Housing Scheme, London Borough of Lewisham
- Broadway Gardens, Wolverhampton
- Northamptonshire and Coventry

B: Half-way houses/hostels
- Domus Unit – Care for older people with severe dementia, South East London

C: Shared Housing
- Dementia Care Initiative independent supported living scheme.

D: Adaptations to ordinary housing or improvement of sub-standard housing
- Handyperson's schemes
- Anchor Hospital Discharge scheme

2. SERVICES AND FACILITIES IN THE HOME (see pp. 195-216)

A: Intensive home support packages
- Kent (Thanet) Community Care Scheme and related schemes (experimental care management)
- Belfast Intensive Domiciliary Care
- Dementia Home Support Project, Ipswich and Newham, London
- Newcastle upon Tyne West End Care Management Project for people with dementia Pilot Project
- Newcastle upon Tyne Dementia Care Initiative Pilot Project
- Wakefield Immediate Support at Home
- Marlow EPICS (Elderly Persons Integrated Care System)
- Stone Rehabilitation Centre, Staffordshire
- Victoria Project: Community Occupational Therapy Rehabilitation Service, London

B: Live in carers
- Homeshare

C: Hospital discharge schemes
- South Derbyshire Hospital at Home (HAH) pilot scheme
- Gloucester Hospital at Home (HAH)

D: Use of technology

■ This is discussed in Chapter 6 of the Report and Appendix 4.

E: Facilities to make older people safer

■ see 1D: Anchor Hospital Discharge scheme

F: Night sitting service

■ Oxford Night Time Home Care Service

3. SERVICES AND FACILITIES OUTSIDE THE HOME (see pp. 217-222)

A: Day care

■ North Edinburgh dementia project

■ Day centres located in multi-purpose residential care homes

B: Night Care

■ CREST (Care And Respite For Elderly People With Support and Treatment)

C: Adult Placement Services

■ Homeshare, London Borough of Lewisham

4. SERVICES TO SUPPORT CARERS (see pp. 222-225)

A: Respite care

■ Respite care in an NHS geriatric ward

B: Counselling/preparation/relaxation services

■ Shiatsu massage for carers

■ Dementia Care Trust counselling service

C: Support groups

■ Carer support groups in Glasgow

1. HOUSING RELATED SERVICES

A: Very sheltered housing/housing with extra-care

NAME OF SCHEME: Somerville Very Sheltered Housing Scheme

1. KEY FACTS
Provider: Care First, provider arm of Lewisham Social Services

Location: London Borough of Lewisham

Funding source: Lewisham Housing Department (capital) and Social Services (care services)

Date: opened September 1996.

2. AIMS AND PHILOSOPHY
Aims: for social services, the primary aim was to extend the range of social care options available to older people living in the community; for housing, the main aims were to re-house vulnerable older people in more appropriate supported accommodation and to make more efficient use of housing stock.

Philosophy: 24-hour supervision, flexible and individually based care packages, the promotion of independence and rehabilitation, tenant involvement in running the scheme, links with relatives and other community resources.

3. DESCRIPTION

Accommodation: The scheme has 26 flats (4 one-bedroom and 22 bed-sitters with small bathroom and kitchen). There is a dining room where a mid-day meal (frozen) is provided, a lounge and two well-used gardens.

Tenants: In 1997, the average age was 72 (age range from 54 to 96). Tenants were predominately women (14 out of 22) and with three exceptions tenants were white. Five tenants attend a day centre. At the opening of Somerville, 7 tenants were relatively independent; 7 were moderately dependent and needed significant amounts of help. None were severely dependent.

Staffing: Included a manager, 8 care staff and 2 domestics. Care staff help with personal care, housework, meal preparation in tenants own flats, mobility around Somerville and help with pension collection and paying bills. A weekly shopping trip is organised for tenants unable to reach the local supermarket independently.

Involvement of relatives: Relatives are also closely involved with shopping, pension collection and helping to clean and decorate tenants' flats.

4. COSTS

Tenants have secure tenancies and are responsible for paying rent and service charges. In 1996/7, these were assessed as follows: rent: £35.89 a week; water and heating, £4.82 a week; service charge £86.15. The total of £126.86 is claimable as Housing Benefit, and the average tenant was contributing £5.60 a week to these charges. The Commissioning and Care Management wing of Lewisham Social Services pay a further £60 a week per tenant for personal and other forms of care services, making a total cost of £186.86 per week per tenant. Day care cost a further £27 a day.

5. FEASIBILITY

Concern was expressed that if all the tenants had higher dependency needs, more staff would be needed.

6. ACCEPTABILITY

Tenants were in general very happy with the scheme.

7. OUTCOMES

The evaluation concluded that Somerville is a successful project which provides a high quality of care to its tenants (Seymour, 1997, p. 22). Issues raised by the evaluation included:

- considerable difficulties in targeting the scheme at those for whom it was most suitable, and most cost effective.

- confusion over the purpose of the scheme. Ordinary sheltered housing tenants in Lewisham were often receiving more help through the home care service than tenants of the extra care scheme (only 8 tenants received more than 10 hours of help a week and 10 received less than 5 hours a week care).

■ one-third of tenants showing an improvement in meeting their own care needs.

8. KEY LESSONS

The question of selecting tenants with an appropriate level of dependency, and then responding as those levels change, is one of the most difficult issues for very sheltered schemes. The evaluation drew the following lessons from Somerville:

■ The selection of tenants for such schemes needs to take place as part of a full assessment.

■ There is an inherent conflict between providing a scheme for those who are most dependent, and one successfully promoting tenants' independence, sense of security and self-confidence. In some instances, the very success of the scheme may render the individual 'less eligible' for the facilities it provides.

■ There must be a shared understanding between commissioner and provider about the service being provided and for whom it is intended (targeted). On-going monitoring of the care needs of tenants is a necessary component of this understanding.

■ People needing 24-hour care should be accepted as tenants of very sheltered housing. These would include those needing direct help or supervision with several activities of daily living on a daily basis, those requiring frequent help at unpredictable times, including the night, and those with complex and multiple needs whom it is difficult to place elsewhere.

Reference
Seymour, P. (1997) Evaluation of very sheltered housing. Lewisham Social Services. Strategy for services for elderly people. 1996-2001.

Acknowledgement
We are grateful to Paul Seymour for comments and the Director of Social Services for the London Borough of Lewisham for permission to use the report.

A: Very sheltered housing/housing with extra care

NAME OF SCHEME: Broadway Gardens, Wolverhampton

1. KEY FACTS
Provider: Touchstone Housing Association in collaboration with Extra Care Charitable Trust commissioned/ purchased by Wolverhampton Social Services.

Location: North West Wolverhampton

Funding source: Capital – local authority housing grant and free land
Revenue – Social Services payment for care, housing benefit, tenants' resources

Date: Opened mid 1995.

2. AIMS AND PHILOSOPHY
Aims: to replace residential care provision.

Philosophy: promotion of independence; establishment of mechanisms for user involvement in operation of scheme; rehabilitative and preventative focus; flexible and responsive care, shared where appropriate with relatives; emphasis on quality of life; locally based with community links through provision of social/activities club; emphasis on the development of volunteering and training opportunities in schemes.

3. DESCRIPTION

Accommodation: Has 56 flats, a social/activities club open to the local community and is staffed 24 hours a day. Meals are available in a communal dining room.

Tenants: Average age of the first 36 tenants was 82. When they moved in 7 tenants were receiving no or a minimal care package, 8 a package costing £10 to £49, 14 a package costing between £50 and £99 a week, 6 were costing between £100 and £199 a week and one person a package of £275 a week.

4. COSTS

Capital costs are in the range of £3 to 4m at current prices. Care is purchased at a set charge per week for tenants with higher dependency levels. No charge is paid for tenants with low dependency. Tenants in receipt of the attendance allowance pay 85% to the scheme provider. Rents and service charges are approximately £110 per week, which is eligible for housing benefit. Wolverhampton are working on the basis that at current prices (January 1998), the cost of a week in very sheltered housing, including a contribution of £54 by social services to care costs, is £257 a week. The quality of life provided is higher than in a residential home and the net cost to Social Services is approximately half of a residential place or a large care package in the community.

5. FEASIBILITY

Wolverhampton have decided to use the Broadway Gardens model as the basis for a long-term strategy involving the closure of all their residential homes. The scheme is staffed and managed by Extra Care Charitable Trust and owned by Touchstone Housing Association. Further partnerships with housing associations such as Anchor, Hanover, and Methodist Homes are in the process of development. The aim is eventually to cease using residential care altogether for people with advanced dementia, and replace it with very sheltered housing provision.

6. ACCEPTABILITY

The first stage of on-going research by Keele University which compared tenants in the scheme to a comparable sample of older people in the community found that 45% of the Broadway gardens residents rated safety as the best thing about living there. In the community sample, 31% rated their neighbours as the best thing.

7. OUTCOME

- Wolverhampton estimate substantial savings of £123,000 for the 36 tenants over the first two years of the scheme, based on a comparison with the package of care that they would otherwise have continued to receive.

- None of the 36 original residents has moved into residential care. Eight have died and one moved to a nursing home 'on trial'.

- Of 34 people, for whom information is available, 7 have remained stable, 10 have shown progressively increased dependency; 17 initially improved, but only 4 have maintained the improvement, 8 have had some setback, but still maintain a higher level of independence than on entry to the scheme and 5 have declined to below their original level of ability.

- Of the 36 tenants, 11 were not receiving any care package before admission.

- Successful promotion of tenant 'ownership' of the scheme and control of their own lives.

- The first stage of the research from Keele has discovered little difference between residents and those living in the community, although Broadway Gardens residents are on average four and a half years older. They tend to rate their own health more positively than those living in the community, but were less able to perform normal social activities.

8. KEY LESSONS

Partnership between a local authority and a non-statutory provider, including housing associations, are a productive way of developing very sheltered schemes. It is felt that close links to community through social/activities club and involvement of relatives and volunteers can be established. The scheme appears successful in enabling tenants to take control of their own lives.

Reference

Biggs, S., Bernard, M. and Kingston, P. (1998) (unpublished) Assessing the health impact of age-specific housing. Department of Applied Social Studies, Keele University.

Papers from Wolverhampton MBC on Implementation of the Very Sheltered Housing Strategy.

Acknowledgement

We are grateful to Anne Bailey, Commissioning Manager, Wolverhampton Metropolitan Borough Social Services and Paul Kingston, Keele University for help.

A: Very sheltered housing/housing with extra care

NAME OF SCHEME: Very Sheltered Housing in Northamptonshire and Coventry

1. KEY FACTS

Provider: Northamptonshire Social Services department in conjunction with Daventry District Council, Northampton Borough Council, South Northants District Council, Bedfordshire Pilgrims Housing Association, ExtraCare Charitable Trust, Minster General Housing Association, and North British Housing Association

Location: Coventry, Daventry, Kilsby, Northampton, Towcester

Funding source: various

Cost: see below

Date: all opened since 1984.

2. AIMS AND PHILOSOPHY

The five Northamptonshire schemes are 'orthodox' very sheltered housing developments which bring together specially designed housing with provision of extra care and support either from the local (social services) home care provider or from an independent provider. The Coventry scheme incorporates a philosophy of 'kaizan', a Japanese idea that everyone, tenants, staff, managers, should all be working for continual improvements in the quality of life; in this scheme, all care is provided by dedicated staff working on the site.

3. DESCRIPTION

The number of tenants range from 26 to 38 in the Northamptonshire schemes, and there are 50 in the Coventry scheme. In 1998, the average age of tenants was 83 and eight out of ten were women. They were overwhelmingly white. More than three-quarters had lived alone before moving into the schemes. All schemes provide residents with self-contained accommodation, incorporating separate bedrooms and kitchens, en-suite baths or showers, controllable heating and a personal alarm system. All have a communal dining room, a central kitchen and a sitting room. The lounges and sitting rooms in the five Northamptonshire schemes are used as day care centres. All schemes have some specialised bath equipment – e.g. with a hoist, or a special bath, or medi-bath or ambu-lift bath, and sometimes these are used also by day centre attendees. Two schemes have small shops on site, all have laundries, whose facilities they shared with external agencies.

4. COSTS

■ The capital costs of schemes varied and also involved different methods of raising finance, some of which were very complex, involving grants from the Housing Corporation, cross-subsidy arrangements with developers, mortgages, donations of land, bank loans and charitable funds. Current capital costs appeared to be in the region of £2m for approximately 30 tenants.

■ Revenue costs are similarly variable. When costs per tenant were calculated, to include care costs, whether provided in-house or by an independent provider, the Northamptonshire schemes ranged from £2,659 per annum to £4,944 per annum, while the Coventry scheme, which was the only one to integrate fully the housing and care provision by employing staff on the site, cost £9,000 a year per tenant.

5. FEASIBILITY (e.g. staffing, premises, transport, practicality)

■ *'Very sheltered housing can make a contribution to the care of older people who may need some form of supported accommodation. This may be either as part of a continuum of supported housing provision, or, if the ExtraCare model described in this report is adopted, effectively as an alternative to (institutional) provision.'*
(Woolham p. iv)

■ Comprehensive assessment is needed to select tenants who can derive most benefit from a tenancy. Wardens of very sheltered schemes should be involved in this.

■ The role of the warden is 'pivotal'. The warden can do their job best if care staff are working directly on the site.

■ Access to public transport was a problem at more than one scheme.

■ Design is very important and tenants have clear views about this.

6. ACCEPTABILITY

The great majority of tenants liked living in the schemes. Only three (out of 148) disliked it, but a varying minority (from 10%-26%) had – perhaps understandably – mixed feelings. Company, care, privacy and security were the factors that people most valued. Tenants were asked if they would prefer to be living somewhere else and overwhelmingly replied no (range 84% to 97%).

7. OUTCOMES

■ Just under a quarter of tenants who responded to a survey (154 respondents in 6 schemes, 75% response rate) thought that they could have stayed at home with help or more help with domestic tasks (range, 11% to 36%); 15% thought that adaptations to their home e.g. a stair lift or shower would have enabled them to 'stay put' (range 11% to 23%); 19% thought that help with heating bills would have made a difference (range 10% to 36%). However, the vast majority (over 85% in three of the schemes, range 65% to 88%) did not think they would have delayed applying even if that help had been forthcoming. Families were influential in urging the older people to move.

■ The vast majority of those in the schemes had received care help since moving in (range 71% to 100%), although those currently receiving such help ranged from 21% to 92%. A number of tenants – very variable by scheme, would have liked more help; bathing or washing all over was a problem for 16 tenants and chiropody 18; general housework for 11, shopping for 16. In the best resourced scheme, in Coventry, where care staff were based in the scheme minimal need was expressed for more help.

■ In the previous 12 months, 29 tenants had moved or died. Thirteen of these had died in the housing scheme; 8 had moved to a nursing home; 4 to residential care; and 4 had moved either to hospital, nursing home or residential care and died. Schemes varied in the extent to which they aimed to help people remain; 6 of the nursing home admissions had come from one scheme, where it was expected that people would move on when they became more frail.

8. KEY LESSONS

■ *'The best arrangements for securing care to tenants seemed to be in those (schemes) where there was either partial or full integration of housing management and care provision in the staff roles.'*
(Woolham, p. v)

■ Appropriate design and well-managed schemes contribute to better levels of physical and mental functioning.

■ The scheme which was most expensive, in Coventry, provided the most care. It also seemed to be the best scheme in terms of quality. The commitment to a philosophy of continual improvement, to staff training, supervision and appraisal, and to a 'key worker' system were the main factors in this.

Reference
The above data has all been drawn from:

Woolham, J. (1998) Very sheltered housing. A study of its impact and effectiveness in meeting the housing and social care needs of older people. Northamptonshire County Council.

Acknowledgement
We are grateful to Dr John Woolham, Senior Research Officer and to the Director of Social Care and Health, Northamptonshire County Council for permission to use and quote from the report.

1. HOUSING RELATED SERVICES

B: Half-way houses/hostels

NAME OF SCHEME: Domus Unit – Care for older people with severe dementia

1. KEY FACTS

Provider: NHS and a Housing Association

Location: Lewisham and North Southwark Health District, South East London.

2. AIMS AND PHILOSOPHY

The domus philosophy was developed by Professor Elaine Murphy to promote quality of care for people with severe dementia including those with particularly challenging behaviour. The aim is to maintain an older person's independence and capacities so far as is possible within the constraints of their illness. The domus unit is a **residential** facility for people with severe dementia, based on the following four assumptions:

1. The domus is the residents' home for life;

2. Staff needs are as important as resident needs;

3. The avoidable consequences of dementia should be corrected and the unavoidable ones accommodated;

4. Residents' individual psychological and emotional needs may take precedence over physical aspects of their care.

3. DESCRIPTION (research focus)

- Both adapted and purpose-built units.

- In-service training programme for all staff.

- Emphasis on the provision of recreational and activity programmes.

- Staff ratios (nursing and domestic) approximately 1.5 staff to 1 resident.

4. FEASIBILITY

Where the NHS was the sole provider, funding did not allow staffing levels or salaries to be sufficiently high to realise the philosophy in full. Nor were management arrangements entirely appropriate to the care philosophy.

5. OUTCOMES

Compared with long-stay hospital wards domus provided:

- more positive and minimal negative interaction between staff and residents;

- more resident activity;

- an increase in the morale and well-being of staff;

- outcomes related to higher staffing levels.

Housing association provision, in conjunction with the NHS, appeared to have significant advantages over solely NHS provision, probably due to expertise in managing special needs housing. Staff training and quality assurance were emphasised and employment policy was more flexible.

6. KEY LESSONS

Adequate staffing levels and appropriate training are critical to a scheme. However on their own, they will not necessarily secure better quality of care. High expectations, wide range of social and recreational activity and maximum autonomy for residents are also critical. There appear to be significant advantages in partnerships between the NHS and housing associations.

References

Dean, R., Proudfoot, R. and Lindesay, J. (1993) 'The quality of interactions schedule (QUIS): development, reliability and use in the evaluation of two domus units'. *International Journal of Geriatric Psychiatry* **8** 819-826

Lindesay, J., Briggs, K., Lawes, M., Macdonald, A. and Herzberg, J. (1991) 'The domus philosophy: a comparative evaluation of a new approach to residential care of the demented elderly'. *International Journal of Geriatric Psychiatry* **6** 727-736

1. HOUSING RELATED SERVICES

C: Shared Housing

NAME OF SCHEME: Dementia Care Initiative independent supported living scheme

1. KEY FACTS

Provider: Dementia Care Initiative, in association with West End Care Management Project (Newcastle Social Services) and Neighbourhood Housing Department

Location: Newcastle upon Tyne

Funding source: Mental Illness Specific Grant, Housing Benefit, Special Transitional Grant, tenant contribution

Date: The first house opened December 1993, followed by a second in January 1995.

2. AIMS AND PHILOSOPHY

A main aim was to promote as normal a life as possible involving the people with dementia and their carers as closely as possible in all aspects of care their care and re-housing, adopting a shared care model.

The Dementia Care Initiative aimed to provide:

- an alternative to residential/nursing home based on a person-centred approach to care and emphasising a 'home for life' philosophy for people with dementia;

- housing for local people with support workers recruited from the same locality as that of the dementia sufferer.

3. DESCRIPTION

The project providing support for dementia sufferers in the community found that there was a real need for some form of independent living arrangement to which people could be re-housed if it was no longer feasible for them to remain in their own homes. Both sufferers and carers identified *supportive housing* in small ordinary houses as less threatening, more acceptable, offering more control to sufferers and increased opportunities for carers to 'share care', which would also reduce carers' feelings of guilt and powerlessness. Two Tyneside flats (one three-bedroom upper flat and one two-bedroom ground floor flat) were connected together by a communicating door, furnished, adapted in line with advice from carers and occupational therapists and connected to the local mobile warden scheme. Prospective tenants met weekly for eight months at an informal day club before moving in. Each tenant was matched with a support worker

4. COSTS

These were £369.20 a week per tenant at 1993/4 prices. Tenants were able to claim Attendance Allowance (£45.70), Severe Disability Premium (£34.30)and housing management element of Housing Benefit (£141.29), reducing the cost to social services to £147.91 per tenant per week.

5. FEASIBILITY

There was some uncertainty by the DSS about whether shared living constituted residential care or not and this delayed payment of higher rate attendance allowance and severe disability premium for 2 out of 4 clients. The concept of 'shared living' and of support workers being visitors to the house took some getting used to all round.

6. ACCEPTABILITY

The initial evaluation suggested a high degree of satisfaction for both tenants and carers.

7. OUTCOME

What the project has clearly shown is that when people are treated sensitively in their 'own' home, they remain less distressed, present with less behaviour problems and are less reliant on tranquillisers and sedatives.

8. KEY LESSONS

Supported living can provide a 'home for life' given considerable determination to make it succeed by staff as well as users. But there has to be some quite careful matching of tenants to each other as well as to support workers for shared living to succeed. It was felt that a better quality of life is achieved because of more individualised attention. Close partnership with the local primary care teams – GPs and district nurses – is vital to the success of this project.

References

Svanberg, R., Tuckwell, M., Stirling, E. and Fairbairn, A. (1995) West End Care Management Pilot Project, July 1992-July 1994. Draft final report. Newcastle-upon-Tyne Social Services Department.

Svanberg, R., Tuckwell, M., Stirling, E. and Fairbairn, A. (1998) 'Ordinary house in an ordinary street'. *The Journal of Dementia Care* (forthcoming).

Acknowledgement

We are grateful to Rani Svanberg, Director, Dementia Care Initiative, for supplying the report and for helping with the above summary.

1. HOUSING RELATED SERVICES

D: Adaptations to ordinary housing or improvement of sub-standard housing

NAME OF SCHEME: Handyperson's schemes

1. KEY FACTS
Provider: A total of 63 schemes were identified in an evaluation; 73% were related to a home improvement agency

Location: Different locations in England and Wales

Funding source: Mixed. Most had initial funding from charitable source or social services departments. There were concerns about long-term funding in all the schemes

Date: Were being developed from the late 1980s.

2. AIMS AND PHILOSOPHY
The aims of the schemes were to provide assistance with small repairs and minor adaptation which would cause great distress to tenants and owners if left undone.

3. DESCRIPTION
The schemes used a paid worker, volunteers or contractors.

4. COSTS
Most schemes had got initial funding from charities or from social services departments. Long-term funding was an issue for all the projects. Charging is an issue in all the projects. Currently 86% were charging.

5. FEASIBILITY
Most schemes were stretched by the current level of demand and a third reported levels above that which the scheme could meet. Only one scheme reported that demand was under-employing current resources.

6. ACCEPTABILITY
A uniformly high level of client satisfaction.

7. OUTCOME
The author concluded that handyperson's schemes provided a valuable service at the intersection of housing and community care. Clients reported a range of benefits; 31% felt that their home had been made more comfortable; 53% that their home was safer and 40% that their home was easier to manage. As many as 91% said that would have found it difficult to get the work done without the project.

8. KEY LESSONS
Although these schemes provide a valuable service and are unable to meet the demand in their areas, it is difficult to obtain mainstream funding.

Reference
Appleton, N. (1996) *Handyperson schemes: Making them work*, York Publishing Services: York.

D: Adaptations to ordinary housing or improvement of sub-standard housing

NAME OF SCHEME: Anchor Hospital Discharge scheme

1. KEY FACTS

Provider: Anchor Housing Trust

Location: Hackney

Funding source: £300,000 from the London Implementation Group.

Date: set up 1994.

2. AIMS AND PHILOSOPHY

To create a fast track of repairs and improvements for people in hospital so that they can be discharged to property which is warm, dry and adapted.

3. DESCRIPTION

The scheme allows 3 minor works grants per property over 3 years with each grant worth up to £1,008 per property.

4. COSTS

£300,000 for 3 years.

5. FEASIBILITY

Difficulties in continuing funding because this type of scheme cuts across so many sectors.

6. ACCEPTABILITY

People are enabled to return to their own homes.

7. OUTCOME

Project accepted 167 people discharged from hospital in the first 2 years. Most clients are over 60 and a high proportion over 80 years of age. It is considered that the scheme has been successful at preventing re-admission to hospital.

8. KEY LESSONS

Older people often from a minority ethnic background have been assisted to return to their own homes.

Reference

Millar, B. (1996) 'Staying Power' *Health Service Journal* 11 January 14-15

2. SERVICES AND FACILITIES IN THE HOME

A: Intensive home support packages

NAME OF SCHEMES: Kent (Thanet) Community Care Scheme and related (experimental care management).
Demonstration projects with research undertaken by the PSSRU (Director, Professor Bleddyn Davies and colleagues) and funded by DoH to examine the impact of devolving budgets to staff directly responsible for enabling highly dependent older people to remain living in the community. Further evaluations

were made of two routine developments implemented in Kent on the lines of the Thanet project. Research has used economic concepts which include **substitution** – in what circumstances do services delivered in the home constitute an alternative to residential care? **marginal productivity** – what is the extent to which more and more home care services, or different combinations of them, can be delivered to individuals to reduce the extent to which they are admitted to residential care?, and hence, **marginal cost** – at what point is the cost of providing these services in people's own homes such that it would be more appropriate to provide residential care? **targeting** – are there rational relationships between what is provided and who receives it? how can scarce resources best be used in relation to the particular needs of individuals in particular localities? **outcomes** – what difference has been made to older people by the care they have received?

1. KEY FACTS

Providers: social services departments in all areas, plus NHS in Darlington

Location: Thanet, Kent; Gateshead; Darlington; Lewisham, London

Funding source: Central and local government

Date: 1980s.

2. AIMS AND PHILOSOPHY

Aims

The aims of the schemes were to devise a means of providing appropriate packages of care for older people with complex needs, that placed them at the risk of admission to institutional care, in a way that maximised flexibility and choice and cut through some of the bureaucratic constraints that arise when control of funding is divorced from delivery of services.

Philosophy

To centre the delivery of services on users and carers in a flexible, responsive and economically efficient way, which was compatible with local needs and resources.

3. DESCRIPTION

The schemes involved organising and managing intensive packages of care targeted specifically on older individuals with complex needs. Those receiving the packages of care were considered to be on the margins of community and residential care, but not actually at the point of entry. The schemes were variously located in social services, and primary and secondary health care. Each care manager had their own budget, with clear expenditure limits of two-thirds of the costs of a place in residential care.

4. COSTS

- costs of delivering the care management scheme were if anything lower than delivering a standard community care package (Challis *et al.*, 1993)

- as an alternative to long-stay hospital care, as in Darlington, care management was decisively less costly, because it excluded capital costs for buildings, involved significant reductions in the levels of care provided by professionally qualified nurses and occurred at a time when the differential between the hospital and home care sectors was probably at its greatest (Davies, 1998)

- higher overhead costs (Challis, 1998)

5. FEASIBILITY

The benefits of these schemes, in terms of efficient use of resources and positive outcomes for users, depended on their being targeted on those clients for whom this intervention was most appropriate. These are not those older people who are actually at the point of entry to residential care. These schemes need to be located in settings which clearly and accurately come into contact with the target population. Care management is a form of service intervention to which appropriate individuals should be referred by those who have a thorough picture of their needs. To be effective, such forms of intervention must involve budget delegation to practitioners and the use of social work skills, in terms of human relations skills, in the management of the care. In Darlington, divisions between social and health care undermined the viability of the home care arrangements (Davies, 1998).

6. ACCEPTABILITY

Users were on the whole very positive.

7. OUTCOMES

Further evaluation of outcomes showed significant differences in Kent and Gateshead between those in the demonstration projects and those in the control group in terms of quality of life, as measured by levels of depression, dissatisfaction, felt ability to cope, morale, social activity, ability to manage basic tasks and reduction of need for basic services. These differences between users and controls were less marked in Darlington, but the user group in Darlington was different, because all those receiving the service would otherwise have been in long-stay hospital care. The impact on carers' well being was marked, particularly in Darlington.

Table 1: Destinational outcomes for matched cases after one year

	Kent social care		Gateshead social care		Gateshead health and social care		Darlington multi-disciplinary care	
	%		%		%		%	
	project	control	project	control	project	control	project	control
Own home	69	34	63	36	64	21	56	9
LA home	4	22	1	37	4	50	(institution)	
Independent home	8	5	–	2	4	–	4	60
Hospital	4	5	7	4	–	4		
Died	14	33	28	20	28	25	40	31
Moved away	1	1	1	1	–	–	–	–
No. of cases	*74*	*74*	*90*	*90*	*28*	*28*	*101*	*113*

Source: Challis, Chesterman, Darton and Traske (1993)

When the routine development of this care management approach was evaluated in two contrasting areas of Kent (Sheppey and Tonbridge) similar positive results were found.(Chesterman, Challis and Davies, 1994). This was ascribed to the accurate targeting of the intervention on those for whom it is most suitable.

Key factors associated with effective outcomes of care management as a service intervention are (Challis, 1998):

- integrated programme funding;

- logical links between objectives of programme (what they are trying to do), model of care (how they are trying to do it) and practice level incentives (what drives people on the coal-face, such as size of caseload, ability to get the services they see as necessary);

- clear service objectives;

- precision and clarity about who is being helped;

- continuity of involvement with the client by practitioners.

8. KEY LESSONS
Care management is a specific form of service intervention, not a generalised administrative process for handling all referrals to a social services department. It is appropriate for a specific group of users i.e. those who are at high risk of moving into institutional care but would prefer to remain in the community.

References
Challis, D. (1998) 'Care management'. DoH briefing paper.

Challis, D., Chesterman, Darton, R. and Traske, K. (1993) 'Case management in the care of the aged: the provision of care in different settings'. In Bornat, J. *et al.,* (eds) *Community Care: a reader.* Macmillan/ Open University: Milton Keynes.

Chesterman, J., Challis, D. and Davies, B. (1994) 'Budget-devolved care management in two routine programmes'. In Challis, D., Davies, B. and Traske, K. (eds), *Community care: new agendas and challenges from the UK and overseas.* Arena. Ashgate Publishing: Aldershot.

Davies, Professor Bleddyn: Personal communication. 24.4.98.

Robbins, D. (ed) (1993) *Community Care. Findings from Department of Health Funded Research, 1988-1992,* HMSO: London.

A: Intensive home support packages

NAME OF SCHEME: Belfast Intensive Domiciliary Care Project

1. KEY FACTS
Provider: South and East Belfast Trust

Location: South and East Belfast

Date: on-going.

2. AIMS AND PHILOSOPHY
- the emphasis of the approach is on the care of the **whole** person without separation between physical, sensory, psychological and social care needs.

3. DESCRIPTION
- the scheme provides an 'intensive level of safe care' in people's own home. It is currently available to around 100 or so older people and to a smaller group of younger physically disabled adults.

- a pilot scheme for six younger severely disabled people, all sufferering from multiple sclerosis was initiated fairly recently and evaluated by Action MS in Belfast. This compared the care provided by the scheme with the care to six comparable sufferers of MS resident in a range of nursing homes. The findings reported here come from their report which was published in 1997.

- the key member of staff is a Primary Health Care worker who is trained to give assistance with daily living activities, but is not trained to the standard of a registered nurse. This worker is responsible to one of four Home Care co-ordinators, each of whom has approximately 35 clients, and offer a 24-hour on-call service. They in turn are responsible to the Intensive Home Care Manager.

4. COSTS

- an upper limit of £410 per week (£21,320 a year) (1996 prices), which was within nursing home care banded costs, was set for each home care package.

- only one client's costs exceeded this amount for a short time, but the package was adjusted

- these figures did not allow for specialised equipment, nor for treatment of health problems over and above those associated with the MS.

5. FEASIBILITY

- the scheme is considerably facilitated by the integration of health and social services in one agency in Northern Ireland.

6. ACCEPTABILITY

- home care staff were *'very much viewed as a friend or family member as well as being a care worker'* whereas nursing home staff *'were very much perceived as a care worker'* (p. 41). Staff were conscious of the fine boundaries between friendship and professional responsibility;

- it may be significant that whereas nursing home staff were all under the age of 25, home care staff were mostly over 25 and usually in their forties.

7. OUTCOMES

- home care delivered a standard of care equivalent to the **best** of the nursing homes

- home care was more effective in focusing upon the 'whole person' and all their needs.

- home care involved and supported the family whereas nursing home care tended to fracture family connections

- at the end of the pilot project, home care recipients thought that the quality of their life had improved significantly, whereas those in the nursing homes reported no change.

- inter-professional barriers were reduced through closer team working.

8. KEY LESSONS

- strengths of the home care model, which were essential to a high standards of care and effective risk management, were staff ltraining, continuity of care, monitoring levels and evaluation of the service by staff and user.

■ the vital requirement for meeting the needs of recipients was *'an attitude of caring that is expressed not only in terms of professional expertise but also in attitudes of compassion and understanding'* (p. vi).

■ effective management and coordination are essential foundations of the project's success

Reference
Action MS (1997) Intensive Domiciliary Care Evaluation Study. Belfast: Action MS.

Acknowledgement
We are grateful to Marie Heaney, South and East Belfast (Health and Social Services) Trust, for providing a copy of the evaluation study and for helpful comments on this summary.

A: Intensive home support packages

NAME OF SCHEME: Dementia Home Support Project

1. KEY FACTS
Provider: Age Concern

Dates: 1984-86

Location: Ipswich and Newham, London.

2. AIMS AND PHILOSOPHY
The scheme aimed to provide a support service in their own home to older people suffering from severe dementia, and to examine whether this was effective in helping them stay out of institutional care. The philosophy of the scheme was that it should be client-centred; flexible, provide seamless collaboration between services and recruit local workers.

3. DESCRIPTION
The scheme aimed at enabling older people (mean age 81) with *severe* dementia to remain at home. A development officer was employed in each area whose tasks were to obtain support from existing services, organise additional support workers and to provide direct help themselves. The development officers worked to a budget and could authorise expenditure of up to £200 a week per person – including the cost of all services provided to the household. Services provided included home care, personal care, meals, day care, visiting and sitting services. The scheme was set up with the direct purpose of assessing the feasibility of enabling people with severe dementia to remain in their own homes. In both areas the older people receiving the service were matched with a control sample of dementia sufferers not receiving the service. Matching was in terms of age, cognitive impairment, mobility, behaviour and carer support.

4. COSTS
(calculated at 31.3.85) The overall costs of £250,000 covered two project development officers and three researchers for three years. Costs of support to dementia sufferers were additional. Overall, costs were greater than the total estimated sum saved on institutional care. This was because there were some beneficiaries of the service who would not have moved to institutional care anyway (p. 137).

5. FEASIBILITY

Psycho-geriatricians apparently varied in their readiness to refer patients to the service. Some households refused the service. There were some issues over recruitment, employment and retention of support workers although these were not critical.

6. ACCEPTABILITY

The acceptability to those suffering from dementia was unknown. Assessments showed no indications that they were happier, or more able to perform a selection of everyday activities than their counterparts in the control sample. For family carers, respite, either through day care, or more extended respite, was the kind of support that made a difference. Extra help in the home, while the dementia sufferer remained at home did not have any effect.

7. OUTCOMES

(i) Deferment of move to institution	Scheme made little difference
(ii) Impact on cognitive impairment	Scheme made no evident difference
(iii) Impact on volume of services received	Scheme made little difference
(iv) Benefit to family carers	Scheme made little difference

However, there was evidence that the scheme enabled a small group to stay at home longer than they might otherwise have done. They all had relatively severe dementia, lived alone and were without caregiver support. Overall, the numbers of people in this category is likely to be small in any one area.

8. KEY LESSONS

Key factors in remaining at home with dementia are the level of risk presented by the older person, the control which others are prepared to exercise and, for family carers, the price they are prepared to pay. It is not so much the presence or absence of a family carer, as their willingness and determination to keep the older person at home that is relevant to institutionalisation. Respite care is the key service that supports them in this task.

Reference

Askham, J. and Thompson, C. (1990) *Dementia and home care*. Age Concern Institute of Gerontology Research Paper, no. 4. Age Concern England.

A: Intensive home support packages

NAME OF SCHEME: Newcastle upon Tyne West End Care Management for people with dementia Pilot Project

This pilot project was the precursor of the Dementia Care Initiative scheme described elsewhere.

1. KEY FACTS

Provider: West End Care Management Pilot Project

Location: Newcastle upon Tyne

Funding source: Mental Illness Specific Grant

Date: 1992-94.

2. AIMS AND PHILOSOPHY

- to enable people with dementia to remain in their own homes for as long as possible and to provide practical and emotional support to their carers.

- to test the process of care management and see whether a needs-led approach could succeed within available resources.

- to empower users and carers, particularly by consulting carers for their advice and guidance.

3. DESCRIPTION

Between July 1992 and July 1994, 22 older people with dementia received services which enabled them to remain in their own homes. A care manager was responsible for arranging: the supply of information to carers, assessments, care planning service delivery and on-going co-ordination, monitoring and review of the situation. Unlike the Kent type care management schemes, the budget was controlled separately, as it was thought that this would help create a genuinely needs-led service. No cost ceiling was put on any one package. Considerable difficulties were experienced initially as existing services were not appropriate to meet the needs of the people with dementia and their carers. In the course of the pilot study, the carers involved set up their own independent provider organisation – Dementia Care Initiative – to fill the gaps left by health and social services.

4. COSTS

The average cost per week per user of these services was £188 in July 1994. This was based on care hours purchased only and did not include care managers' or other professionals' time. Costs fluctuated quite sharply, both between users and also for the same user based on changing needs. Thus for one user, costs ranged from £160 in one week to £908 (when offering terminal care, or 24-hour care while the carer was away), whereas for another the range was only from £225 to £234. As disability increased, so did cost. Overall costs were estimated to be £50,000 over 2 years.

5. FEASIBILITY

- comprehensive assessment was essential for all users;

- very detailed planning was required to get reliable, continuous acceptable sets of arrangements in place;

- the co-ordinating role and the continuity provided by the care manager was essential;

- as the needs of the person with dementia change, so must the care package;

- in general, existing services were inadequate to meet flexibly and appropriately the needs of users and carers; carers highlighted the need for flexible day care, community respite facilities, 24-hour live-in companion/befriending scheme and independent supported living houses;

- staff from independent provider organisations at the time of the project were less satisfactory than locally recruited staff, initially with self-employed status;

- carers wished to have control of their relatives' packages;

- training of staff was crucial;

- assessment and service barely began to address the need of ethnic minority sufferers of dementia;

6. ACCEPTABILITY

The original scheme of purchasing care packages from independent provider organisations was not acceptable to carers. The following points were among those they saw as most crucial to caring for people with dementia:

1. A **person centred approach** to care, focusing on the abilities not a disease and disabling approach.

2. The need to train a support worker whose job is to act as a **substitute carer carrying out all or most tasks carried out by an informal carer**, thus doing away with task versus sitting or social bath versus nursing bath and similar dilemmas.

3. The need for stability, **continuity** and flexibility of staff, including full 24-hour cover, provided by **a small team of support workers** preferably coming from the same locality as that of the client, so that they can enable the person to be participating members of their own community.

7. OUTCOME

People with severe dementia were enabled to remain in their own homes, but there were significant problems in making the appropriate arrangements. This led to the Dementia Care Initiative scheme which was set up by carers and former carers advising the West End Care Management pilot project. There was a felt need for an independent supported living house, as an alternative to residential care from some of those with serious difficulties and an alternative independent living home was established (See Section 1C).

8. KEY LESSONS

Artificial service boundaries, particularly between the delivery of health and social care, posed major obstacles to the delivery of person-centred, needs-led community care (Svanberg *et al.*, 1995, p. 78). Empowering people with dementia and their carers in the community is related to empowering care providers – care providers will only respond adaptively so long as they are engaged in a process which is defined by themselves and by others, as being meaningful and successful (*ibid.*, p. 78). A person-centred approach to care and continuity provided by a small team of support workers from the same community as the client, is crucial to success.

References

Svanberg, R., Stirling, E. and Fairbairn, A. (1997) The process of care management with people with dementia. *Health and Social Care in the Community*, 5 (2) 134-136.

Svanberg, R., Stirling, E. and Fairbairn, A. (1995) *West End Care Management Pilot Project, July 1992-July 1994*. Draft final report. Social Services Department. Newcastle upon Tyne.

Acknowledgement

We are grateful to Rani Svanberg, Director, Dementia Care Initiative for supplying the report and for helping with the summary.

A: Intensive home support packages

NAME OF SCHEME: Newcastle upon Tyne Dementia Care Initiative Pilot Project

1. KEY FACTS

Provider: Dementia Care Initiative

Location: Newcastle upon Tyne

Funding source: Joint funding: Primary Care Development Fund (PCDF) – for 10 people at any one time, and Newcastle Social Services

Cost: PCDF. £120,000 per annum; Social Services: £122,720

Date: 1995-98.

This project succeeded the West End Care Management Pilot Project outlined above.

2. AIMS AND PHILOSOPHY

■ to enable people with severe dementia who would otherwise have gone into NHS continuing care or nursing homes for the elderly mentally ill to remain in their own homes for as long as possible and to provide practical and emotional support to their carers;

■ to use a joint health and social services approach to partnership and funding;

■ to enable people to live as 'normally' as possible, continuing with life styles and routines as before, e.g. by letting them get up and go to bed when they liked, eat what they wanted to, go out when they wanted to and so on.

3. DESCRIPTION

■ the project provides care up to 24 hours for people living alone and living with carers. Support workers work flexible hours based on need for clients living with carers and a 24-hour shift system of one day on, and two days off for those living alone;

■ a minimum number of staff – usually three – work to ensure that confusion is not increased by too many people going into the user's home;

■ up to 10 older people have been beneficiaries of the project at any one moment in time. In total 23 older people received the service between November 1994 and April 1998.

■ to be eligible, the older person has to want to remain in their own home, and have the explicit support of any carer for this, and to suffer from severe dementia or another serious psychiatric disorder involving *'sustained or frequently recurrent difficult behaviour'*.

4. COSTS

■ in 1995/6 the average weekly costs of 24-hour support 7 days a week ranged from £460 to £601 and in 1997/8 from £449 to £625.

■ the actual support costs could be higher (because of additional staff time, or double pay), or lower (because the patient was in hospital, or the family carer took over for a short period). They ranged from £219-£789 a week for one patient, and from £357 to £865 for another.

- £238 a week was allowed by social services and extra funding was provided by the Primary Care Development Fund.

5. FEASIBILITY

- all the older people in the research study had family who did not wish them to go into institutional care;

- *'it is the determination of carers which seems to be an important factor in maintaining this client group in their own homes'* (p. 34);

- dependent on the quality and commitment of support staff;

- substantial flexibility required of staff in the hours that they worked, having to cover for one another during holidays and sickness;

- support staff *'continually expressed'* the value of teamwork and sharing;

- the 24-hour shift system (one day on, two days off) was much preferred by workers to the 12-hour one.

6. ACCEPTABILITY

- importance of accessible and easily available information for carers;

- four out of 23 older people involved in the scheme moved into nursing home care because they would not accept people coming into their home; in two cases *'the working conditions were also inappropriate'*.

- support staff were very satisfied with their employment conditions.

7. OUTCOME

- *'the majority of GPs stated that their clients would be in (institutional) care if they had not been part of this project'* (p. 29);

- *'all social workers interviewed who had clients in the pilot study considered that they were receiving a better quality of life than they would in residential care'* (p. 30);

- of nine older people involved in the project in 1998, six have been involved for more than two years, one for over one year, and two for over nine months.

- *'It was evident that there were older people in the project who had experienced periods in institutional care and had not settled at all, but were much more content at home in surroundings they were familiar with'* (p. 28);

- eight out of eleven carers rated the care as excellent, two as good and one as adequate

- half had experienced problems with the package of care, particularly in the early stages, largely due to staff changes;

- there can be problems of coordination between health and support staff, and between support staff and social services. There is some evidence that the social worker is redundant as the care manager when the support staff are providing 24-hour care.

8. KEY LESSONS

- *'people with severe dementia can be looked after in their own homes and be provided with a good quality of life which would be difficult to achieve in a residential setting'* (p. 35);

- the overriding factor in improving quality of life to which people drew attention was the one-to-one individualised attention which people could receive in their own homes;

- *'the importance of contact and communication between professionals, support workers and carers involved in the care of clients cannot be overstated'* (p. 34).

Reference
Caring for people with severe dementia in their own homes. An evaluation of Dementia Care Initiative Pilot project. Newcastle upon Tyne City Council Research and Information Services.

Acknowledgement
We are grateful to Rani Svanberg, Director, Dementia Care Initiative for making the evaluation available and for helpful comments with this summary.

A: Intensive home support packages

NAME OF SCHEME: Wakefield Immediate Support at Home

1. KEY FACTS
Dates: Launched April 1993; on-going

Funding source: Joint finance

Location: Wakefield and Pontefract Community NHS Trust.

2. AIMS AND PHILOSOPHY
The aim was to provide an immediate package of care in response to sudden illness, accident or crisis in order to prevent inappropriate admission to hospital or residential care; provide a safe space whilst assessment is taking place; to improve the quality of life by increasing the options available at a difficult time. The underlying philosophy was to provide the same quality and type of care as a family member would provide.

3. DESCRIPTION
This scheme aims to enable older people (over 60) to remain at home during an emergency, when no alternative carer is available to help them. It is run by the Community Nursing Service, which employs workers on a pool basis, paying them only for work undertaken. Workers are not qualified nurses, but may have experience of caring for older people. In-service training is provided and all staff have a development portfolio. Care can be provided for a maximum of five days and can vary from two hours of help a day to constant care and from one day of help to five days. The referrer assesses the care that the older person will require for the five days and is responsible for arranging the follow-on care.

Tasks undertaken include personal care, meals, cleaning, overnight support, day-time supervision but the major task appears to be the provision of support and comfort. Referrals increased from 69 in the first year to 177 in 1996/7. Approximately 50% of individuals referred are over 80. The main sources of referral are Accident and Emergency departments, district nurses and social services. The main reasons for referral are accident or illness of the client, illness of the carer or need for crisis care.

4. COSTS

There is limited information. In terms of the actual service, between April and September 1997, 1000 hours of service were provided at a cost of £7,500 i.e. £7.50 an hour. This does not take account of the *full* cost of the service, e.g. it excludes any element of overhead for the community nursing service. Estimates are that the service costs approximately £20,000 a year.

5. FEASIBILITY

(i)   Staffing. Stable workforce. Uniformly praised for quality.

(ii) Target group. In 8 cases in 1996/7, there were insufficient workers to cover the complex packages of care required to keep the older person at home; of these, 3 were admitted to hospital, 2 to residential care, 2 remained in the community at risk and for 1 the outcome was unknown.

(iii) Collaboration between providers. Collaboration between district nurses and social services teams is 'excellent'.

6. ACCEPTABILITY

The service is valued by clients, particularly the comfort and support provided by staff. Users see this as instrumental in helping them regain confidence and enabling them to stay at home. Referrers are less conscientious about returning evaluation forms, but where they have done so they are positive about the benefits of the service.

7. OUTCOME

Estimates of outcome were only available for about 50% of clients in 1996/7. Referrers predicted that about half of these would have been in hospital or residential care (the vast majority in hospital) without the service. The other half would have been at risk in the community. Between June and December 1997, estimates were very similar.

8. KEY LESSONS

A service like this can be valuable in keeping older people out of hospital. We do not know from the data provided whether the same people received the service on more than one occasion, or whether subsequent to receipt of the service they ended up in hospital or other institutional care.

Reference
Wakefield and Pontefract Community NHS Trust.

A: Intensive home support packages

NAME OF SCHEME: Marlow EPICS (Elderly Persons Integrated Care System)
Note: This is an example of an EPICS scheme that has been evaluated recently and was cited in a recent Audit Commission report. EPICS is a system of providing co-ordinated home support to older people which has been pioneered in the United Kingdom by the Helen Hamlyn Foundation. Essentially it involves, as this Marlow scheme illustrates, the integration of different services and budgets in a way that means users and carers experience a single agency meeting their needs. The Foundation supported the establishment of demonstration projects in North

Kensington, Derby and Shropshire which are all on-going. Analysis of these projects indicated that *'EPICS principles are sound and workable, and provide a framework within which to develop integrated services for elderly people'* (Hollingberry, 1997).

1. KEY FACTS

Provider: South Buckinghamshire NHS Trust

Location: Marlow, Bucks

Funding source: joint finance for five years, tapering to Health plus additional set-up funding from the DoH for information systems

Date: established 1994; on-going.

2. AIMS AND PHILOSOPHY

The aim of the service has been *'to provide one-stop flexible care which provides the older person and their carer with choices which meet expectations and are compatible with their values'* (Calviou *et al.*, 1997, p. 3). Particular emphasis was originally placed on speed of response to prevent inappropriate admissions to hospital, and on providing care that is totally integrated with community resources. This has meant a commitment to multi-agency, multi-disciplinary working. Central to this idea was the development of an information system relating patients' clinical and social data and needs to a geographical locality. Current goals stress optimising options for users and carers within legal, budgetary and other resource constraints, and providing a co-ordinated care and support network. There are ambitions to call on local community resources, for example, by involving the local pub in providing an emergency meal, but these still have to be realised.

3. DESCRIPTION

The scheme, which employs a special co-ordinator, operates from the local GP practice. It may be accessed 24 hours a day throughout the year. The co-ordinator is responsible for an immediate initial assessment. This leads to co-ordination of a care package in association with other agencies and input of care from special EPICS care workers. They provide anything from 24-hour attendance to a visit to help an older person in and out of bed. Sixty-three per cent of referrals use the EPICS care service. The scheme has one reserved place at the local day hospital for multi-disciplinary assessments which can be arranged within 48 hours. Approximately one-third of cases require a complex assessment. The average length of intervention by the EPICS scheme is 7.5 days.

4. COSTS

The main costs of the scheme arise from employment of a special co-ordinator and the EPICS care staff. In 1995/6 the average cost (including full costs such as accommodation and equipment) of a basic referral for an average of 7.5 days of intervention was estimated to be £180 per person. The additional cost for services provided by the EPICS care workers (average 15.6 hours of help to 63% of the referrals) was estimated to cost £128 per person. Other support services were additional to this. This compared with £1,304 a week in a general medical bed in hospital, and £285 per week for a week in local authority residential care, inclusive of the client's financial contribution. Total costs in 1997/8 were estimated to be £34,580.

5. FEASIBILITY

No problems reported.

6. ACCEPTABILITY

A detailed study of 31 users' and 8 carers' experience of the scheme found very positive attitudes, particularly to the immediacy of response, the flexibility of approach and the quality and reliability of the staff.

7. OUTCOMES

A questionnaire to all potential referrers in the area (76% response, n=66) found that the service was mainly used to provide additional support for the client at home and to provide assistance with hospital discharge. The service was largely appreciated and appeared to work well from their point of view, but some criticisms were made reflecting difficulties in securing sufficient trained nursing care and the need for hospital staff to become more aware of the scheme. Between 1 January and 31 May 1996, 331 admissions to the local hospital took place, representing 271 patients, Records of these patients were examined by a GP and a consultant to decide whether use of the EPICS scheme would have been possible. They agreed that 51 episodes (15%) could have been avoided, either by reducing the length of stay in hospital, or by preventing admission. This equated to 564 bed days over the five months. There was therefore still a need to communicate the potential of the scheme. Those who had used the service found it provided a seamless approach to care which linked smoothly to subsequent support services.

8. KEY LESSONS

- It is essential for potential referrers to have proper information about the scheme, if it is to be properly exploited;

- A GP practice is the most appropriate place for the one-stop access point, one of the most important advantages of such a scheme;

- Multi-disciplinary working and collaboration is essential to the success of such a scheme.

Reference

Calviou, A., Hockley, J. and Schofield, L. (1997) *An evaluation of Marlow EPICS.* South Buckinghamshire NHS Trust and Buckinghamshire County Council Social Services.

Hollingberry, R. (1997) *Elderly People's Integrated Care System (EPICS): a general outline.* ConsultAge: Petersfield.

A: Intensive home support packages

NAME OF SCHEME: Stone Rehabilitation Centre

1. KEY FACTS

Provider: North Staffordshire Combined Healthcare NHS Trust

Location: Stone, Staffordshire

Funding source: South Staffordshire Health Authority purchaser

Date: opened January 1996.

2. AIMS AND PHILOSOPHY

- to provide an enabling service for local people, that offers rehabilitation and support for adults with acquired physical and/or sensory disabilities, and also offer support and help to carers.

- the service is **therapy** based, e.g. occupational therapy, physiotherapy.

- staff work as a team and see themselves as *'rehabilitationists'* with different skills to offer. There is one set of case notes per patient.

- practitioner skills are geared to community living

- emphasis on 'holistic practice' – *'the right ingredients correctly mixed'*

- 'one-stop shop' – one referral provides the means of accessing many different services

- the (largely unqualified) rehabilitation assistants provide continuity and co-ordination of services.

3. DESCRIPTION

- the service is for adults with sensory/physical disabilities. It is primarily a domiciliary service offering assessment and treatment in people's own homes but includes nursing/residential homes.

- approximately 80% of those referred to the service are over 65. Key reasons for referral are loss of mobility, difficulties in coping with daily living, falls, swallowing difficulties, communication problems and chronic chest conditions.

- it developed from the closure of the local day hospital and involved new purpose-designed building. This includes an equipment store (equipment can be bought or loaned short-term), office space for other agencies such as social services, carers' organisations and voluntary groups, a bathroom, for assessment and carer training in the use of specialised equipment and a reception area with advice and information provision.

- The service manages six respite care beds in a local nursing home. Use of these has been reviewed in relation to the *health needs* of the older person and rehabilitative objectives introduced during the short-term stay.

- the rehabilitation team of 12.5 w.t.e. staff comprises physiotherapists, occupational therapists, speech and language therapists, a nurse, a chiropodist, rehabilitation assistants, and support staff.

- currently, there are approximately 750 patient contacts per month.

- referrals have mainly come from the two local GP practices, independent nursing/residential homes and hospital consultants, although increasingly people are referring themselves.

4. COST

Revenue £200,000.

5. KEY LESSONS

- the importance of integration of different therapies involved in rehabilitation;

- the potential of the rehabilitation assistant, working in conjunction with qualified therapists;

- value of one service – rehabilitation – over a mix of individual services.

References

Stone Rehabilitation report, October 1996;

Shield, F. (1998) *Developing a therapy-led community rehabilitation team.*

Acknowledgements

We are grateful to Fiona Shield, Service Manager, Stone Rehabilitation Service, for papers and comments on this summary.

A: Intensive home support packages

NAME OF SCHEME: The Victoria Project: Community Occupational Therapy Rehabilitation Service

1. KEY FACTS

Provider: Riverside Community NHS Healthcare Trust

Location: Victoria, South West London

Funding source: The King's Fund, Kensington, Chelsea and Westminster Commissioning Agency and Westminster Social Services

Date: 1996 on-going.

2. AIMS AND PHILOSOPHY

- provision of a community occupational therapy rehabilitation service for people aged 65 and over living in Victoria.

- provision of client-centred, holistic assessment and rehabilitation, addressing all aspects of a person's life.

- maximising functional independence and reducing effects of disability.

3. DESCRIPTION

Between November 1996 and January 1998, 161 referrals were received by the project. The major reasons for referral were orthopaedic (42), general medical conditions (35) and neurological (presumably dementia) conditions (26). Psychological problems were present in a significant minority of cases (25%) as a secondary diagnosis.

4. OUTCOMES

Of 125 clients discharged from the service between November 1996 and January 1998 25% (31) had received rehabilitation, were in improved health, and needed less social care; 22% (27) had a health gain and 46% (57) had received a comprehensive assessment and were in receipt of some equipment and/or services.

5. KEY LESSONS

- travel time is a significant element in time and cost of service. Locality based services are more efficient and promote integration of services;

- successful rehabilitation is multi-disciplinary;

- occupational therapists are key staff for their skills in assessment and promotion of independence.

Reference
Hill, Hauxner and Furner (1998) *The Victoria Project. Community Occupational Therapy Rehabilitation Service. Research findings and recommendations.* Riverside Community Healthcare NHS Trust.

2. SERVICES AND FACILITIES IN THE HOME

B: Live in carers

NAME OF SCHEME: Homeshare

1. KEY FACTS
Provider: The Community Care Trust, a registered charity

Location: London area and South West Hertfordshire

Funding source: the charity receives a grant from the Department of Health; various charitable trusts and foundations; contributions from users. Local authorities are also able to purchase Homeshare arrangements

Date: set up in 1993 as a two-year pilot scheme. Since 1995 has developed and has plans currently for further expansion.

2. AIMS AND PHILOSOPHY
Aim: A scheme which aims to provide low-cost, high quality help to people who need help at home with everyday tasks by matching them with a younger person – usually professional, often from overseas – who needs accommodation.

Philosophy: *'The philosophy of homesharing is centred around the home itself and an appreciation of what the loss of that home means. The elderly person wants to remain in their home and the younger person wants to find somewhere to live. By sharing the home in a clearly defined and mutually beneficial way, each is giving and each receiving . . . The understanding of, and respect for, the wishes of older people is paramount'* (Annual Review, 1997).

3. DESCRIPTION
An elderly 'householder' offers a room and share of their home's facilities rent-free plus a £5 weekly charge for utility use in exchange for ten hours help a week with everyday tasks. The Community Care Trust assesses the older person, vets the homesharer scrupulously, matches them carefully and then monitors the on-going arrangements to make sure they are working satisfactorily. The younger person pays for their own food, cooks for themselves etc and goes out to work and study each day. A written agreement outlines the obligations on each party.

Most arrangements last for at least six months. Homesharers are largely over 25 years old, either single or couples, mainly from Australia, New Zealand and South Africa, committed to helping other people, but using the scheme as part of a year travelling in Europe. Recruitment is through a magazine read by those seeking accommodation or employment in Britain. This is still a small enterprise. Although 115 householders were matched during 1996/7, 58 were current at the time of the annual review. The matching and monitoring tasks are shared out among a small group of coordinators.

4. COSTS

Householders pay a modest monthly charge to the charity. Inability to pay does not make someone ineligible. Charges contribute only a very small part of the income needed to run the charity.

5. FEASIBILITY

- Housing must be appropriate. Almost all 31 householders using the service in the first two years lived in relatively spacious and comfortable accommodation.

- Homesharing provides basic help and companionship and crucially overnight security, but is not a substitute for other forms of help and support. The homesharer may well work in conjunction with other care providers and family members. Of 58 matches current in 1997, 43% were receiving help from social services during the day.

- In 1997 over 50% of clients had some form of dementia

6. ACCEPTABILITY

An evaluation of the first two years placements found general satisfaction (Thornton, 1995). Many householders were prepared to have a second or third homesharer.

7. OUTCOME

There were sometimes benefits to co-resident carers of the arrangement. Professionals valued the flexibility of Homeshare and thought that the arrangements could meet a very real need for an older person whose needs were primarily for companionship and the security of having someone sleep in the house overnight.

8. KEY LESSONS

It appears valuable for the 'right' person but is not appropriate on its own for someone very vulnerable or frail. It can act as support for carers as well as users as part of a wider 'package' of care.

References

The Community Care Trust (1997), Annual review, 1997.

Thornton, P. (1995) *The Homeshare Project. Report to the Community Care Trust* SPRU: York.

2. SERVICES AND FACILITIES IN THE HOME

C: Hospital discharge schemes

NAME OF SCHEME: South Derbyshire Hospital at Home (HAH) pilot scheme

1. KEY FACTS

Provider: South Derbyshire Community Health Services in conjunction with an acute hospital

Location: South Derbyshire

Funding source: Waiting Initiatives money

Date: scheme established 1990.

2. AIMS AND PHILOSOPHY

To increase the choice available to consumers of health services and to move away from hospital based care if this is not necessary and to allow purchasers to make an informed choice.

3. DESCRIPTION

A pilot scheme was established for the early discharge of fractured neck of femur patients from hospital to their own homes. One group of patients using HAH were compared with a second matched group of patients receiving hospital care only. HAH patients were discharged an average of 7 days earlier than full hospital based patients.

4. COSTS

- £200,000 for first year.

- Providers of HAH quoted a lower price than providers of acute orthopaedic beds.

5. FEASIBILITY

One group of patients were discharged to a community health team under the clinical responsibility of the GP for a maximum of 12 days. The second group of patients stayed in hospital for longer and were not discharged to a community team.

6. ACCEPTABILITY

Patients in both groups were satisfied with the care they received.

7. OUTCOME

Three-month mortality rate for two groups the same. Readmission rate for HAH patients appeared slightly higher but this was not statistically significant.

8. KEY LESSONS

HAH is a feasible and acceptable form of care for early discharge patients with fractured neck of femur. Patients appear to suffer no ill effects.

Reference

Cathain, A. O. (1994) 'Evaluation of a Hospital at Home scheme to facilitate early discharge of patients with fractured neck of femur' *Journal of Public Health Medicine* 16 2 205-210

C: Hospital discharge schemes

NAME OF SCHEME: Gloucester Hospital at Home (HAH)

1. KEY FACTS

Provider: Gloucester District Health Authority

Location: Gloucester City

Funding source: NHS

Date: scheme established 1992.

2. AIMS AND PHILOSOPHY

To achieve earlier discharge, improved rehabilitation and prolonged independence at home with less use of hospital and nursing home care.

3. DESCRIPTION

A randomised controlled trial was established for the early discharge of older people from medical wards. The scheme provided a team of people to support older people in their own homes after they had been discharged earlier than would normally have been possible with conventional discharge arrangements. This team had a manager, a physiotherapist, an occupational therapist and part-time rehabilitation assistants. The team was available for a maximum of 4 weeks. Thirty patients were allocated at random to the HAH and 30 to the normal discharge procedures.

4. COSTS

A thorough cost analysis was not carried out. The costs of the scheme was thought to be half per day what it would cost to keep a patient in hospital.

5. FEASIBILITY

Patients were discharged to a community health team under clinical responsibility of the hospital consultant.

6. ACCEPTABILITY

Scheme was unanimously well received.

7. OUTCOME

Patients were visited by the HAH for an average of 20.6 days after discharge. Patients in both groups were followed up at three and six months. 64% of each group was still living at home at the six-month follow up. There was little obvious difference between the two groups. There was no discernible ill effect from earlier discharge for the HAH patient.

8. KEY LESSONS

HAH is a feasible and acceptable form of care for early discharge patients that is cost effective compared with hospital care. Patients appear to suffer no ill effects.

Reference

Donald, I. P., Baldwin, R. N. and Bannerjee, M. (1995) 'Gloucester Hospital at Home: A Randomised Control Trial' *Age and Ageing* 24 434-439.

D: Use of technology

This is discussed in Chapter 6 of the main report and in Appendix 4 of this volume.

E: Facilities to make older people safer

See 1F: Anchor Hospital Discharge scheme.

F: Night sitting service

NAME OF SCHEME: Oxford Night Time Home Care Service

1. KEY FACTS

Provider: Oxford Social Services Department and Oxford City Council Housing Department

Location: Oxford

Funding source: King's Fund

Date: 1993.

2. AIMS AND PHILOSOPHY

- to relieve carers;

- to prevent emergency admission to care homes;

- to provide short-term support on hospital discharge;

- to give greater personal choice over getting up and going to bed;

- to provide care input in a crisis;

- to provide reassurance and security for people who are anxious or lonely at night;

- to monitor night-time problems;

- to provide support in cases of terminal illness.

3. DESCRIPTION

A team of two night care assistants deal with an average of 27 users in one night (1994 figures) a few needed two calls so the average was 33 calls in a night. Toileting was the most frequent task and monitoring was the second most frequent.

4. COSTS

On-going costs approximately £80,000 p.a.

5. FEASIBILITY

Four night care assistants employed. Two work each night They are trained in personal care. There are 250-300 people on the register who can ask for help at night.

6. ACCEPTABILITY

Semi-structured interviews with users and carers reported that Nursing Care Assistants had been totally sensitive to their needs.

7. OUTCOME

The most common action was in providing reassurance and security. The scheme was able to respond to clients on the register providing care input in a crisis. The service was successful in preventing a number of emergency admissions.

8. KEY LESSONS

It is possible to provide a high quality night service but there are problems in the potentiality of the service being dominated by highly dependent long-term users.

Reference

Seal, H. (1994) Evaluation Report to the King's Fund *The setting up of a night-time home care service.*

3. SERVICES AND FACILITIES OUTSIDE THE HOME

A: Day Care

NAME OF SCHEME: North Edinburgh dementia project

1. KEY FACTS
Provider: Voluntary organisation

Location: Edinburgh

Funding source: not reported

Date: centre opened May 1993.

2. AIMS AND PHILOSOPHY
Aim to provide high quality day care with an individualised programme of activities.

3. DESCRIPTION
This new day centre offered 15 places 5 days a week for 5 hours a day. Referrals were taken from a defined catchment area of approximately 6,000 people.

4. COSTS
Not yet established.

5. FEASIBILITY
The centre is staffed by a day care co-ordinator, three care assistants and up to three volunteers. Close links are maintained with local old-age psychiatry services, social services and non-statutory service providers through monthly multi-agency liaison meetings.

6. ACCEPTABILITY/OUTCOME
The focus of the research was the impact of day care on the day care attender. Specifically the research looked at whether attending day care improved the mood, well-being or enhanced the self-esteem of the dementia sufferer. Family caregivers were interviewed within three months of the dementia sufferer joining the day centre and followed up three months later. No less than 42% of the attenders were reported to show a marked improvement in mood and behaviour which was attributed to attending the day centre.

7. KEY LESSONS
High-quality day care can have a beneficial impact on the behaviour of the individual dementia sufferer. Day care is normally discussed in terms of the impact it has on the carers.

Reference
Curran, J. (1996) 'The impact of day care on people with dementia' *International Journal of International Psychiatry* Vol.11 813-817.

A: Day care: day centres located in multi-purpose residential care homes

1. KEY FACTS

Provider: Local authorities

Location: Day centres in six multi-purpose residential homes in different locations, a seaside town, a rural setting, a Welsh city, a London suburb, a Midland inner city area and a Northern town rooted in the wool industry

Funding source: Local Authority

Date: Research carried out 1990/91.

2. AIMS AND PHILOSOPHY

Common broad aims for the day centre users included:

- an integrated package of care;

- a continuum of care for day centre users i.e. that day centre users would become resident if they became more dependent;

- support for carers.

3. DESCRIPTION

Multi-purpose residential homes have become increasingly common. In addition to short and long-term residential care and day care, many have offices for social workers and home care organisers on the premises. All six case study homes had either been new-built or refurbished to accommodate the day centre and other facilities.

4. COSTS

Revenue cost per day centre place per week range from £199 to £20 at 1989/90 prices.

5. FEASIBILITY

Practical problems existed with staffing. Most day centres were unable to allocate sufficient staff to meet the requirements of day centre users for bathing.

6. ACCEPTABILITY

Although the sample of day centre users were enthusiastic about the quality of the facilities in the multi-purpose home, only one in four thought they would have been willing to become residents. Few day centre users appeared to be willing to mix with residents.

7. OUTCOME

All six homes offered assisted bathing in the residential care bathrooms. But only half of the day centre users wanting such support got it. Such a service is labour intensive and only one of six homes was able to allocate sufficient staff to meet the demand. Many of the day centre users had used a respite care facility to give a carer a break. Carers were very grateful for the breaks from caring provided by day care. Some carers perceived themselves as receiving extensive support from the multi-purpose residential home. But others did not. Spouses were particularly likely to report that they had never talked to anybody at the day centre about their own needs for support. Only one of the day centres had a specified worker with a responsibility to talk to any carer before a dependent person was admitted to day care and again several weeks after the admission.

8. KEY LESSONS

Bathing is an area of personal care difficult for many day centre users as they are reluctant to ask relatives for assistance. Day centres able to provide bathing assistance need a high enough level of staffing to meet the demand. It is important for a member of staff to have a designated role of contact with carers to ascertain their needs for information and support.

Reference

Wright, F. (1995) *Opening Doors: a case study of multi-purpose residential homes* HMSO: London.

3. SERVICES AND FACILITIES OUTSIDE THE HOME

B: Night Care

Night care service for dementia sufferers

NAME OF SCHEME: CREST (Care And Respite For Elderly People With Support and Treatment)

1. KEY FACTS

Provider: District Health Authority

Location: London

Funding source: NHS

Date: 1995.

2. AIMS AND PHILOSOPHY

1. To provide, as part of the comprehensive community-orientated mental health services for a London district, support of elderly mentally confused people and their families.

2. To provide relief for relatives caring for elderly mentally infirm people at home.

3. To provide individualised programmes of night care for each patient, which are orientated towards facilitating patients' independence and dignity.

4. To provide a service which supports informal carers by working in partnership with them to deliver quality care to patients.

3. DESCRIPTION

A service catering for up to 15 people each night was designed to run four nights a week. Patients were collected from their homes between 8 p.m. and 9 p.m. and returned home the following day. The majority of their nights were spent sleeping but they received encouragement for self care from staff and where necessary assistance from staff to fulfil activities of living.

4. COSTS

Not reported.

5. FEASIBILITY

A nursing team was set up which included an ambulance driver, qualified nurses and nursing assistants (numbers not specified). Unless the carer preferred otherwise all the patients were picked up at home and taken to the night care unit.

6. ACCEPTABILITY

Not all patients were considered suitable for CREST and not all patients accepted the service. Out of 55 referrals, 36 accepted, and were accepted by CREST, nursing staff assessed 7 potential patients as unsuitable and 12 potential patients with their carers decided they did not wish to use the service.

7. OUTCOME

Out of 34 patients attending CREST, 3 did so for more than a year, 8 died, 10 were discharged home and 13 admitted to long-term care. CREST contributed to 8 patients remaining at home in the community until they died. Half the CREST patients were admitted to long-term care because carers felt unable to continue supporting them. For some carers their relatives attendance at CREST enabled them to make the decision to give up the caring role. Carers were successively interviewed and 21 out of the 34 reported that there had been some beneficial changes such as being to get a good night's sleep.

8. KEY LESSONS

It was concluded that structured night nursing care away from home has positive benefits for patients and should be provided as part of a comprehensive set of alternative packages of care.

Reference

Watkins, M. and Redfern, S. (1997) 'Evaluation of a new night nursing service for elderly people suffering from dementia' *Journal of Clinical Nursing* 6 485-494.

3. SERVICES AND FACILITIES OUTSIDE THE HOME

C: Adult Placement Services

NAME OF SCHEME: Homeshare, London Borough of Lewisham

1. KEY FACTS

Provider: London Borough of Lewisham

Location: London Borough of Lewisham

Funding source: Local authority funding, social security and Housing Benefits

Date: service for people with learning disabilities since 1979, service for older people since 1985, generic service since 1995.

2. AIMS AND PHILOSOPHY

The Lewisham scheme was originally a series of schemes related to different client groups – people with learning disabilities, older people and people with mental health needs. These schemes were merged in 1995. Aims and philosophy vary between the client groups. Confusion has arisen amongst purchasers over exactly what the service is providing and this has been exacerbated by differences in eligibility criteria between client groups It is little used for long term care for older people. In 1997, there were three long-term elderly users, compared with 22 elderly users of respite and 20 elderly users of day care placements.

3. DESCRIPTION
The scheme provides long-term care, short-term care, befriending help, day care and respite care. Carers are recruited through the Homeshare service and are then trained.

4. COSTS
For elderly people, in 1997/8, unit costs, including the costs of running the scheme, fees to carers and transport costs, were estimated at £392 a week for respite care and £63 a day for day care. This assumes a take-up of 370 carer weeks for respite care and 12 carer days a week for day care. Carers' fees are costed at £217 a week for respite care, and £25 a day for day care.

5. FEASIBILITY
There are serious problems in relating the service to the eligibility criteria currently operating. The review of the service concluded that users were less likely to receive respite care from the service if already receiving a domiciliary care package, since the costs of that package would be such that they would go 'over budget' if respite was added as well. Consequently, the service was more likely to be accessed by people with lower dependency needs.

6. ACCEPTABILITY
It appears that the service is valued by users.

7. OUTCOME
This particular service was running into some difficulties, which arose from a combination of factors, including the merger of the different client groups, the changes in benefit regulations and the application of eligibility criteria to potential users of the service. The service review recommended that the service for older people should be independent. The purpose of the service would be:

1. To provide an information and advice source for users, carers and care managers;

2. To co-ordinate requests for planned short-term care, especially respite;

3. To match, place and monitor placements on behalf of care managers in a variety of settings including family based and residential – including small homes;

4. To develop or negotiate new placements;

5. To monitor standards in accordance with regulation/accreditation and contract requirements (Homeshare Review second stage, p. 9).

8. KEY LESSONS
Adult placement schemes are best run for a specific user group, rather than as a generic service but the placement service for older people is particularly suitable for short-term and respite care.

References

Denne, C. and Morrison, K. (1997) *Homeshare Review. Interim report.* Lewisham Social Services.

Denne, C. and Morrison, K. (1997) *Homeshare Review Second stage.* Lewisham Social Services.

Acknowledgement

We are grateful to Carolyn Denne and to the Director of Social Services for the London Borough of Lewisham for permission to use the reports.

4. SERVICES TO SUPPORT CARERS

A: Respite care

NAME OF SCHEME: Respite care in an NHS geriatric ward

1. KEY FACTS

Provider: NHS Putney and Barnes geriatric service and Wandsworth geriatric service

Location: London

Funding source: NHS

Date: undated.

2. AIMS AND PHILOSOPHY

Respite care was seen as important to maintain the carers in their caring role.

3. DESCRIPTION

This small evaluative study interviewed a sample of carers in their own homes and again after the person being cared for at home had been admitted to a geriatric ward for respite care. A behavioural rating scale to measure the dependent person's level of functioning was completed by the carer at the first interview. The scale was completed again by nursing staff when the dependant was interviewed during the respite care stay.

4. COSTS

Not known.

5. FEASIBILITY

Many of the carers would have liked more respite care.

6. ACCEPTABILITY

Respite care was very acceptable to most carers.

7. OUTCOME

No difference was discernible in the carers' levels of stress whether the dependent person was at home or in the hospital. As far as the dependants were concerned there was a significant reduction in overall dependency when they were in the hospital setting. The greatest improvement in functioning was found between the people being looked after by the most highly stressed carers.

8. KEY LESSONS

The problems associated with caring for an older dependant are not necessarily solved by removing that person from the carer.

Reference

Homer, A. C. and Gilleard, C. J. (1994) 'The effect of inpatient care on elderly patients and their carers' *Age and Ageing* 23 274-276.

B: Counselling/preparation/relaxation services

NAME OF SCHEME: Shiatsu massage for carers

1. KEY FACTS

Provider: Hoxton Health Group, a registered charity providing complementary health care for people over 60

Location: London Borough of Hackney and the City of London

Funding source: Originally NHS funded. Since 1997, voluntary donations from individuals and trusts

Date: established 1987 through Inner City Partnership.

2. AIMS AND PHILOSOPHY

Shiatsu massage is a very relaxing form of massage which works on pressure points in the body. It is a full body treatment done through clothing.

3. DESCRIPTION

Six weekly massage sessions were offered to 62 carers aged 50 and over in their own homes. Fifty participated in research on the effects of the treatment.

4. COSTS

One treatment costs £16.

5. ACCEPTABILITY

Carers greatly valued the massage in comparison with medication.

6. OUTCOME

The treatment was effective in many cases in alleviating stress and tension, and associated pain and discomfort. Carers in general felt that they were better able to cope with everyday activities as a result of the massage treatment, but would have welcomed an on-going service.

7. KEY LESSONS

Complementary medicine may contribute very useful therapies to support carers. There would appear to be some scope for substituting such treatments for medication and carers would welcome this.

Reference

Formby, J. (1995) *Who cares for the carers? A report on the benefits of Shiatsu massage for carers.*

B: Counselling/preparation/relaxation services

NAME OF SCHEME: Dementia Care Trust counselling service

1. KEY FACTS

Provider: Dementia Care Trust

Location: Bristol, North Somerset, parts of Gloucestershire

Funding source: NHS, social services and charitable donations.

2. AIMS AND PHILOSOPHY

The counselling service offered by the Dementia Care Trust is part of their wider aims of providing support for those caring for people with any form of dementia.

3. DESCRIPTION

Two salaried counsellors, and eight volunteers who are undertaking a diploma in counselling are employed. Annually they provide 1000 sessions of three hours, comprising one hour of counselling, one hour of travelling and one hour of recording. Carers have a variable amount of counselling, agreed in a contract. Bereavement counselling is included. All carers are asked to complete a questionnaire about their experience of the counselling service.

4. FEASIBILITY

Funding is the main identified issue.

5. ACCEPTABILITY

Carers praise highly the counselling service.

6. COST

1998: £40,000 a year.

Reference

Communication from Dementia Care Trust.

4. SERVICES SPECIFICALLY TO SUPPORT FAMILY CARERS

C: Support groups

NAME OF SCHEME: Carer support groups in Glasgow

1. KEY FACTS

Provider: The Social Services Department supported six local carers support groups by providing the services of a professional worker and by meeting costs such as leaflets, printing.

Location: Glasgow

Funding source: local authority

Date: not clear.

2. AIMS AND PHILOSOPHY

To give carers effective support.

3. DESCRIPTION

Six diverse support groups were evaluated. Two were off-shoots of day centres (one a centre for adults with learning difficulties and the other one for adults with physical disabilities, two were 'free standing' and open to carers from all types of dependency situations, one was carers of stroke patients and the sixth for carers from ethnic minorities).

4. COSTS

Not specified.

5. FEASIBILITY

One of the free standing groups had difficulties in attracting members.

6. ACCEPTABILITY

High levels of satisfaction were expressed with the groups and the professional workers.

7. OUTCOME

Carers expressed a high level of satisfaction with the groups and with the support of the professional worker. The day centre groups attached to day centres acted as a bridge between the carers and the people running the day centre but were less effective in terms of emotional support and helping group members form a self-identity as carers. They were less able than the free-standing groups to allow carers emotional space to focus on their own needs. The free-standing groups were more successful in these respects.

8. KEY LESSONS

Carer support groups are not all the same. Carers need a range of different types of support groups to chose between.

Reference

Mitchell, F. (1996) 'Carer support groups: the effects of organisational factors on the character of the groups' *Health and Social care in the Community* 4(2) 113-121

Acknowledgments

The authors would like to thank the following individuals and organisations:

Age Concern England: Evelyn McEwen, Louise Russell, Pauline Thompson

Anchor Housing Association

Anne Bailey, Commissioning Manager, Wolverhampton Metropolitan Borough Council Social Services

Bournemouth Social Services

Kathleen Boyle, National Housing Federation

Carers National Association

Dr Ruth Chadwick, Department of Health

Continuing Care Conference

Professor Bleddyn Davies, Universities of Kent and Manchester and the London School of Economics

Department of the Environment, Transport and the Regions: Andy Britain, Brian Turk, Henry Small, Tania Capstick

Peter Dunn, Social Services Inspectorate, Department of Health

Chris Elliston, The Community Care Trust

Farnborough Women's Institute

Hanover Housing Association

Tessa Harding, Help the Aged

Marie Heaney, South and East Belfast (Health and Social Services) Trust

Oliver Holder, Chief Executive, Dementia Care Trust, Bristol

Richard Hollingberry, ConsultAge, and formerly Director of the Helen Hamlyn Foundation

Prof Malcolm Johnson, University of Bristol

Paul Kingston, Keele University

William Laing, Laing and Buisson

London Borough of Lewisham: Carolyn Denne, Pam Seymour and the Director of Social Services

John Payne, ExtraCare Charitable Trust

Bridget Penhale, University of Hull

Melinda Phillipson, Helen Pinch, Housing 21

The Princess Royal Trust for Carers, Lewisham

Moyra Riseborough, University of Birmingham

Martin Shreeve, Director of Social Services, Wolverhampton Metropolitan Borough Council

Southwark Pensioners Centre

Fiona Shield, Stone Rehabilitation Service, Nuffield Centre for Community Care Studies, University of Glasgow

Rani Svanberg, Dementia Care Initiative, Newcastle upon Tyne

Prof Tony Warnes, University of Sheffield

John Woolham and the Director of Social Care and Health, Northamptonshire County Council

Carol Wright, Solihull Social Services Department

The Joseph Rowntree Foundation and the Nuffield Foundation for financial support which allowed the development of the computer models used in Chapter 9.

The Department of Health for permission to reproduce Anthea Tinker's Paper (Appendix 2).

The work based on the SARs (Table 2.1) is provided through the Census Microdata Unit of the University of Manchester. Reproduced with the permission of the controller of the Stationery Office Crown Copyright.

The authors are particularly grateful to Emily Taylor (ACIOG) for putting together this report.

References

Adams, A. and Wilson, D. (1997) *Older People with Mental Health Difficulties: User Preferences - Housing Options.* Age Concern Scotland and Edinburgh Association for Mental Health: Edinburgh.

Age Concern England (1998) *Beyond Bricks and Mortar: Dignity and Security in the Home.* Submission to the Royal Commission on Long Term Care: London.

AgeNet (1998) *Using the Internet to Improve the Quality of Life of Older People.* Report of a conference, 3.6.98, AgeNet: London.

Allen, C., Clapham D., Franklin, B. and Parker, J. (1998) *The Right Home? Assessing Housing Needs in Community Care.* Centre of Housing Management and Development, Department of City and Regional Planning, Cardiff University: Cardiff.

Allen, I. (1983) *Short Stay Residential Care for the Elderly.* Policy Studies Institute: London.

Allen, I., Hogg, D. and Peace, S. (1992) *Elderly People: Choice, Participation and Satisfaction.* PSI: London.

Alzheimer's Disease Society (1998) *Submission to the Royal Commission on Long Term Care for Older People.*

Appleton, N. (1996) *The Value of Handyperson's Schemes for Older People*, JRF Findings Housing, Research 179, JRF: York.

Arber, S. and Ginn, J. (1990) 'The meaning of informal care: gender and the contribution of elderly people'. *Ageing and Society 104: 429-454.*

Arber, S. and Ginn, J. (1991) *Gender and Later Life. A Sociological Analysis of Resources and Constraints.* Sage Publications: London.

Arblaster, L., Conway, J., Foreman, A. and Hawtin, M. (1996) *Asking the Impossible: Interagency Working to Address the Housing, Health and Social Care Needs of People in Ordinary Housing.* Policy Press: Bristol.

Askham, J. and Thompson, C. (1990) *Dementia and Home Care.* Age Concern Institute of Gerontology Research Paper, no. 4. Age Concern England: London.

Askham, J. (1997) 'Supporting Elderly People and Informal Carers at Home' in Redfern, S. and Norman, I. (eds.) *Mental Health Care for Elderly People.* Churchill Livingstone: London.

Askham, J., Nelson, H., Tinker, A. and Hancock, R. (forthcoming) *Attitudes of Older Owner Occupiers.*

Association of Directors of Social Services (1994) *Towards Community Care, Review of the First Year.* ADSS.

Association of Directors of Social Services (1995/6) Evidence to House of Commons Health Committee 1995/6b *Long-Term Care: Future Provision and Funding.* Vol. 11, HMSO: London.

Audit Commission (1992a) *Lying in Wait: The Use of Medical Beds in Acute Hospitals.* HMSO: London.

Audit Commission (1992b) *Homeward Bound: A New Course for Community Care.* HMSO: London.

Audit Commission (1992c) *Community Care: Managing the Cascade of Change.* HMSO: London.

Audit Commission (1992d) *The Community Revolution: Personal Social Services and Community Care.* HMSO: London.

Audit Commission (1994) *Taking Stock: Progress with Community Care.* Community Care Bulletin, no. 2. HMSO: London.

Audit Commission (1995) *United They Stand.* HMSO: London.

Audit Commission (1996) *Balancing the Care Equation.* Community Care Bulletin, no. 3. Audit Commission Publications: Abingdon.

Audit Commission (1997) *The Coming of Age. Improving Care Services for Older People.* Audit Commission Publications: Abingdon.

Audit Commission (1998) *Home Alone.* Audit Commission Publications: Abingdon.

Audit Commission/SSI (1997) *Joint Reviews of Local Authority Social Services.* Barking and Dagenham (1997), Barnet (1998), Bury (1998), Calderdale (1998), Lincolnshire (1997), Oxfordshire (1997), Sandwell (1997), Sefton (1997), Somerset (1997), Southwark (1997), Wandsworth (1997). Audit Commission: London.

Baldock, J. (1997) 'Social Care in Old Age: More Than a Funding Problem'. *Social Policy and Administration*, 31, 1, 73-89.

Baldwin, S. and Lunt, N. (1996) *Charging Ahead: Local Authority Charging Policies for Community Care.* The Policy Press: York.

Banerjee, S. and Macdonald, A. (1996) 'Mental Disorder in an Elderly Home Care Population: Associations with Health and Social Service Use'. *British Journal of Psychiatry* 168, 750-756.

Bebbington, A., Brown, P. and Darton, R. (1996) *Survey of Admissions to Residential Care.* Discussion paper 1222. University of Kent, PSSRU: Kent.

Bennett, F. (1996) *Highly Charged: Policy Issues Surrounding Charging for Non-Residential Care.* York Publishing Services: York.

Bennett, M., Smith, E. and Millard, P. (1995) *The Right Time? The Right Place? An Audit of the Appropriateness of Nursing Home Placements Post Community Care Act.* St George's Hospital, Department of Geriatric Medicine.

Bernabei, R., Landi, F., Gambassi, G., Sgadari, A., Zuccala, G. *et al.* (1998) 'Randomised Trial of Impact of Model of Integrated Care and Case Management for Older People Living in the Community'. *British Medical Journal* 316, 1348-51.

Bjorneby, S. (1998) 'The BESTA Flats in Tonsberg: Using Smart House Technology For People with Dementia' Paper to Dementia Conference 14.7.98: Bristol.

Bland, R. (1996) 'On the Margins: Care Management and Dementia'. In Phillips, J. and Penhale, B. (eds) *Reviewing Care Management for Older People.* Jessica Kingsley: London.

Blom-Cooper, L. (1989) *Occupational Therapy: An Emerging Profession in Health Care.* Report of an Enquiry. Duckworth: London.

Blunden, R. (1998) *Terms of Engagement: Engaging Older People in the Development of Community Services.* King's Fund: London.

Brearley, P. and Mandelstam, M. (1992) *A Review of the Literature 1986-91 on Day Care Services for Adults.* HMSO: London.

Brown, A. and Mulley, G. (1997) 'Injuries Sustained by Caregivers of Disabled Elderly People'. *Age and Ageing* 26, 21-23.

Bullivant, M. (1992) *What Kind of Care?* Leeds Community Health Council: Leeds.

Calling for Help Group (1994) *Community Alarms Services: A National Survey.* Anchor/Help the Aged/National Housing and Town Planning Council/Research Institute for Consumer Affairs: London.

Calviou, A., Hockley, J. and Schofield, L. (1997) *An Evaluation of Marlow EPICS.* South Buckinghamshire NHS Trust and Buckinghamshire County Council Social Services.

Carers National Association (1997) *Still Battling? The Carers Act One Year on.* Carers National Association: London

Carter, J. (1981) *Day Services for Adults.* George Allen and Unwin: Hemel Hempstead.

Centre for Policy on Ageing (1996) *A Better Home Life.* CPA: London.

Challis, D. (1989) 'Elderly Dementia Sufferers in the Community: The Needs Service and Policy Background'. In Morton, J. (ed.), *Enabling Elderly People with Dementia to Live in the Community.* Proceedings of an Ageing Update conference, 18.6.89. Age Concern Institute of Gerontology, King's College London: London.

Challis, D. (1998) Care management. Department of Health briefing paper. Seminar 27.3.98.

Challis, D., Chesterman, J., Darton, R. and Traske, K. (1993) 'Case Management in the Care of the Aged: The Provision of Care in Different Settings'. In Bornat, J. *et al.* (eds) *Community Care: A Reader.* Macmillan/ Open University

Chesterman, J., Challis, D. and Davies, B. (1994) 'Budget-Devolved Care Management in Two Routine Programmes'. In Challis, D., Davies, B. and Traske, K. (eds), *Community Care: New Agendas and Challenges from the UK and Overseas.* Arena. Ashgate Publishing: Aldershot.

Clark, H., Dyer, S. and Hartman, L. (1996) *Going Home, Older People Leaving Hospital.* The Policy Press: Bristol.

Clark, H., Dyer, S. and Hartman, L. (1997) *Going Home. Community Care*/JRF.

Clark, H., Dyer, S. and Horwood, J. (1998) *The Importance of 'Low Level' Preventive Services to Older People.* JRF Findings, JRF: York.

Clark, J. (1998) *Community Health Care for Elderly People: Report of a Clinical Standards Advisory Group.* Stationery Office: London.

Clemson, L. and Martin, R. (1996) 'Usage and Effectiveness of Rails, Bathing and Toiletting Aids' *Occupational Therapy in Healthcare* 10, 1, 41-60.

Clifford, D. (1990) *The Social Costs and Rewards of Care.* Aldershot: Gower.

Cobbold, C. (1997) *A Cost Benefit Analysis of Lifetime Homes.* Joseph Rowntree Foundation: York.

Cowan, D. and Turner-Smith, A. (1998) *The Role of Assistive Technology and Alternative Models of Care for Elderly People.* Centre for Rehabilitation and Engineering, King's College London: London. Appendix 4.

Cowan, D. and Turner-Smith, A. R. (1999) 'The funding agencies perspective on the provision of electronic assistive technology – Equipping for life?' *British Journal of Occupational Therapy* (in press).

Curran, J. (1996) 'The Impact of Day Care on People with Dementia'. *International Journal of Psychiatry* Vol. III, 813-817.

Davies, B. (1998) 'Shelter with Care and the Community Care Reforms – Notes on the Evolution of Essential Species'. In Jack, R. (ed), *Residential Versus Community Care.* Macmillan: London.

Davies, B. (24.4.98) Personal communication.

Davies, B., Bebbington, A. and Charnley, H. (1990) *Resources, Needs and Outcomes in Community-Based Care.* Avebury: Aldershot.

Davis, A., Ellis, K. and Rummery, K. (1997) *Access to Assessment: Perspectives of Practitioners, Disabled People and Carers.* Policy Press: Bristol.

Dementia Care Trust – Communication.

Denne, C. and Morrison, K. (1997) *Homeshare Review. Interim Report.* Lewisham Social Services: London.

Denne C and Morrison K (1997) *Homeshare Review. Second Stage.* Lewisham Social Services: London.

Department of Environment (1996) *An Evaluation of the Disabled Facilities Grant Scheme.* HMSO: London.

Department of Environment, Transport and the Regions (1998) *Housing and Construction Statistics Part 1.* HMSO: London.

DoH (1989) *Discharge of Patients from Hospital*, HC (89)5 and LAC(89)7. Department of Health: London.

DoH (1994a) *Community Care Packages for Older People. Implementing caring for people.* Department of Health: London.

DoH (1994b) *Feet First: Report of the Joint Department of Health and NHS Chiropody Task Force.* NHS Executive, Department of Health: London.

DoH (1994c) *Hospital Discharge Workbook: A Manual on Hospital Discharge Practice.* Department of Health: London.

DoH (1995) *NHS Responsibilities for Meeting Continuing Health Care Needs*, HSG(95)8 and LAC(95)5. Department of Health: London.

DoH (1996) Carers (Recognition and Services) Act: Policy guidance. HMSO: London.

DoH (1998) *Community Care Statistics.* Government Statistical Service: London.

DoH (Sept 1998) *Partnership in Action: New Opportunities for Joint Working Between Health and Social Services.* DoH: London.

DoH/ Department of Environment (1997) *Housing and Community Care. Establishing a Strategic Framework.* Department of Health Publications.

DoH OSCA (Outcomes of Social Care for Adults) (1998) *Social Care Outcomes* Newsletter No. 1, Jan. Nuffield Institute for Health: Leeds.

DoH/SSI (1995a) *Moving On.* HMSO: London.

DoH/SSI (1995b) *Moving On: A Further Year.* HMSO: London.

DoH/SSI (1995c) *Caring Today: A National Inspection of Local Authority Support to Carers.* DoH/SSI/: London.

DoH/SSI (1997a) *At Home with Dementia: Inspection of Services for Older People with Dementia in the Community.* DoH: London.

DoH/SSI (1997b) *The Cornerstone of Care: Inspection of Care Planning for Older People.* DoH: London.

DoH/SSI (1997c) *They Look After Their Own, Don't They? Inspection of Community Care Services for Black and Ethnic Minority Older People.* DoH: London.

DoH/SSI (1997d) *Inspection of Local Authority Support for Carers: City of York.* DoH: London.

DoH/SSI (1998a) *Inspection of Local Authority Support for Carers: London Borough of Merton.* DoH/SSI/: London.

DoH/SSI (1998b) *Getting Better? Inspection of Hospital Discharge (Care Management) Arrangements for Older People.* DoH: London.

DoH/SSI (1998c) *Inspection of Local Authority Support for Carers.* DoH/SSI: London.

DoH/ SSI/ NHS Executive (1994) *The F Factor: Reasons Why Some Older People Choose Residential Care.* DoH/SSI/NHS: London.

Department of Social Security (1998) *The Pensioners' Income Series 1995/6 – revised edition.* DSS Analytical Services Division: London.

Edinvar (1998) *Assistive Interactive Dwelling-House* leaflet. Edinvar: Edinburgh.

Ernst and Young (1994) *The Cost of Specialised Housing,* DoE Housing Research Report No. 2, DoE: London.

Etim, N. (1993) *An evaluation of the Greenhill Way Continuing Care Scheme.* Solihull Social Services Performance Review.

Evandrou, M. (1997) 'Social Care: Today and Beyond' in Evandrou (ed.) *Baby Boomers: Ageing in the 21st Century.* Age Concern England: London.

Fielder, S., McIntosh, A. and Tremlett, N. (1994) *Review of the Home Improvement Agency Grant Programme.* DoE: London.

Fisher, M. (1994) 'Man-Made Care: Community Care and Older Male Carers'. *British Journal of Social Work* 24, 659-680.

Fisk, M. (1997) *Telemedicine and Telecare – Technologies to Help Support Independent Living at Home.* Paper to Politecnico di Torino conference 23.5.97.

Fleiss, A. (1985) *Home Ownership Alternatives for the Elderly.* HMSO: London.

Fletcher, P. (1991) *The Future of Sheltered Housing – Who Cares? Policy Report.* National Federation of Housing Associations: London.

Formby, J. (1995) *Who Cares for the Carers? A Report on the Benefits of Shiatsu Massage for Carers.*

Gage, M. and Kinney, J. (1995) 'They aren't for Everyone: The Impact of Support Group Participation on Caregivers Well-Being'. *Clinical Gerontologist* 16(2) 21-34.

Glennerster, H. (1996) *Caring for the Very Old: Public and Private Solutions. WSP 126.* London School of Economics/STICERD: London.

Gordon, D. and Spicker, P. (1997) *Planning for the Needs of People with Dementia.* Avebury: London.

Goss, S. (1996) 'Bringing Housing into Community Care'. *Journal of Interprofessional Care* 10, 3, 231-239.

Government Statistical Service (November 1992) OPCS Monitor, General Household Survey: Carers in 1990. OPCS: London.

Graafmans, J., Taipale, V. and Charness, N. (eds) (1998) *Gerontechnology: A Sustainable Investment in the Future.* IOS Press: Amsterdam, Netherlands.

Green, H. (1988) *General Household Survey 1985: Informal Carers.* OPCS, HMSO: London.

Green, S., Girling, D., Lough, S., Ng, A. and Whitcher, S. (1997) 'Service Provision for Elderly People with Long-Term Functional Illness'. *Psychiatric Bulletin* 21, 353-7.

Griffiths, R. (1988) *Community Care: Agenda for Action. A Report to the Secretary of State for Social Services.* HMSO: London.

Gurney, C. and Means, R. (1993) 'The Meaning of Home in Later Life' in Arber, S. and Evandrou, M. (eds) *Ageing, Independence and the Life Course.* Jessica Kingsley: London.

Hancock, R. and Jarvis, C. (1994) *The Long Term Effects of Being a Carer.* HMSO: London.

Hancock, R. (1998) 'Can Housing Wealth Alleviate poverty Among Britain's Older People?' *Fiscal Studies* 19, 3, 249-272.

Hanson, L. (1997) *Who Cares in the Long Term?* Townswomens Guilds: Birmingham.

Harding, T. (1998) *A Life Worth Living.* Help the Aged: London.

Hasler, J. and Page, D. (1998) *Sheltered Housing is Changing: The Emerging Role of the Warden.* Metropolitan Housing Trust Ltd: Nottingham.

Health Advisory Service (1997) *Services for people who are elderly.* The Stationery Office: London.

Helps, L. (1997) *Rationing Community Care: CAB Clients' Experience of Home Care Services.* National Association of Citizen's Advice Bureaux: London.

Henwood, M. (1995*) Implementation of the Community Care Reforms Two Years On*. Nuffield Institute for Health/King's Fund Centre: London.

Henwood, M. (1998) *Our Turn Next. A Fresh Look At Home Support Services for Older People*. Joint Initiative for Community Care/Nuffield Institute for Health/King's Fund: London.

Henwood, M., Lewis, H. and Waddington, E. (1998) *Listening to Users of Domiciliary Care Services*. Nuffield Institute for Health and UKHCA: Leeds.

Henwood, M., Wistow, G. and Robinson, J. (1996) 'Halfway There? Policy, Politics and Outcomes in Community Care'. *Social Policy and Administration* 30, 1, 39-53.

Heumann, L. and Boldy, D. (eds) (1993) *Ageing in Place with Dignity*. Praeger: New York.

Heywood, F. and Smart, G. (1996) 'Funding Adaptations, the Need to Cooperate'. SAUS/JRF: Bristol.

Heywood, F. (1994) *Adaptations, Finding Ways to Say Yes*. SAUS/JRF: Bristol.

Hill, Hauxner and Furner (1998) *The Victoria Project. Community Occupational Therapy Rehabilitation Service. Research Findings and Recommendations*. Riverside Community Healthcare NHS Trust.

Hirst, J. (1996) A Fresh Start. *Community Care*, 4-10 July.

Homer, A. and Gilleard, C. (1994) 'The Effect of Inpatient Respite Care on Elderly Patients and Their Carers'. *Age and Ageing* 23, 4, 274-276.

House of Commons (1996) *Long Term Care: Future Provision and Funding. Volume 1. Health Committee. House of Commons session 1995/6*. The Stationery Office: London.

House of Commons (1997) *The Implementation of Community Care in Scotland. Scottish Affairs Committee. House of Commons session 1996/7*. The Stationery Office: London.

Housing Corporation (1996a) *Future Directions for Housing Associations. Research note no. 14*.

Housing Corporation (1996b) *Housing for Older People*. The Housing Corporation: London.

Hunt, G. (1998) 'Technologies to Support Carers' in Graafmans *et al.*, pp. 158-164.

Inquilab Housing Association (1998) *The Case for Sheltered Housing Amongst Black and Minority Ethnic Elderly Communities in West London*. Inquilab HA: Southall, Middlesex.

Institute of Health Services Management (1998) *Telemedicine and Telecare: Impact on Healthcare*, Institute of Health Services Management: London.

Johnson, L. (1995) *Getting the message. Users and carers experience of community care in Leeds*. Leeds Community Health Council: Leeds.

Jones, A. (1994) *The Numbers Game: Black and Minority Ethnic Elders and Sheltered Accommodation*. Anchor Trust: Oxford.

Joseph Rowntree Enquiry (1996) *Meeting the costs of continuing care*. Joseph Rowntree Foundation: York.

Joseph Rowntree Foundation (1995) *Adult placement services and the effect of the Registered Homes (Amendment) Act. Social Care Research findings, no. 71*. Joseph Rowntree Foundation: York.

Joseph Rowntree Foundation (1995) *Older people's satisfaction with their housing. Housing research findings 146.* JRF: York.

Joseph Rowntree Foundation (1996) *Accommodation for older people with mental health problems. Social Care research findings 87.* JRF: York.

Joseph Rowntree Foundation (1997) *Building Lifetime Homes.* JRF: York.

Journal of Housing for the Elderly (1985) Special Double issue 'Continuing Care Retirement Communities' Vol. 3, Nos. 2/3.

Judge, K. and Sinclair, I. (eds) (1986) *Residential Care for Elderly People.* HMSO: London.

Kitwood, T., Buckland, S. and Petre, T. (1995) *Brighter Futures: A Report on Research into Provision for Persons with Dementia in Residential Homes, Nursing Homes and Sheltered Housing.* Anchor Housing Association: Oxford

Knight, J. (1992) *Sheltered Housing: The Positive Choice – A Professional Care Guide for Wardens,* Anchor Housing Association: Oxford

Laing, W. and Buisson (1997) *UK Domiciliary Care Market Report.* Laing and Buisson: London.

Laing, W. (1998) *Disparity Between Market Rates and State Funding of Residential Care,* Joseph Rowntree Foundation, Findings series June 1998: York.

Lamb, B. and Layzell, S. (1994) *Disabled in Britain – a World Apart.* SCOPE: London.

Lane, J. P., Usiak, D. J., Stone, V. I. and Scherer, M. J. (1997) 'The Voice of the Customer: Consumers Defiine the Ideal Battery Charger'. *Assistive Technology* 9, 2, 130-139.

Langan, J., Means, R. and Rolfe, S. (1996) *Maintaining Independence in Later Life: Older People Speaking.* Anchor Trust: Oxford.

Leat, D. and Perkins, E. (1998) 'Juggling and Dealing: The Creative Work of Care Package Purchasing'. *Social Policy and Administration* 32, 2, 166-181.

Leat, D. (1992) 'Innovations and Special Schemes'. In Twigg, J. (ed.) *Carers: Research and Practice.* HMSO: London.

Leather, P. and Morrison, T. (1997) *The State of UK Housing.* The Policy Press: Bristol.

Leather, P. and Sykes, R. (1996) *The Future of Community Care: A Consumer Perspective.* Anchor Trust: Oxford.

Leicester, M. and Pollock, A. (1996) 'Community Care in South Thames (West) Region: Is Needs Assessment Working?' *Public Health* 110, 2 109-113.

Levin, E. and Moriarty, J. (1996) 'Evaluating Respite Services' In Bland, R. (ed.) *Developing Services for Older People and Their Families.* Jessica Kingsley: London.

Levin, E., Moriarty, J. and Gorbach, P. (1994) *Better for the Break.* HMSO: London.

Levin, E., Sinclair, I. and Gorbach, P. (1989) *Families, Services and Confusion in Old Age.* Gower: Aldershot.

Lindsay, M., Kols, M. and Collins, J. (1993) *The Patchwork Quilt: A Study of Respite Care Services in Scotland.* Scottish Office: Scotland.

Livingston, G., Manela, M. and Katona, C. (1997) 'Cost of Community Care for Older People'. *British Journal of Psychiatry* 171, 56-69.

Lupton, C. (1990) *Sheltered Independence.* Social Services Research and Information Unit, Portsmouth Polytechnic: Portsmouth.

Mackintosh, S. and Leather, P. (1993) *The Performance of Home Improvement Agencies in 1990.* HMSO: London.

Mackintosh, S., Leather, P. and McCafferty, P. (1993) *The Role of Home Improvement Agencies in Helping Disabled People.* HMSO: London.

Marshall, M. (1997) *Dementia and Technology.* Counsel and Care: London.

Martin, J., Meltzer, H. and Elliott, D. (1988) *The Prevalence of Disability Among Adults.* OPCS Surveys of Disability in Great Britain. HMSO: London.

McCafferty, P. (1994) *Living Independently: A Study of the Housing Needs of Elderly and Disabled People.* HMSO: London.

Means, R. (1997) 'Home, Independence and Community Care: Time for a Wider Vision'. *Policy and Politics* 25, 409-419.

Means, R. (1998) *Housing and Housing Organisations: A Review of their Contribution to Alternative Models of Care for Elderly People,* Paper commissioned by ACIOG for the Royal Commission (Appendix 3): London.

Means, R., Phillips, J. and Russell, L. (1998) *Towards a Broader Vision of Community Care: Innovative Examples from Finland, Sweden and England.* Anchor: Oxford.

Means, R. and Smith, R. (1985) *The Development of Welfare Services.* Croom Helm: London.

Medical Research Council (1994) *The Health of the UK's Elderly People.* MRC: London.

Midgley, G., Munlo, I. and Brown, M. (1997) *Sharing Power.* The Policy Press: Bristol.

Mitchell, F. (1996) 'Carer Support Groups: The Effect of Organisational Factors on the Character of the Groups'. *Health and Social Care in the Community* 4, 2, 113-121.

Mittelmann, M., Ferris, S., Steinberg, G., Shulman, E., Mackell, J., Ambinder, A. and Cohen, J. (1993) 'An Intervention that Delays Institutionalization of Alzheimer's Disease Patient: Treatment of Spouse-Givers.' *The Gerontologist* 33, 6, 730-740.

Monahan, D., Greene, V. and Coleman, P. (1992) 'Caregiver Support Groups: Factors Effecting Use of Services'. *Social Work* 37, 254-260

Moriarty, J. and Levin, E. (1998) 'Respite Care in Homes and Hospitals' in Jack, R. (ed.) *Residential Versus Community Care.* Macmillan: London.

Morris, A. (1998) 'Technology to Help Family Carers: Innovative US Dissemination Strategies' in Graafmans *et al.,* pp. 165-168.

National Consumer Council (1995) *Charging Consumers for Social Services: Local Authority Policy and Practice.* National Consumer Council: London.

National Federation of Housing Associations (1991) *Getting Involved. Housing Associations and Community Initiatives. Research Report 11.* NFHA: London.

References

National Housing Federation (1996) *Appraisal Guide for Sheltered Housing.* National Housing Federation: London.

National Housing Federation (1997) *The Fifth Pillar. Towards New Housing Policies Policy Briefing.* NHF: London.

National Housing Federation (1998) Memo to ACIOG on Very Sheltered Housing.

Neill, J. and Williams, J. (1992) *Leaving Hospital: Elderly People and Their Discharge to Community Care.* HMSO: London.

Neill, J. *et al.* (1998) *A Need for Care.* Avebury: London.

Netten, A. and Dennett, J. (1997) *Unit Costs of Health and Social Care,* Personal Social Services Unit, University of Kent: Canterbury.

Nocon, A. and Baldwin, S. (1998) *Trends in Rehabilitation Policy: A Review of the Literature.* King's Fund: London.

Nocon, A., Qureshi, H. and Thornton, P. (1997) *Outcomes in Social Care: The Perspectives of Users' and Carers' Organisations.* Social Policy Research Unit, University of York.

Nolan, M., Grant, G. and Keady, J. (1996) *Understanding Family Care.* Open University Press: Buckingham.

Nolan, M. and Grant, G. (1989) 'Addressing the Needs of Informal Carers: A Neglected Area of Nursing Practice'. *Journal of Advanced Nursing* 14, 950-961.

Nuttall, S., Blackwood, R., Bussell, D., Cliff, J., Cornall, M., Gatenrby, P. and Webber, J. (1994) 'Financing Long-Term Care in Britain'. *Journal of the Institute of Actuaries* no. 121.

Office for National Statistics (1998) *Housing in England 1996/97,* Stationery Office: London

Office of National Statistics (1997) *Population Trends* Autumn No. 89, Stationery Office: London.

Office of Population, Census and Surveys (1993) *1991 Census: Communal Establishments.* HMSO: London.

Office of Population Census and Surveys (1996) *Living in Britain: Results from the 1995 General Household Survey.* HMSO: London.

Ohlin, P., Fagerberg, G. and Lagerwall, T. (1995) *Technology for Assisting Disabled and Older People in Europe.* The Heart Study, EU. TIDE: Brussels.

Oldman, C., Quilgars, D. and Carlisle, J. (1998) *Living in a Home.* Anchor Research: Oxford.

Oldman, C., Quilgars, D. and Oldfield, N. (1996) *Housing Benefit and Service Charges, DSS Research report No. 55.* The Stationery Office: London.

Opit, L. and Pahl, J. (1993) 'Institutional Care for Elderly People: Can We Predict Admissions?' *Resesarch, Policy and Planning* Vol. 10.

Pahl, J. 1988) 'Day Services for Elderly People: Misunderstandings and Mixed Metaphors' in Morton, J. (ed.) *New Approaches to Day Care for Elderly People.* ACIOG, King's College London: London.

Palmer, S., Gann, D., Adams, C., MacFarlane, B., McCosh, A. (1998) *House from the Rising Sun – Timber Housing in Japan*. Department of Trade and Industry Overseas Science and Technology Expert Mission Visit Report, October 1998.

Parker, G. (1992) 'Counting Care: Numbers and Types of Informal Carers' in Twigg, S. (ed.) *Carers: Research and practice*. HMSO: London.

Parker, G. (1993) *With this body*. HMSO: London.

Parker, G. (1996) 'The Needs of Co-Residers: Support for Spouses and Siblings' in Bland, R. (ed.) *Developing Services for Older People and Their Families*. Jessica Kingsley: London.

Parker, G. (1997) 'Coping With Caring for a Person with Dementia' in Hunter, S. (ed.) *Dementia: Challenges and New Directions*. Jessica Kingsley: London.

Parker, G. and Lawton, D. (1994) *Different Types of Care: Evidence from the General Household* Survey. HMSO: London.

Peak, T., Toseland, R. and Banks, S. (1995) 'The Impact of a Spouse-Caregiver Support Group on Care Recipient Health Care Costs'. *Journal of Aging and Health* 7, 3, 427-449.

Perkins, E. and Allen, I. (1997) *Creating partnerships in social care: evaluation of the Caring for People at Home Initiative*. Policy Studies Institute: London.

Petch, A. (1996) 'New Concepts, Old Responses: Assessment and Care Management Pilot Projects in Scotland'. In Phillips, J. and Penhale, B (eds) *Reviewing Care Management for Older People*. Jessica Kingsley: London.

Petch, A., Cheetham, J., Fuller, R., Macdonald, C., Myers, F. with Hallam, A. and Knapp, M. (1996) *Delivering Community Care: Initial Implementation of Care Management in Scotland*. The Scottish Office Central Research Unit. The Stationery Office: Edinburgh.

Pettitt, G. (1997) *Non-Residential Services in London*. London Research Centre: London.

Phelps, L. (1997) *Rationing Community Care: CAB Clients' Experience Of Home Care Services*. National Association of Citizen Advice Bureaux: London.

Philp, I., McKee, K., Meldrum, P., Ballinger, B., Gilhooly, M., Gordon, D., Mutch, W. and Whittick, J. (1995) 'Community Care for Demented and Non-Demented Elderly People: A Comparison Study of Financial Burden, Service User, and Unmet Needs in Family Supporters'. *British Medical Journal* 310, 1503-6.

Quereshi, H. and Walker, A. (1989) *The Caring Relationship*. Macmillan: London.

Quilgars, D., Oldman, C. and Carlisle, J. (1997) *Supporting independence*. Anchor Trust: Oxford.

Randall, B. (1995) *Staying Put: The best move I'll never make*. Anchor Housing Association: Oxford.

Redfern, S. and Norman, I. (eds) *Mental Health Care for Elderly People*. Churchill Livingstone: London.

Reed, R. and Gilleard, C. (1995) 'Elderly Patients' Satisfaction with a Community Nursing Service'. In Wilson, G. (ed.) *Community Care, Asking The Users*. Chapman and Hall: London.

Research Institute for Consumer Affairs (RICA) (1986) *Dispersed Alarms: A Guide for Organisations installing Systems.* RICA: London.

RICA (1997) *Which Guide to Community Alarms.* RICA: London.

Richards, E., Wilsdon, T. and Lyons, S. (1996) *Paying for Long-Term Care.* Institute for Public Policy Research: London.

Riseborough, M. (ed.) (1995) *Opening up the Resources of Sheltered Housing to the Wider Community.* Anchor Housing Association: Oxford.

Riseborough, M. (1997) *Community Alarm Services Today and Tomorrow.* Anchor Trust: Oxford.

Riseborough, M. and Niner, P. (1994) *I Didn't Know You Cared!* Anchor Housing Trust: London.

Riseborough, M. and Sykes, R. (1995) 'From Paternalism to Dialogue: An Analysis of the Changing Relationships Between Social Housing Providers and Older Tenants'. Paper to the British Society of Gerontology, University of Keele.

Robbins, D. (ed.) (1993) *Community Care. Findings from Department of Health Funded Research, 1988-1992.* HMSO: London.

Robinson, C. and Simons, K. (1995) *In safe hands? Quality and Regulation in Adult Placements for People with Learning Difficulties.* Community Care/Joint Unit for Social Research, University of Sheffield.

Robinson, J. and Turnock, S. (1998) Investing in Rehabilitation. King's Fund/Audit Commission: London.

Rolfe, S., Mackintosh, S. and Leather, P. (1995) *Retirement Housing: Ownership and Independence.* Anchor Housing Association: Oxford.

Rowlands, O. (1998) *Informal Carers.* Office of National Statistics, The Stationery Office: London.

Royal College of Physicians (1994) *Ensuring Equity and Quality of Care for Elderly People.* Royal College of Physicians: London.

Russell, L. (1998) *Disabled Facilities Grants and Older People.* Age Concern England. Briefings: London.

Russell, L. and Arnold, S. (1998) *Repair or Despair?* Age Concern England: London.

Salvage, A. (1986) *Attitudes of the Over 75s to Health and Social Services.* University College of Wales College of Medicine: Cardiff.

Salvage, A. (1998) *On Your Feet! Older People and Chiropody Services.* Age Concern England: London.

Scottish Office (1991) *Care Management. Circular SWSC 11/91.* The Scottish Office.

Seal, H. (1994) *Evaluation Report to the King's Fund. The Setting Up of a Night-Time Home Care Service.*

Secretary of State for Health (1996) *A New Partnership for Care in Old Age.* HMSO: London.

Secretary of State for Health, Social Security, Wales and Scotland (1989) *Caring for People: Community Care in the Next Decade and Beyond.* HMSO: London.

Shield, F. (1998) *Developing a Therapy-Led Community Rehabilitation Team.*

Sim, B. (1990) 'Women and the Welfare State' in Ungerson (ed.) *Gender and Caring: Work and Welfare in Britain and Scandinavia.* Harvester Wheatsheaf: Hemel Hempstead.

Sinclair, I. (1986) 'The Residents: Characteristics and Reasons for Admission'. Chapter in Judge, K. and Sinclair, I.

Sinclair, I. (1988) *Residential Care: The Research Reviewed.* (Wagner Report) HMSO: London.

Sixsmith, A. (1986) 'Independence and Home in Later Life' in Philipson, C., Bernard, M. and Strang, R. *Dependency and Interdependency in Old Age.* Croom Helm: London.

Smale, G., Tuson, G., Ahmad, B., Darvill, G., Domoney, L. and Sainsbury, E. (1994) *Negotiating Care in the Community.* HMSO: London.

Smith, G. and Cantley, V. (1985) *Assessing Health Care: a Study in Organisational Evaluation.* Milton Keynes: Open University Press.

Smith, K. (1986) *I'm Not Complaining.* Shelter Housing Advice Centre: London.

Soldo, B. and Myllyluoma, J. (1983) Caregivers Who Live with the Dependent Elderly. *The Gerontologist,* 23, 605-11.

Stone Rehabilitation Report. October 1996.

Stout, R. and Orr, J. (1997) The Challenges of Professional Training. *Age and Ageing* 26-S4 24-29.

Sunday Times (1998) 'Robonurse Takes Care of Elderly' 4.1.98, p. 19.

Svanberg, R., Stirling, E. and Fairbairn, A. (1997) The Process of Care Management with People with Dementia. *Health and Social Care in the Community* 5, 2, 134-146.

Svanberg, R., Stirling, E. and Fairbairn, A. (1995) *West End Care Management Pilot Project, July 1992-July 1994. Draft final report.* Social Services Department, Newcastle upon Tyne.

Taylor, M., Langan, J. and Hoggett, P. (1995) *Encouraging Diversity: Voluntary and Private Organisations in Community Care.* Arena Ashgate: London.

Tester, S. 1989) *Caring by Day.* Centre for Policy on Ageing: London.

Thomas, M. (1995) *Home Care Users' Views and Service Guidelines.* Age Concern Scotland.

Thompson, C. and West, P. (1984) The Public Appeal of Sheltered Housing'. *Ageing and Society* 305-326.

Thornton, P. and Mountain, G. (1992) *A Positive Response: Developing Community Alarm Services for Older People.* Joseph Rowntree Foundation: York.

Tinker, A. (1976) *Housing and the Elderly: How Successful are Granny Annexes.* London: Department of the Environment, Housing Development Directorate (1976) reprinted HMSO, 1980: London.

Tinker, A. (1984) *Staying at Home: Helping Elderly People to Stay at Home.* HMSO: London.

Tinker, A. (1989) *An Evaluation of Very Sheltered Housing.* HMSO: London.

Tinker, A. (1994) 'Ethical Issues' in Stevenson, O. (ed.) *Community Care for Very Old People: Technology for Living at Home.* Akontes Publishing for the EU: Netherlands.

Tinker, A. (1996) *Older People in Modern Society.* Longman: London.

Tinker, A. (1997) 'The Environment of Ageing' in Evans, J., Holliday, R., Kirkwood, T., Laslett, P. and Tyler, L. (eds) *Ageing: Science, Medicine and Society.* The Royal Society Philosophical Transactions: Biological Sciences, Vol. 352, No. 1363, pp. 1861-1869.

Tinker, A. (1998) *Helping Older People to Stay at Home: Supported Accommodation,* Paper for the Department of Health, Seminar, March 1998 (Appendix 2).

Tinker, A. and Jarvis, C. (in press) *Older Tenants in Housing Associations in 1995,* The Housing Corporation: London.

Tinker, A., McCreadie, C. and Salvage, A. (1993) *The Information Needs of Elderly People – An exploratory study.* ACIOG: London.

Tinker, A., McCreadie, C., Wright, F., and Salvage, A. (1994) *The Care of Frail Elderly People in the UK.* HMSO: London.

Tinker, A. and McCreadie, C. (1998) *A Research Strategy for Hanover Housing Association.* Report to Hanover Housing Association (unpublished).

Tinker, A., Wright, F. and Zeilig, H. (1995) *Difficult to Let Sheltered Housing.* HMSO: London.

Trotter, E. and Phillips, M. (1997) *Remodelling Sheltered Housing.* Housing 21: Beaconsfield, Bucks.

Twigg, J. and Atkin, K. (1994) *Carers Perceived: Policy and Practice in Informal Care.* Open University Press: Buckingham.

Twigg, J. (1997) 'Bathing and the Politics of Care'. *Social Policy and Administration* 31, 1, 61-72.

Twigg, J., Atkin, K. and Perring, C. (1990) *Carers and Services: A Review of Research.* HMSO: London.

UK Central Council for Nursing, Midwifery, and Health Visiting (1997) *The Nursing and Health Visiting Contribution to the Continuing Care of Older People.* UK CCNMHV: London.

Von Mering, O. and Neff, L. (1993) 'Joining a Life Care Community: An Alternative to going into a Nursing Home in the USA', *Generations Review,* 3, 4, pp. 5-8.

Wagner Report (1988) *Residential Care: A Positive Choice.* HMSO: London.

Walker, A. and Warren, L. (1996) *Changing services for older people.* Open University Press: Buckingham.

Warburton, W. (1994) *Home and Away: A Review of Recent Evidence to Explain Why Some Elderly People Enter Residential Care Homes While Others Stay at Home.* Department of Health: London.

Warner, N. (1995) *Better Tomorrows: A Report of a National Study of Carers and Community Care Charges.* Carers National Association: London.

Warrington, J. and Eagles, J. (1995) 'Day Care for the Elderly Mentally Ill: Diurnal Confusion?' *Health Bulletin* 53, 2, 99-104.

Watkins, M. and Redfern, S. (1997) 'Evaluation of a New Night Nursing Service for Elderly People Suffering from Dementia' *Journal of Clinical Nursing* 6, 485-494.

Watson, L. and Conway, T. (1995) *Homes for Independent Living: Housing and Community Care Strategies.* Chartered Institute of Housing: Coventry.

Weaver, T. and Peace, S. (undated) *Continuing Care Communities: A Review of Current Themes.* The Polytechnic of North London, Centre for Environmental and Social Studies in Ageing: London.

Wenger, C. (1984) *The Supportive Network.* Allen and Unwin: Hemel Hempstead.

Wenger, C. (1990) 'Elderly Carers the Need for Appropriate Intervention'. *Ageing and Society* 10, 2, 197-219.

Wertheimer, A. (1993) *Innovative Older People's Housing Projects.* National Federation of Housing Associations: London.

West, P., Illsley, R. and Kelman, A. (1984) 'Public preferences for the care of dependency groups' *Social Science and Medicine* 18, 4, 287-195.

West, S. (1997) *Your Rights 1997-98: A Guide to Money Benefits for Older People.* Age Concern England: London.

Williams, E. and Wallace, P. (1993) *Health Checks of People Aged 75 and Over. Occasional Paper 59.* Royal College of General Practitioners: London.

Williams, G., Spicer, L. and Doughty, K. (1998) 'A Remote Electronic Monitoring System for the Prevention of Pressure Sores'. One of a number of Papers presented at the 19th Annual International Conference of the IEEE Engineering in Medicine and Biology Section, Chicago, USA, 30.10-2.11. 98.

Wistow, G. and Lewis, H. (1997) *Preventative Services for Older People: Current Approaches and Future Opportunities.* Anchor Trust: Oxford.

Wooldridge, D. (1997) *Care and the Community. An Analysis of Community Care Issues Affecting CAB Clients in Hampshire, Berkshire, Dorset, Isle Of Wight and West Sussex in 1995 and 1996.* National Association of Citizens Advice Bureaux., Southern Area Social Policy Group.

Woolham, J. (1998 draft but unpublished) *Very Sheltered Housing: A study of its Impact and Effectiveness in Meeting the Housing and Social Care Needs of Older People.* Northamptonshire Social Services: Northampton.

Wright, F. (1986) *Left to Care Alone.* Gower: Aldershot.

Wright, F. (1994) 'Multi-Purpose Homes: A Fair Deal for Residents?' *Ageing and Society* 14, 3, 383-404.

Wright, F. (1996) *Opening Doors: A Case Study of Multi-Purpose Residential Homes.* HMSO: London.

Wright, F. (1998) *Continuing to Care: The Financial and Emotional Effect on Carers of an Older Persons' Admission to a Care Home.* York Publishing Services: York.

Young, R. and Wistow, G. (1995) *Experiences of Independent Sector Home Care Providers: Analysis of the January 1995 UKHCA Survey.* Nuffield Institute for Health: Leeds.

Zarit, S. and Toseland, R. (1989) 'Current and Future Direction in Family Caregiving Research'. *The Gerontologist* 29, 481-483.

Alternative Models of Care for Older People

Appendices

by

Anthea Tinker, Fay Wright, Claudine McCreadie, Janet Askham, Ruth Hancock & Alan Holmans

Age Concern Institute of Gerontology

King's College London

Contents

1 Focus Groups. Discussions with Older People
and their Carers
Research undertaken by Dr. Fay Wright, ACIOG 245

2 Helping Older People to Stay at Home - The
Role of Supported Accommodation
Paper commissioned by the Department of Health
from Professor Anthea Tinker, ACIOG 265

3 Housing and Housing Organisations: A Review of
their Contribution to Alternative Models of Care for
Elderly People
Paper commissioned by ACIOG from Professor Robin Means . 299

4 The Role of Assistive Technology in Alternative
Models of Care for Elderly People
Paper commissioned by ACIOG from
Dr. Alan Turner-Smith by Dr. Donna Cowan
and Dr. Alan Turner-Smith 325

Alternative Models of Care for Older People

Appendix 1

Focus Group Discussions with Older People and Caregivers

Dr Fay Wright
Age Concern Institute of Gerontology,
King's College London

INTRODUCTION

Because of time constraints it was not feasible to carry out a survey of older people's views and attitudes to community care policies. Several focus group discussions were set up to inform the research process. A focus group interview is a qualitative research technique widely used in market research for many years and now fast becoming popular in social research. It is a form of group interview that is recorded and transcribed. A focus group interview is an interview in a social context. Participants have to consider their views in relation to the views of others and can make contributions beyond their original responses as they hear what others in the group have to say. The interaction between participants is important in people formulating their views. A focus group transcript is analysed qualitatively to explore participants' views.

Seven focus group discussions were held, four with older people and three with people currently defining themselves as in a caregiving situation. In reality there was no clear distinction between people taking part in the carers' groups and those taking part in the older people's discussions. It emerged that many of those taking part in the older people's discussions had either been carers or were currently giving other older people support. The following four groups of older people took part in the research:

- attenders with a severe disability at a day centre on the south coast;

- a Women's Institute discussion group in Kent;

- sheltered housing tenants from East Anglia;

- people attending a pensioner's centre in a London borough.

Forty-four people took part in the groups. Two of the groups were all female but two had both men and women taking part.

People with a current caregiving responsibility taking part in the three focus group discussions were predominantly caring for older people but in each group there were one or two people caring for a younger person. The following three focus groups took part:

■ carers from several different London boroughs in contact with the Princess Royal Trust for Carers;

■ carers in contact with Lewisham Carers;

■ carers in contact with a carers' support worker in Bournemouth.

Twenty individuals took part in the three groups. Although women predominated, four men took part. The oldest daughter taking part was aged 80 and caring for her mother who had just reached 100 years of age. Several spouses taking part were also in their eighties. Although most of the carers taking part were either the spouse of the person being cared for or the offspring, a few people were caring for a friend or a more distant relative.

The distinction between older people's and carers' groups was inevitably blurred. Many of those taking part in the carers' focus group discussions were over retirement age. A majority of those taking part in the older people's discussions had themselves been carers at various points in their lives. Although some were giving support to people unable to be totally independent, they were not defining themselves as carers.

A vignette of a growing dependency situation was used in each of the discussion groups and participants discussed the advice they would give to the central character. Although all the groups considered the same dependency situation, the vignette for carers was written from a carer's perspective and the one for older people from the perspective of an older person becoming increasingly dependent.

The discussions of the two types of groups are presented separately below but the conclusion pulls together the common themes.

FOCUS GROUPS WITH OLDER PEOPLE

The vignette and the group questions

> Mrs S is a widow aged 87 living in the same terraced house since her marriage 60 years ago. She has had arthritis for some years and finds it difficult now to get up and down stairs and is beginning to find difficulty in getting in and out of bed. After a few weeks in hospital following a fall, Mrs S has become less confident and has to rely on other people to prepare meals and do the shopping. She is becoming rather confused and worried about her situation. Up to now her daughter Julia has been able to give her mother any help needed. Julia works part-time as a secretary for her husband who runs a small business. Her own two children are now at university. Mrs S's increasing dependency makes it difficult for Julia to give the amount of help needed. Mrs S herself does not have clear ideas about the future.

A. Should Mrs S ask Social Services for a package of care in her own home?

B. Should Mrs S move to Julia's house?

C. Should Mrs S move into very sheltered housing in the town? [Very sheltered housing usually has flats, 24-hour warden cover, help with domiciliary and care tasks and some meals]

D. Should Mrs S move into a residential care home?

1. Some underlying themes

An interesting issue is when individuals perceive old age to begin. As one woman commented:

> *Old age is always 10 years on from you!*

There was a definite sense for those people in their sixties and seventies that old age had not yet begun. The one group in a day centre contained participants in their mid-eighties and just one woman who was 75. She waited until after the discussion to comment that she was far too young to mix with such old people.

A common view from those in their sixties and seventies was that they did not want to live to very old age:

> *I don't think any of us wants to live until we're over 90 do we?*

There was a clear sense from participants that older people are not wanted in our society:

> *No, because we're not wanted really.*

> *The National Health doesn't want us.*

> *No, society can't cope, this is the thing. It really can't.*

2. A package of care in one's own home

Participants were doubtful about a highly dependent person getting adequate support at home. Three areas of particular concern were a lack of support from the GP, the difficulties of re-establishing life at home after hospital treatment and role of the home care services in some areas.

(a) Lack of support from GP

Several participants expressed concerns about the difficulty of getting medical attention from GPs nowadays:

> *You have to have someone telephone. Fourty-eight hours to get an appointment as a rule, unless it's an emergency, which is another system that's fallen by the wayside. I think that is very bad. I think the doctor should be able to visit an elderly person on their rounds more frequently.*

> *They don't seem to bother. If you don't go, they forget you don't they?*

(b) Problems following hospital discharge

Several participants focused on hospital discharge and there had been a wide range of experiences. At one extreme some had experienced a lack of support on returning home in a weakened state from hospital:

> *Well, I was ill last year. When I came out of hospital, I rang them and asked for a home carer and they said, 'You'll have to wait at least another month'.*

There were several similar anecdotes. One related to a friend who suffered from dementia and had been discharged from hospital with no follow up:

> *They're not very quick on coming. I mean I've got a friend came out of hospital and she really is getting very bad in that sense. She's about this age, on her own. And I go up there and. I'm worried in case she might go out and not be able to find her way back. She's been about three weeks, to my knowledge, waiting for a home help. Nothing.*

At the other end of the spectrum, some who had been seriously ill had nothing but praise for the trouble taken in hospital and in follow up after care. One woman, in her mid-eighties, had been delighted to return finally to her own home after months in hospital:

> *I can't speak highly enough of them. I had a stroke last April and I was in hospital for five months. When I came home I had this help in the morning, to help me to get up and dressed and washed, make my bed for me, and get my breakfast, and wash up afterwards, and hoover the floor or do any little jobs around the flat. Then at lunch time another different one would come and get me my lunch, and, in the evening, another one would come and make sure I got into bed safely, 'cos I was all paralysed down one side. They give me a drink or a sandwich before I went to bed. They made sure I was safely in bed before they left the flat. And they did that every day right until I was well enough to start to help myself a wee bit. Because I could walk when I came home, you see.*

One issue identified was carrying out an assessment too swiftly after a major operation. One of the participants recounted how her mother had been swept off to her flat in an occupational therapist's car only three days after a major operation to try out her tea-making skills:

It was all hasty – get a move on, you know – not good psychology. The whole flat was completely changed in a matter of minutes, before she'd had a chance really of thinking about it. I think that really caused her a little bit of stress, it was far too quick, for this lady to go in and say, 'Well make me a cup of tea, and can you do this, and can you do that? You're going to have to have this rug up'.

(c) The role of the home care service

Individuals had widely differing experiences of home care. The issue of equity between people in different local authorities came out strongly in one of the groups held in a day centre for people with high levels of disability. Participants came from two neighbouring local authorities. One authority was reported as willing to provide extensive care packages with a high home care input but the other was reluctant to give much support of this kind.

The following weaknesses of the home care service were identified when people needed intensive support in their own homes:

■ *visits at inappropriate times* for people unable to put themselves to bed or to get up unaided without home carer support. Several participants knew people who had to rely on home care assistance to get in and out of bed. They were often confined to bed for lengthy periods because an assistant might arrive late in the morning or early in the evening;

She needed someone to come and dress her in the morning, and she was sometimes waiting hours and hours for someone to come in, and having to pay a lot of money obviously, because she was able to pay.

■ *failing to turn up at all* leaving the person without any support;

The carer system is a hit and miss. I think we all know people who depend on carers who have a day off, nobody turns up to see that they either get out of bed or have their breakfast or whatever.

■ *an apparent lack of training for home care assistants;*

The home helps who come round are not trained. They get them from a lot of these agencies or they want a day's work or something. They come along and they do bully the old people because I've had it tried on with me. And they should be from social services shouldn't they? A proper department where they see to it that people come along, and they should be supervised before they go in to help these people.

■ *difficulties for the service in matching some people's needs for assistance in using the toilet;*

That's a big problem for people – toileting. You can manage many other things on your own, but you can't always manage that. And it's a thing you can't time. You can time people going to bed, you can time them having a meal, but you can't time them as to what their toilet requisites are.

3. Moving to a daughter's home

For many participants in their sixties or indeed seventies the issue of a parent moving in was very much a live issue. Several had shared a house with their parents or in-laws in the past and several were currently giving some support to a parent in a different household. A few participants currently had a parent living in the same household. Co-resident households were not thought to be a comfortable experience for the younger generation. One woman in her sixties was finding life uncomfortable now that her father had moved in with her and her husband:

I find with my father and my husband, I feel very much piggy-in-the-middle. I find it a difficult situation, even sitting in the same room with them both, as to who's vying for my attention!

My family had left home by the time my mother came, but we felt that we had to offer her a home. It worked out all right. I can't say that we were overjoyed with the prospect really.

One participant had cared for no less than three elderly relatives in her time:

I know of the other end. I looked after my mother, an old aunt and a mother-in-law.

Interestingly participants were adamant that they themselves would never want to move to live with one of their children. Various reasons were put forward in support of this view:

■ older people prefer their independence;

I think this is the main thing. I think people are so afraid of losing, at this age, their independence, and frustrated at having to be a person in somebody else's home. No longer having any say in anything, or when the television should go on or, how loud, or anything.

And then, you see, your children, they might have young children as well, and you feel as though you're in the way sometimes. So it's better if the elderly person has a place of their own. They can get up when they like, they can go to bed when they like, they can do what they like during the day

You've got to have your independence.

You've got to. That's what keeps us going. We know that it's our home. Although we're happy with the family, it's not your own, and you'd think perhaps twice before making a cup of tea. If they knew they'd be cross. You can go in your kitchen, you can make a cup of tea, and do what you want, and keep your independence.

■ daughters and daughters-in-law could be too bossy;

And she's very good, and my other daughter is the same. But then I wouldn't live with them, not on no account. Because I'd tell them they were too bossy, but they're not. They tell me for my own good. Oh yes if I do things that are wrong, our girls will tell me in a minute, but they're very kind to me, and that's the main thing.

- different generations do not gel;

> *I go for the weekend now, because I don't think it's fair, because I have in the past had the older people when I was young. They're good but we've got different thoughts, different ideas, and I'll go to my son's every weekend, but I like to keep my own flat and I like to be independent, and make a cup of tea – but when you're in your own home it's that little bit different.*

> *And as far as my children are concerned, there's a generation gap you see. We think differently.*

> *I think it's a mistake, because you see, there's always one or two generation gaps, and they have different ideas. They think differently. And they have their life to lead. We've had ours. We're coming to the twilight years of our life. So they just don't gel you see.*

- a strong sense that their own children's first responsibility had to be to the grandchildren;

> *This is very much against, I think, anything. I, myself, would hate my family to think they were duty-bound to look after me if I was ill. They have enough problems of their own. They are working to either educate their kids or whatever. They do not need an extra elderly person to look after.*

4. Very sheltered housing

Although participants in one of the groups were sheltered housing tenants, several participants in the other three groups were uncertain what was meant by sheltered housing. There was some confusion between the difference between sheltered housing and residential care:

> *And I said that if, when it comes that I can't do the stairs any more, or I can't cope any more, then I probably would move. In fact when I was at the town hall a few weeks ago, to sort my benefits out, I asked them for the appropriate forms for this. I presume that's the one with the warden isn't it?*

Other participants had been discouraged from sheltered housing after direct experience. One woman visiting her mother in sheltered housing had been dismayed by the cutting of the warden service:

> *Gradually the warden's hours were cut and cut and cut, and in the end they were on what they called 'control', which mean that there was pullcords all over the place, and then 'cos I had to pull it myself when I had to call an ambulance. Now when I used to go into my mother's and she would always tell me, 'Oh Pat's not on duty this week', and she didn't like that because they like a human contact.*

Another woman had visited a friend in sheltered housing with bed sit accommodation and thought all sheltered housing was like that:

> *The only thing that I complain about. A lot of people that are on their own, have to go into bedsits. And this is the one thing that I . . . And I think it's wrong, to make single people go into a bedsit. They wouldn't give me a one-bedroom place. That's the only drawback.*

Interestingly two of the focus groups, one based in sheltered housing and the other with several participants living in sheltered housing were critical of the concept of sheltered housing. It was argued that sheltered housing only met the needs of those who were fit and able:

> *We were saying there about the sheltered housing. That once you become infirm, sheltered housing is not the answer. You've got to be self-caring to go into sheltered houses.*

Vigorous discussion developed about the need for continuing care communities that contained independent living units, sheltered housing, residential care and nursing facilities on the same site. It was seen as detrimental to the well-being of older people that it often became necessary to move to get the appropriate support services:

> *The other idea that I've seen is a senior citizen's village, that I know of, and I think there's two or three up and down the country, and where they have their own little unit, like a sheltered unit, like bungalows or flats. And once they become too infirm, they also have their own nursing home and they're own small cottage hospital, in this village. They guarantee to look after you from when you elect to go there, if possible acquiring a place, but when you become infirm you're then – it's suggested that you go into the nursing home, which is still retaining your own room, within the nursing home, but you are cared for, and you're not left.*

> *That's right, or flats, but into accommodation that allows them to be independent without too much responsibility. They then get to a stage where they're needing a lot of extra care, so they haven't got to move to the other side of town, they can keep their friends and just move to another portion of the same estate, or another building, or whatever. And they get to the stage then where they're needing a lot of care, they move into a nursing home. But it would seem to me logical. It would keep people in an area that they liked. They've got their friends still around them.*

A perceived advantage of retirement communities was that older people would be able to help each other:

> *You'd find friends you see, you'd become like a little community, so you can continue helping each other.*

> *It's a wonderful idea.*

> *I think that councils and government, if they want to solve the problem of the senior citizens, that that is what they should think along the lines. And the communities I've seen, where they've got every facility, to the grave.*

Feeling safe from crime was an issue for some people and it was thought that continuing care communities would provide greater security than living in normal mixed age communities:

> *And elderly people, in those little communities, they feel safe, they can go out.*

Some reservations were expressed about the conveyor belt aspects of a continuing care community:

Should they (the government) put their money into producing custom-built property that people can go into when they retire? And then as they get less infirm they can move to another adaptable unit, and then another adaptable unit, until eventually they end their days in a crematorium. But if it sounds like a conveyor belt.

5. Moving into residential care

Reactions to residential care were varied. The group of people in a day centre who had serious physical disabilities and already had an intensive package of care at home accepted that inevitably they would enter a care home one day. This was seen as a preferable alternative to moving into a household with one of their children:

The time will come when none of us can cope on our own any more, in our own private accommodation. So that will be soon enough to go into a rest home or a nursing home. But I think it's inevitable that we all end up in one of those places. You do, of course, it's got to happen.

So you see, I don't you think you've got to give as you get older, and they might say to me (the council) you'll have to go into a rest home or you might have to go into a nursing home. So I'm quite ready for that you see. I've accepted my illness, and I've seen people that are much worse than myself. And I used to say, 'Thank God, I'm not too badly off after all!'

Participants in the other three groups were physically far fitter and had some stringent comments to make the quality of care in some care homes. The lack of privacy was commented on:

But when he went into this, although he had his own room, and he had one or two of his own bits in there, they insisted that he had the door open – which I suppose in a way you can understand – but then everybody had their door open, and his hearing was very acute still. He hadn't gone deaf like everybody else. And there was somebody yelling all the time down the corridor, two or people with radios and televisions all on different stations blaring away. It was really quite horrendous.

The lack of activities was commented on:

We went into the sitting room, and there was all the patients, residents, that had got Alzheimer's or dementia, and they were sitting all in a room these people. And what was on . . . Mickey Mouse or something. And they were all sitting, not occupied, but all playing with bits of paper and folding their handkerchiefs.

Some people commented on the extensive closure of local authority homes feeling that older people were being forced to use up their money by paying for care in the private sector:

Well they're doing that now aren't they? They're closing homes down. I mean what you're saying, they're doing that, they're forcing you into it. You've got no choice because they don't listen to you, they just close the homes down. There's no care. When you get on and say you want to go into care, you can't get into care, even if you can pay for it now you can't get in care. They're just closing everything down.

CARERS FOCUS GROUPS

The vignette and the group questions

> Julia is 55 and has a part-time job as a secretary for her husband who runs a small home decorating business. She has two children both at university. Her 87-year-old mother is a widow living nearby in a terraced house. Mrs S has had arthritis for some years and finds it difficult now to get up and down stairs and is beginning to find difficulty in getting in and out of bed. After a few weeks in hospital following a fall, Mrs S has become less confident and has to rely on other people to prepare meals and do the shopping. She is becoming rather confused and worried about her situation. Up to now Julia has given her mother any help needed. Mrs S's increasing dependency now makes this difficult. Mrs S herself does not have clear ideas about the future. For her part Julia is uncertain what to do for the best.

A. Should Julia ask Social Services for a package of care?

B. Should Julia invite her mother to move to her house?

C. Should Mrs S move into very sheltered housing in the town? [Very sheltered housing usually has flats, 24 hour warden cover, help with domiciliary and care tasks and some meals]

D. Should Julia think about residential care for her mother?

1. Some underlying themes

Although it is difficult to generalise about caring situations, some underlying issues identified during the discussions were noted:

(a) A carer experiencing more than one dependency situation

Some of the married daughters in their sixties and seventies caring for a parent in her nineties were also experiencing a developing dependency of a spouse:

> *I must admit that at the moment I'm between the devil and the deep-blue sea. My mother's 97, my husband's only 70, and my duty is which way? I mean the situation is becoming more difficult. At the present moment I'm beginning to think well perhaps I ought to divert more attention to my husband, because at the moment 24-hour care is geared to a 97-year-old.*

> *That's right, I'm the only one. It falls on me. Everything falls on me. I've an elderly aunt and I have to look after her as well, I get the shopping and do the house for both my mother and my aunt, I don't get much time for myself.*

(b) Carers of working age usually lose income

There were carers of working age in all three groups. Some had had to totally give up work because of their caring responsibilities and others were working part time instead of full time. Inevitably this led to a current loss of income and would eventually lead to a reduced pension.

2. A package of care in the cared-for person's own home

Carers raised many significant points about packages of support in the course of the discussions. In addition they raised other key issues. These included a need for:

- the cared-for person to acknowledge the dependency;

- a proper carer assessment;

- adequate information about supportive health and social services;

- the cared-for person to accept support services;

- professionals to communicate with each other;

- support from the GP;

- professionals to receive appropriate training to understand about carers and their needs for support;

- a supportive home care service;

- adequate respite from caregiving.

(a) A need to acknowledge that a caring situation exists

Caring situations commonly progress from one individual in a relationship having a need for some support in certain aspects of daily living to having more substantial needs for support. Indeed giving some support with an aspect of daily living is commonplace in many relationships including that between a husband and wife. It was a spouse in one of the groups who commented that it needed a professional person, in this case a community nurse, to point out that he was in a caring situation and needed some support from outside:

> *It was our district nurse, who first of all said, 'You need some help'. And from the district nurse, so all the help that we eventually received came and it was discussed with us in a very humanitarian way.*

(b) A carer's assessment

Under the Carers (Recognition and Services) Act 1995, carers are entitled to ask for an assessment in their own right of their ability to provide and continue to provide care. A local authority must take into account the result of a carer's assessment when it decides what services to provide for the person being cared for. Some of the participants in the groups had been assessed and had some comments on the process. Amongst the views expressed were:

- An assessment may be superficial and unhelpful;

> *We had a lady come to see us one time and she was very young, and I don't think she was the right person to do the job. She just came in and she looked around and asked, Where does he sleep? and, Where does he eat? Have you got a toilet upstairs, I said,*

'No, there's only the one that's downstairs'. 'And how does he manage to get up and down?' She just said, 'Oh yes, you're fine', and she went. But I mean if it had been an older person, had the experience of people that need help, she'd probably have asked questions like, 'How do you manage to do this? Have you got a social worker that comes round?'.

■ need to get advice from carer support workers or other carers at carers centres about different kinds of support so that they can be proactive in an assessment;

You do need to know though, before you go for assessment, what you want. If you don't – we were lucky we had a very good assessment, but I think that was because I knew exactly what I wanted before they came.

But I think people need a lot of help before they have an assessment. I think just going into an assessment, it can be very confusing, it can sometimes the social worker has wanted to be so informal that people aren't even aware that this is a real assessment, things are going to hang from this. So they need preparation, help and preparation, before having the assessment.

■ An initial assessment could be particularly constructive if followed up at regular intervals. One carer in her eighties caring for a husband with severe physical disabilities was delighted at the attention;

And the garden, the social services, as I say, I've got these rails put in, and they phone me every single week to see if I need any other help.

(c) A need for information about supportive health and social services

A theme in each of the three groups was the need for carers to be given information about all the different potential kinds of support. Only then could decisions be made about what might be helpful and acceptable to both carer and user. Inevitably carers felt angry and cheated if they had had difficulty in getting support that could easily have been made available. One daughter herself above retirement age had only found out about a bathing service after 18 years of caring for her 95-year-old mother:

When I approached the doctor he said, 'Well why doesn't she go to the day centre and have day care, and have her bath there?' which was wonderful. And that was the first information I had regarding help. And it was a godsend. So I looked forward to her going for her bath.

Carers were bemused at the difficulty of accessing the local information they needed. As one carer said:

I've been caring for ten years, and it was hit or miss whether I stumbled on information. Everyone should be even more enlightened as to how and where and what information is available. But it's still very difficult. It's exceedingly difficult.

People needed an information system that was accessible to them in their own homes:

> *This is the trouble . . . it's up to the carer to ask for things. But you don't know what to ask for. Whereas in this situation, people will say 'Well it's all in library'. Hang on a minute, when does a carer get time to go to the library?*

As one of the carers commented:

> *Nobody's told me what the system is. To me the system is the things I've found out. I don't know what the bits are that I haven't found out. An awful lot of the system I'm not even aware of.*

(d) Need for the cared-for person to accept help

A problem that several daughters had experienced was a parent refusing to accept a service and insisting that care should continue to be provided by the daughter. The view was expressed that for the carer's sake it was important for a third party with authority such as a social worker to intervene and offer some protection to a carer:

> *If my mother wouldn't have people in the house I couldn't do anything about it. She'd actually see people off. But what I felt was needed was someone to come in and force the issue, but it was never done.*

> *My mother, she was very difficult, she didn't want to leave home, she didn't want to do this, she didn't want to do that. But when you've got the third person (the social worker) headlining about, 'All we want to do is make life easier for your daughter', because they can't wriggle for the minute, and they do go along. 'Oh I'll give it a try'.*

(e) A need for professionals to communicate with each other

Some of the worries that carers had related to the failure of professionals in contact with the cared-for person to communicate with each other. There were various anecdotes. For example, a community nurse relieving a colleague who had gone on holiday failed to read the notes that explained that she was treating a leg ulcer for a dementia sufferer who could not be left alone with medicines. The dementia sufferer proceeded to rip up ointment containers and dressings leaving a mess that had to be cleared up by the caregiver.

(f) A need for support from the GP

Some carers felt there could have been more support from the doctor. Sometimes the complaint was that there was no continuity of care and understanding of what was wrong with the person being cared for:

> *Yes, well I find that – we've got a doctor, just the one doctor, we haven't seen him for a couple of years, never been in. Every time you ask for somebody to come it's a different doctor and they don't know anything about her. You have to explain everything every time they come, exactly know what's the matter with her. It's frustrating.*

A doctor could fail to make the necessary home visit:

> *She was really sick and he'd say, 'Oh I'll come tomorrow'. And still tomorrow would come, and he wouldn't come.*

Sometimes a carer could be expected to carry out medical procedures. One husband was rather startled to find he was expected to give his wife an enema, a procedure he found both distasteful and difficult. His comment was that explaining to him how to give the enema was the first time either the doctor or the community nurse had really acknowledged his role as his wife's sole carer.

(g) A need for appropriate training for professionals

Carers were quite clear that they expected that social workers and doctors should have more understanding of both the situations for, and the needs of, carers.

(h) A need for a supportive home care service

Several participants had experienced enormous support from home care staff. Experiences varied widely. Some had nothing but praise for the quality of the care assistants and the conscientious way that the social services departments concerned ensured that the help was always put into the home:

> *The advantage of having help through the social services (and it's definitely not cheaper unless you are on income support) the advantage is the carry-through. If anything happens to your carer they put somebody in. I've never been let down in four years by the home care services. The quality of workers if very high. Moreover if they're dealing with someone who's got dementia they realise the importance of continuity. You can't have different people coming in on different days. There's one who comes in five days a week, then two at the weekends.*

Others had quite different experiences. One carer lamented:

> *Every day it's different – four times a day you can have four different carers, some better than others. Some have no idea about caring whatsoever. I don't know why they're doing the job. They have no idea of the apparatus, nor do they care, nor are they really interested.*

Some carers had been refused assistance because the cared-for person could pay privately for care. But, it could be very difficult for a caregiver to sort out a reliable and appropriate care package through agencies. In effect, in these circumstances a relative had to take on the role of a care manager. Using a private agency could be particularly worrying when it was felt that there was an absence of police checks on an assistant sent along to look after the cared-for person:

> *You can't get a list of people who would help you perhaps, care or something like that. For example if I want private care to look after my mother for an hour, it's £7 an hour. But you don't know who you're going to get. There's no list or anything else like this. Whereas with children there's a list. I mean with children, you can't look after a child unless you're registered.*

Refusal to provide a cleaning service

An issue raised by several carers was the refusal of the home care services in many areas to provide a cleaning service. When the carer was a frail and elderly spouse providing a partner with considerable personal care this refusal seemed difficult to justify. One of the participants in her eighties was bemused at a cleaning service being refused when she had discharged herself early from hospital after an operation because her husband could not cope in the house on his own:

> I tried to get one of those reclining armchairs, so that I could be downstairs with my husband and just go to the kitchen when necessary, and still have the rest for my legs. I couldn't get anything, and when I asked for a home help, they wanted £9 an hour, but they won't do any housework. I said, 'But that's what home helps are supposed to do'. They said, 'Oh well they're for personal care and they will not do any housework'.

Charges for home care

Local authorities set individual charging policies for community support services. Some carers reported that there was no charge for home in their area. Others that there was quite a hefty one. In some areas receiving an Attendance Allowance was the reason for not making a charge but in others it was a reason for making a charge:

> Now because my mother was on an Attendance Allowance, they wanted to charge £9 an hour for her care.

(i) A need for adequate respite from caregiving

Different forms of respite from caring include day care, short breaks (with an overnight stop) and sitting services. Important considerations for carers are the availability, the reliability and the costs of these services.

Day care

Participants were generally very appreciative of day care for the cared-for person:

> My mother goes to day care Tuesday, Wednesday and Friday and that's good. That's my time. We usually go off to the allotment.

One carer for an Alzheimer's sufferer was particularly grateful because:

> the stimulation there is great. It really works.

It meant a great deal to one of the carers that her mother went to a day centre in a residential home where she was also able to stay for a short break.

An important issue identified by one of the carers was that day centres often have strict age criteria. Her husband, incapacitated by a stroke in his fifties, had recovered sufficiently to attend a day centre so that she could continue working. The day centre for younger people with a physical disability had proved very constructive to her husband. She was anticipating that at the age of 60 he would be upset by being transferred to a day centre specifically for older people most of whom would be an older generation and in their eighties.

Short breaks

Having a break from a caring situation if only for a few days can be very important in sustaining a caring situation. Several issues arose around getting a short break. These included:

- **a shortage of respite care places.** All the participants acknowledged that there were difficulties in finding good quality short-term places in residential care homes. It was felt that it had become even more difficult as local authority homes which had been reliable providers of short stay places in the past were closing. Carers had to scramble for the few places available. One carer trying to find a week's stay for the cared-for person in March had to be content with locating a respite care place for the last week in October.

- **local differences in locating available respite care places.** In some areas local authorities were reported providing a home support service that had a computerised database of respite care places and their bookings. But, in other areas, carers reported that the only way to locate a respite care place was to use Yellow Pages and ring up each local residential home.

- **variations in charging policies.** Although some local authorities provide free respite care, in other areas carers reported having to pay the full price. Some participants expected to pay up to £400 a week for the cared-for person's short stay in a care home.

- **trauma for some cared-for people staying in respite care.** One of the wives acknowledged the effect of respite care on her husband;

    And I have a week's break, every three months. And he hates going away.

In some areas this trauma had been avoided by a care assistant staying in the home. One husband reported a Crossroads care attendant staying with his wife at home at the local authority's expense:

Last year I went away for four or five days because otherwise I'm unable to escape from the situation you see, and the local authority arranged Crossroads and it was all right.

- **lack of weekend cover.** A significant problem mentioned by several participants was getting a weekend break. Few care homes were prepared to provide such a service because of the loss of revenue on the place during week days.

Sitting Services

Major differences exist between areas in the availability of a sitting service. Some participants reported no access to a sitting service. Others reported extensive support. A carer from one London Borough, for example, reported that the local authority provided her with 14 hours a week care assistance in the home:

. . . so that we can go out, or do our own thing, and the council covers this.

A carer from a different area was very grateful for a sitting service provided by her local authority at a modest charge but commented:

They're highly subsidised, they're not expensive, but they are on ration. I mean you can't have as much as you'd like. But it's very helpful to be able to go off and have a lunch on your own, or to the park or something, and know that someone trained and police vetted will be there.

3. Having a parent move into an offspring's home

A substantial proportion of the carers in the groups were co-resident with the person being cared for. Some were the spouses and others the married or single daughter or son. Although some reservations were expressed participants in all three groups were far more positive about co-residence than those taking part in the four groups of older people. One of the daughters had moved her family into a house with a granny flat so that her mother could live with them. Her comment was:

It's worked for us. I also have a very supportive husband and I think you need a supporting family.

In the end because her mother needed so much care that the separate granny flat was no longer feasible and they became a joint household. Another carer had set up a similar living situation by splitting a house into two flats so that her mother and handicapped brother could live nearby but in a separate household. Again, over time and with increasing dependency, separate households on the same premises had not proved feasible and a joint household had been set up.

For one carer the decision to share a household with a parent was seen as a moral one:

And so you have to make that decision in the end with your conscience. It is between you and your conscience, whether you abandon people really, or whether you don't. And at the end of the day I think that it is up to the individual, and your conscience.

One carer now looking after a spouse felt from his own personal experience that setting up a joint household with parents could be a disaster:

So we got them down here. Disaster! Because illness came and all the rest of it – they nearly drove us bonkers. I say, you love them by all means, but don't burden yourself with it if there is an alternative.

One carer saw the main reason for co-residence as a pragmatic one:

The reason why people take them in is because they think it's going to be easier under one roof. And also you think . . . also there's a huge guilt thing because you don't want to put her or him out.

4. Having a parent move into sheltered housing

Few carers had had any personal experience of sheltered housing. One carer was delighted when her mother moved into a scheme and her caring role was reduced. A few people related anecdotes about the loneliness of people in sheltered housing and the exposure to risks of conmen when there were concentrations of older people which made them uncertain about it. As many of the carers taking part were looking after people who had become very dependent, it may have been difficult for them to see the relevance of sheltered housing to their situations.

5. Having a parent move into residential care

Most of the carers in the groups were very sceptical about the quality of care in residential homes. One carer had experienced the cared-for person staying in a care home for an assessment:

> *it really was a nice place, nice rooms and everything. But the quality of care was abysmal, absolutely abysmal.*

Many carers had some experience of care homes through a short stay place for respite and tended to get an impression of poor standards:

> *They don't have the freedom to be able to get up and wander around, or do fiddly bits that they're doing anyway.*

> *There's no stimulation there. They've got up and they've been looked after and they're stuck in a room like this and there's television, and that's it. There's nothing.*

One of the carers had reached the end of her tether with her mother's behaviour and had accepted a care home place very recently because the tension in the situation had affected the quality of the care at home:

> *But then I was looking at the quality I'm giving my mother in the end. I didn't think our relationship was getting much better. Now, she's in a home it's different. I'm giving her quality time now, whereas before it was so much hard work, that the relationship was changing. But you do battle with your conscience.*

CONCLUSIONS

Focus group discussions are an increasingly popular qualitative research technique for exploring views and attitudes. Like all research techniques there are drawbacks as well as positive aspects. One drawback is that in the course of an hour's group discussion, participants have only a limited opportunity to express their views. There are both negative and positive aspects to participants currently having caregiving responsibilities. On the one hand, they have a unique insight into the strong emotions generated both by their own feelings and by the responses of health and social services. But, on the other hand, the distress of some caregivers means that they need some space to vent anger and frustration with their own situation. This can sometimes inhibit rather than facilitate group discussion.

Each focus group discussion generated a lengthy transcript and the synthesising process inevitably meant that not all the material generated could be used. A brief report such as this one can only identify some of the key issues arising. The above report presents the themes emerging in the focus groups for older people separately from those emerging in the caregivers' focus groups. This conclusion draws together some of the common themes emerged for both carers and older people taking part in the seven groups.

1. A care package at home in the community

There was common agreement that GPs have a key role to play in identifying a developing dependency situation and in referring the dependent person and any involved carer to appropriate support services. Common complaints were that GPs were not always giving the support needed. Getting home visits for housebound dependent people could be problematic. Referrals for appropriate support services could easily be non-existent.

Discharge from hospital was identified as a point in time at which an older person continuing to live at home in the community was under threat. Early discharge can mean that a person returns home in a weakened state with difficulties in coping with normal life. If the older person concerned has caring responsibilities, a lack of practical support at home can lead to the cared-for person being permanently admitted to institutional care. In some areas of the country there is practical support for older people and carers on discharge from hospital.

Views about the quality of the home care service were very mixed. Some participants described extensive and excellent support. Others were very concerned about issues such as the quality of home care assistants and the high charge for the service. Participants were commonly bemused by the refusal of home care staff to give practical housework assistance.

Participants currently in a caregiving role had an additional agenda. Although the right to a carer's assessment is a relatively recent innovation, carers in the groups were very conscious of this right and were very positive about its potentialities. Nevertheless a major cause of concern for many was the difficulty of getting respite such as a short break from caregiving. Carers commonly experienced great difficulty in obtaining a short-stay place in a care home for the cared-for person. If a place was obtained, the carer often had to pay the full cost. A break just for a weekend was particularly difficult to obtain. Few had had the experience of a break through a paid carer coming to stay in the home with the cared-for person.

2. Moving to live in a daughter's household

Differences were evident between people currently in a caregiving situation and participants in the older people's focus groups. Many of the caregivers thought that this could be a viable option in a situation of an older person's increasing dependency. It was argued that although there might be difficulties some of the tensions would be taken out of the situation. The older people, on the other hand, were virtually unanimous in thinking that such a move would be detrimental to the older person and to the daughter. Maintaining independence was seen as of paramount importance. To move into another household would be to lose the right to make decisions about the little and the big things in life. A common theme was that different generations in the same household would not gel.

3. Moving to live in very sheltered housing

It was difficult for some groups to discuss sheltered housing because it was outside their experience. Nevertheless when people lived in sheltered housing or had visited such schemes they had strong views. A common point was that much sheltered housing could not meet the need of an older person with high dependency because it was intended for the more active older people. Two of the groups were very interested in the idea of a continuing care community of older people in which there were different types of accommodation and support appropriate for people with very different needs.

4. *Moving to a residential care home*

Differences of view were in evidence between people currently caregiving and other group participants. On the whole carers thought that the quality of life in a residential home would be poor and thought it was not an option. Although many older participants had something negative to say about residential care homes, they were more likely than carers to be sympathetic to this option. Participants with a high level of disability in the day centre discussion group expressed a virtually unanimous view that residential care was the only way that their increasing needs for support could eventually be met.

Appendix 2

Helping Older People to Stay at Home: The Role of Supported Accommodation

Professor Anthea Tinker
Age Concern Institute of Gerontology,
King's College London
(Paper prepared for a Department of Health
Seminar March 1998. See note on p. 298)

INTRODUCTION

1. Definitions

For the purposes of this paper **supported accommodation** is interpreted in its widest sense i.e. support that is given to someone who needs some kind of help either in mainstream or specialised housing. However, it should be realised that the term 'supported accommodation' is used by the Housing Corporation for funding purposes. 'Special needs accommodation' used to be the term used and was often associated with special buildings such as hostels, the congregation of specific groups and agency-managed systems of support (Watson and Conway, 1995). The subsequent 'supported accommodation' is much wider and includes 'floating support' which is not linked to particular housing or scheme. The whole concept of 'supported accommodation' is currently under discussion by the Housing Corporation in the context of registered social landlords (Housing Corporation, 1997). They argue that:

> 'Supported housing is intended for people who need a range of services over and above basic housing management. This may include those in general needs stock who require floating support services. Such services can range from intensive housing management and practical advice on benefit matters, through counselling and emotional support to personal assistance with bathing and dressing. The balance between these different kinds of services varies greatly between schemes. The balance of regulatory and funding responsibilities can also vary.

> Each of the funding streams for supported housing has a different eligibility criteria and therefore a different set of accountability requirements. Confusions can arise.'
> (ibid., p. 7)

Staying at home is interpreted as older people staying in homes of their own i.e. this is not necessarily in their own home in mainstream housing but can be a home of their own in sheltered housing. As well as those who want to remain in their current home the paper will include a discussion of provision for those who wish to move to alternative accommodation. This may be moving on from specialist housing or as a result of closures of institutions such as hospitals and residential care homes. The potential demand for supported housing arising from the closure of residential care homes needs to be addressed seriously in the light of the prediction by the Association of Directors of Social Services to the Royal Commission on Long Term Care of the Elderly that these homes are outdated and unlikely to survive into the next century (reported in *Community Care*, 1998).

One of the key themes in 'Staying at Home' policies is the concept of 'Independent Living'. The term has been particularly used by the disability movement but also applies to older people as well. As Watson and Conway put it in their Good Practice Guide *Homes for Independent Living: Housing and Community Care Strategies* (1995) 'Independent living is not intended to imply that everyone should establish their own separate household, or that support should be withdrawn at the earliest possible moment. It may be that it is only with continuing support that independent living, in the sense of having control over decisions about one's life, can be maintained in the long term' (Watson and Conway, 1995, p. 29). In research on older people, carers, professionals and campaigners about an 'ideal' (interpreted as the best possible practice and not a vision of utopia) housing system for older people it was agreed that independent living and appropriate housing should be treated as basic rights (Midgley *et al.*, 1997).

2. Scope of the paper

There are five preliminary points that need to be made as caveats to this paper. First the main focus requested by the Department of Health (DOH) is on people who are likely to have had some contact with a hospital and who are therefore the most frail and vulnerable. Although there are lessons to be learned from research about these groups **there is need to look at research on other groups** in order to plan preventive strategies. For example there is a good deal of evidence that many people who fall either do not present themselves even to the General Practitioner or, if they do, are not referred to hospital (Graham and Firth, 1992). Similarly research on older people with depression and dementia shows that by no means all of them will have had contact with a hospital.

Second **there is very little research specifically on housing issues which relate to the two groups under discussion**. (These groups were the focus of the seminar) i.e.:

(a) those who are recovering from acute episodes of ill health such as people who have had strokes or broken bones through falling at home (most of whom it is stated will have received treatment or surgery in hospital);

(b) those who have long-standing or degenerative conditions such as depression or dementia (where it is stated that many of these people will also have received treatment in hospital).

Third although concentration was requested on studies since 1993 other **older studies have to be referred to** because of the dearth of current work in certain areas of this topic.

Fourth **comparisons with other countries can prove problematical**. Although there are lessons from abroad other factors such as the financial regimes are often different as is the cultural background.

Fifth **housing must be set in the context of other services such as income, transport and leisure**.

3. Sources

The sources that have been used are both quantitative and qualitative and can be roughly grouped into studies of:

- a range of general topics which cover housing and other issues e.g. *The General Household Surveys*, hospital discharge etc.

- general housing research such as *The English House Condition Survey* (Department of the Environment (DOE), 1993)

- specific research on housing for older people (note the importance of the DOE study *Living Independently: A Study of the Housing Needs of Elderly and Disabled People* (McCafferty, 1994). The neglect of this large and important study in the literature is surprising. Is this because of the lack of peer reviewed articles?

- general research on older people

- other relevant research e.g. on health and homelessness which has implications for vulnerable older people.

A number of research findings are now discussed:

- first research on a number of overarching topics are examined

- second research on specific kinds of supported accommodation is considered

- third the paper concludes with key messages for policy makers and practitioners on how policies are working within and between health, social care and other agencies and for good practice within health social care and other agencies which lead to positive outcomes for service users.

KEY RESEARCH FINDINGS WHICH INFORM THE DEVELOPMENT OF THE POLICY AND PRACTICE AGENDA FOR THE CARE OF OLDER PEOPLE AND KEY MESSAGES FOR POLICY AND PRACTICE — OVERARCHING TOPICS

1. The neglect of housing

It appears from both empirical research and from expert opinion that housing is neglected in policy, practice and research. There is much concentration on building links between health and social services but housing seems to appear as an add on. There is now a considerable literature on community care which shows that, while the situation is improving, health and social services are seen as the main elements in community care.

> '*At a* local level *research shows that Community Care Plans, introduced after the National Health Service and Community Care Act, 1990 are "widely variable in the attention given to housing. Those that do include a separate section on housing, or that incorporate housing issues under other headings, tend to focus on three areas: processes of consultation with housing agencies; assessment of housing needs and supply (usually as a plan or intention); and specialist housing projects which have been given or are to be given priority for bids to the Housing Corporation and/or social services revenue funding".*'
> (Watson and Conway, 1995, pp. 10-11)

At the level of the **individual older person** assessment is an obvious area for housing to be brought in. Although some recent research shows that community care assessments often do include housing departments and associations this is usually only where access to public rented housing or to aids and adaptations is the issue (Parker *et al.*, 1998).

It is not just at a policy level that there is a neglect of housing but also among researchers. For example a current research project by the author and others is looking at older people who have moved out owner occupation in old age. Many of these people have subsequently moved into some form of supported accommodation or institutional care. The research on residential or nursing care will sometimes give some indication that moves have taken place because of health reasons. Maybe, if the researcher is lucky, the report will state poor housing but give virtually no other information such as the kind of home let alone the tenure.

Among **professionals** too research shows that there is ignorance about housing, especially options. A study of the housing preferences of people with extra support needs, and the way they gained access to accommodation and support, showed that many of the professionals who were helping relied on specialist rather than mainstream housing and few had had specific training on housing issues. (Hudson *et al.*, 1996). Professionals, however, do face problems such as lack of time and resources as well as organisational issues to do with different planning and organisational cycles (Goss and Kent, 1995).

Why is it so important to bring in housing when discussing the care of vulnerable older people? Three examples of the need to bring in housing are over health. First over temperature, mortality and morbidity there is concern about issues to do with heating of homes. A large national survey of older people found that, despite the increase in central heating, 81% of the respondents had living room temperatures in the morning below those recommended by the World Health Organisation (Salvage, 1993). Substantial proportions had housing problems such as condensation and draughts. But what this study also showed was that as well as the need for policies for more insulation and energy-efficient measures a major problem was an inability to afford heating. Research on housing and health has to go hand in hand with other social policies.

Research by MORI in 1997, commissioned by Anchor Trust, amongst 50 (half of all) Health Authorities in England found that few thought that winter payments to pensioners would have a major impact on cold related deaths of older people (Anchor Trust, 1998). Seventy four per cent felt that the money would be better targeted at those in the worst housing and 54% felt that the money would be better used on home energy checks.

A second example is over **homelessness** where research shows that loss of home, as well as a breakdown in relationships and other factors, contributes to people becoming homeless (Crane, 1990; Crane, 1993; Crane, 1997; Kelling 1991). The link between health and housing is clear here.

Third a major contributory cause to **accidents**, especially falls, is the condition of the home. While it is difficult to disentangle the causes of many accidents, homes that are in poor condition, stairs and uneven surfaces are one of the reasons why older people fall. Falls are the leading cause of accidental death in the over 75s and the main type of non-fatal accident for them is also a fall (Lilley *et al.*, 1995). The consequences of accidents such as falls for older people are physical and mental and may also be a reason for entry into institutional care (Warburton, 1994). (See also 7 in this section.)

The final section will discuss what is being done about this neglect of housing.

2. The importance of home

Recent research endorses the importance of home to older people (Gurney and Means, 1993, Langan *et al.*, 1996; Dupuis and Thorns, 1996). The concept of 'home' as opposed to the bleak terms used by policy makers 'accommodation' or 'dwelling' is increasingly being recognised in the sociology and psychology literature. 'I've got my own front door' must be one of the most quoted statements for those of us who do research on people in their own homes.

Research in 1996 on the meaning of home to older people based on a qualitative study showed the importance of home in terms of security, a refuge, a place where they could express their individuality and above all where they could retain control over their own lives and not be dependent (Means, 1997). The research found that:

> *'Overall these older people were often asking for very modest forms of help in order to maintain their independence and their sense of being "at home" in their present accommodation. And the help required was often outside narrow definitions of community care services with priorities often relating to housing issues and with concerns about mobility and transport.'*
> (Means, 1997, p. 416)

3. Responding to the changing profile of households

There is general awareness about the projected increase in numbers of very elderly people but what must also be taken into account is the trend towards smaller households. In 1995 51% of people aged 75 and over lived alone (Office for National Statistics (ONS), 1997, p. 21) and the implications for the future of very large numbers of very old people living alone must be thought through very carefully. Arising out of this are the housing implications of underoccupation. (See also 5 in this section.)

4. Responding to changes in tenure

One of the most important wider issues about housing where there is currently research activity is over changing tenure patterns in old age. For example the Age Concern Institute of Gerontology (ACIOG) has a programme of both quantitative and qualitative research on the benefits and burdens of owner occupation in old age. Currently 67% of the heads of households are **owner occupiers**, and the figures for those aged 60-64 is 76%, 65-69 67%, 70-79 63% and 80 and over 56% (OPCS, 1996, p. 233). For the coming generation of older people – those aged 45-59 – the figure is 77% (*Ibid*.). The trend to owner occupation among the population has a number of implications for the groups we are concerned with. We know that there is higher satisfaction with this tenure (DOE, 1993; Riseborough and Niner, 1994; Green and Hansbro, 1995) but that there are often problems with upkeep of the home. In a study of home owners and housing repairs it was generally found that while home owners are generally aware of the main problems with their properties older people and those on low incomes were the least aware (Leather *et al.*, 1998). Specific problems identified for older households included on-going diminution of amounts of work undertaken and the neglect of even responsive repair work. At the same time there may be a diminishing DIY capacity and an unwillingness to face disruption. Among the solutions for all home owners it was suggested that there needed to be a raised awareness about the need for and costs of repair and maintenance, more information on the nature of disrepair and ways of dealing with it and ways of making it easier for home-owners to find a trustworthy builder.

One of the most striking potential advantages for home is to release housing equity to pay for long-term care (Hamnett, 1995). A survey of older people who had taken up equity release schemes in 1995 showed that relatively small amounts of additional income was released (an average of £35 per week) (Davey, 1996). However, while this small amount was unlikely to be used for major expenditure on housing repairs or care services, it did make an important contribution to the living standards of the older people. Despite more widespread owner occupation, most of the increase for older people has been for those on middle to high incomes. It is still the case that lower income older people are much less likely to own their own homes than those on high incomes (Hancock, 1998a). In the poorest fifth of the income distribution more than three-quarters of the household population aged 65 and over do not own their own homes and in the next fifth the proportion is nearly 60%. There is not much difference in the proportions of those aged 65-79 and those aged 80+ (Hancock *et al.*, forthcoming). There are therefore significant limits on the extent to which equity release could help the poorest older people. Modelling the potential effect of one type of equity release on older people's income it was found that about 80% of home-owners aged 75 and over could gain something from equity release but the median increase in income would be only just over £1,000 a year (Hancock, 1998b). For many the sums generated would probably be too small to be worthwhile.

One problem for poor owner occupiers who later want to go into some kind of specialised housing, such as sheltered or very sheltered, is that they are still often excluded by local authorities from obtaining this kind of housing (DOE, 1997). Housing associations are more likely to accept owner occupiers.

In the **social rented sector**, local authorities and housing associations, there is a decline in the proportion of older people as tenants. They are still disproportionately represented but there may be great problems in the future with the decline in the number of social housing homes (from 7 million in the UK in 1981 to 5.7 million in 1994 (Wilcox, 1997, p. 85). Past policies of bringing new build in the social rented sector to an almost stop, right-to buy policies and privatisation of much of the housing stock pose serious problems for those who cannot afford to buy. What is going to be the effect of the growing residualisation of this sector? For vulnerable older people the contraction of social housing may mean that they remain in unsuitable housing in the community or in residential care.

The **private rented sector** in Britain is small compared with many European countries. A comparison of five (France, Germany, The Netherlands, Spain and Sweden) based on material from each country and interviews with experts in each one shows that they all subsidise private renting in contrast with Britain (McCrone and Stephens, 1994). It is interesting that very little research in the UK on older people in privately rented property has taken place. But we do know from the *English House Condition Survey* that lone older households are the most likely to live in private housing in the worst condition (DOE, 1993).

5. The design, condition and size of the home

Clearly the **design,** condition and size of the home will have an effect on whether the two groups under discussion can remain there and/or return after a spell in hospital. On the positive side there is some early evidence – but this needs to be done in more detail – that homes that are built to 'lifetime' standards enable people to live there with a range of disabilities and are relatively inexpensive (Bonnet, 1996; Joseph Rowntree Foundation, 1997; Cobbold, 1997). 'Lifetime' means that the home has the potentiality to have adaptations so that someone can remain there for the whole of their lives. There are sixteen standards which include turning circles for wheelchairs in ground floor living rooms, wheelchair accessible downstairs lavatory, ground floor bedspace, level or gently sloping approach to the home and room for a future stair lift. If most housing was designed to this standard, then people who had suffered strokes and/or falls and were left with some physical disability would be able to visit family and friends in these kinds of homes.

Common sense dictates that the absence of a downstairs lavatory may prevent the return to home of someone with impaired physical ability or to remain there. Research indicates that this is indeed the case. For example research on discharge from hospital shows that a hindrance is often home conditions or the absence of an occupational therapist to make an assessment of the home. There is evidence of bed blocking for such reasons.

Both wheelchair and mobility housing also have a role to play for people with severe physical problems (summarised in Tinker, 1997).

The **condition** of homes that some older people live in must give cause for concern. The 1991 *English House Condition Survey* showed that one in five homes in England suffered from dampness, condensation or mould growth and one in 13 was unfit (Leather *et al.*, 1994). In Great Britain the highest proportion of disrepair existed in the private rented sector where about one in five was unfit (Leather and Morrison, 1997). In a major Scottish housing survey it was found that the physical quality of the housing that people occupied was the most important factor in explaining older people's satisfaction with their housing (Wilson *et al.*, 1995). Older people who rented were more likely to be dissatisfied with their accommodation and this was because of the poorer physical conditions rather than the tenure. The main problems which they identified were damp, draughts and defects. How can the groups we are concerned with hope to survive in such conditions? One problem shown by the *English House Condition Survey*, and previously noted from other research, is that home-owners are often unaware of the need for regular maintenance (Leather and Mackintosh, 1995). More information and education of home-owners would help but for the wider problems of poor housing conditions lack of resources may be the determining factor.

There is now extensive research on ways of repairing and improving homes and the value of home improvement agencies such as Care and Repair or Staying Put schemes (e.g. Smart and Means, 1997). The latter give advice and practical assistance to householders to repair and maintain the fabric of their homes. But research also shows that there is a complex system of grants (renovation and home repair) and that most of them are discretionary. Leather, who has done much research on older people and the condition of their homes, suggests that a range of new policies is needed to make best use of public spending and generate more private spending (Leather, 1997). He suggests that the way forward is:

- to end major grants replacing them with loans and some means tested grants;

- to give emergency grants aimed at particular client groups and would be given for health reasons;

- to prevent someone going into care, to enable someone to leave hospital etc.;

- to emphasise prevention by persuading people that they need to save for repairs;

- have greater regulation and control such as vetting schemes run by home improvement;

- agencies and also educating people so that they understand the risks of going for cheap options.

(Leather, 1997)

For those older people who need help with minor repairs a number of schemes have been set up. A pioneering scheme to set up a repair and maintenance service by two housing associations was unable to find ways of subsidising the service through the Social Security system, local authority grants or by equity release schemes (Mackintosh and Leather, 1995). The service failed because potential clients thought that it was too expensive. More successful have been handyperson's schemes for older people. A national study of all schemes which could be identified found that they provided a valuable service (Appleton, 1996). Most of the work done was very minor and was a key component in enabling the older person to remain in their home. The majority of clients were elderly women, living alone and on low incomes. However, demand was usually more than could be met and mainstream funding was difficult to secure.

The **size** of the home is of relevance. Many older people underoccupy and it could be argued that smaller accommodation might be more suitable for those with health problems especially if it is all one level. There is no statutory definition of underoccupation but it is usually defined as having two or more bedrooms above the bedroom standard (Central Statistical Office (CSO), 1996, p. 180). In 1994-95 half of two-person households where one or both were aged 60 or over underoccupied as did one in three single adults of that age (CSO, 1996, p. 180). There is general reluctance to persuade older people to move from a home which they may have occupied for a number of years. However for some it may be the sensible option and the need is for advice, help for those who do want to move and above all for an adequate supply of small accommodation in the right place. In addition policy makers have to take into account the needs of families who are either homeless or overcrowded who need family accommodation. Where this home is in the socially rented sector decisions need to be made *vis-à-vis* the older person and a homeless family with needs for a home of this size. The research agenda cannot solve the ethical problems but it could help by investigating what might help or hinder older people moving.

6. Making use of technology

The kinds of needs which technology might meet include contact, help with personal, domestic and mobility problems and medical (telemedicine). Looking at these in more detail it can be seen that a variety of different ways may be needed.

(a) The need for contact

There are many reasons why older people may wish to contact other people including relatives and professionals. This may be for:

- information (for example to find out what services are available);

- reassurance (for example if they feel vulnerable to intruders);

- emotional/psychological (for example to confide in someone);

- social (to participate or to share an experience – for example to chat to someone);

- practical (for example to ask for a service).

A new area of interest is the use of computers by older people. There are interesting developments both in the UK and elsewhere where older (sometimes very old) people are using computers both to communicate with others and for their own benefit e.g. to write their biographies. These developments may enhance the quality of life and well-being of older people.

(b) Help with personal, domestic and mobility problems

For older people who have problems at home technology can help in a number of ways including the provision of various aids to daily living which involve the manipulation of objects:

- nutrition (for personal help to aid eating and drinking and cooking);

- hygiene aids (for personal washing/bathing/showering or with the laundry);

- mobility (such as help to get up from a chair);

- environmental (help to open and close doors and windows).

(see Cullen and Moran, 1992, p. 36).

(c) Medical

The use of telemedicine is included in this heading and can be used for diagnosis, treatment and rehabilitation. It is used much more for obstetrics at the moment but systems that allow for monitoring medical conditions without the person having to go to the doctor or him/her to have to visit could be immense. For example it is suggested that 'Very small hand held devices allow patients to record their own ECGs when they suffer pain or arrhythmia. This can be transmitted by telephone to a monitoring centre' (Institute of Health Services Management, 1998, p. 11). Other measurements could include temperature, respiration rates, breathing patterns, restlessness etc. Community nursing services have also been established via the home television so that a video can help the nurse to monitor or advise a patient and to give advice (*Ibid.*). Another use is for professionals to consult one another, for example a GP could ask the opinion of a consultant about a patient's condition without him or her having to go to hospital. Yet another use is for patients to have access to skilled professional advice.

Recent research on telemedicine and telecare shows that its development would enable more people both to remain in their own home and/or not to be admitted to hospital (*Ibid.*). The important wider issue of empowering patients and giving them better information is also stressed. But the research also sounds a word of caution about a number of issues including:

- patient confidentiality and data protection;

- unclear legal issues;

- lack of agreed technical standards;

- a lack of economic evaluation;

- no clear agreement on funding responsibilities.

(d) Issues to do with the use of alarms, telephones and smart houses

Alarms and telephones are the most common ways in which technology is used. *Alarms* have the potential for use in emergencies, for reassurance, as sensors (passive alarms), for environmental monitoring, intruder alert, for bodily monitoring and electronic tagging (Butler, 1989). After the early research on alarms and telephones there is now need for more evidence about the value of these ways of enabling vulnerable people to get in touch with others. The early research showed reluctance of older people to use alarms, and sometimes phones, but a more ready use would allow someone to stay at, or return to, their own home. Research now shows that most alarms work reasonably well (*Which*, March 1997).

It is estimated that alarms are installed in the homes of over one million people in the UK (Riseborough, 1997). The Calling for Help group estimate that 300,000 of these people live in mainstream housing in all tenures (Calling for Help Group, 1994). Riseborough's recent study comprised information from 2,243 older people and 554 staff involved in the schemes. Few people used the alarms for life and death situations, and still fewer because they were lonely or isolated. But they were used for everyday emergencies and, in areas where there was a lot of crime, calls were common. They were also used when care arrangements broke down. The research indicates that there is need to define the purpose of the alarms and to give practical demonstrations and information to older people and staff. It was also found that the alarm centres were often providing other services such as out of hours repairs services. A series of helpful recommendations were produced including the need to have much more of a consumer focus, such as by involving them in monitoring performance and standards. A code of practice for alarm providers was also suggested.

Currently 98% of households where one or both adults are aged 60 or over and 90% where there is one adult aged 60 or over in GB have a *telephone* (ONS, 1997, p. 41). The future use of mobile phones by an older generation may prove of immense use and will not have the stigma which is often associated with alarms.

'*Smart*' (sometimes called intelligent) *homes* are rare and usually only provided as demonstration models. For example Edinvar housing association has a demonstration flat in Edinburgh which shows a range of 'smart' technology (Edinvar, 1998). It has numerous mechanisms that operate windows, curtains and doors and a video entryphone system. But it also has equipment that will, for example, track the movements of the occupant or give audible reminders of important times or dates.

There is a limited use for technology for people with dementia but research abroad is beginning to show the potential for some schemes e.g. for them to use a phone by pressing a button which has a picture of the daughter instead of a number. The potentiality of passive alarms e.g. that alert someone when the older person has fallen or has failed to get out of bed for a period is immense. But so are the ethical issues.

7. Specific issues to do with older people who are recovering from acute episodes of ill health including issues to do with hospital discharge

There is particular interest in older people who are recovering from acute episodes of ill health such as a stroke or broken bones through falling at home (and see also 1 in this section). Most of these will have received treatment or surgery in hospital. A large national study of the hospital discharge of older people found that 'almost all had lived in their present accommodation for many years, wished to remain there and had roots in the local community' (Neill and Williams, 1992, p. 154).

Looking at the causes of accidents helps an understanding of potential hazards for anyone recovering from an acute episode of ill health and for those who are discharged from hospital. A number of studies have shown that over one third of falls to elderly people in the community are caused by **environmental factors** (Lilley *et al.*, 1995). These include poor lighting, uneven surfaces and floor hazards. However there remains a dearth of research on the association between falls and housing circumstances (Askham *et al.*, 1990). Some recent research provides only very limited evidence that home hazards are an important cause of fractures and falls (Clemson *et al.*, 1996). The authors call for large randomised trials of home assessment and modifications. A professional consensus at a recent World

Conference on Injuries and Accidents (Amsterdam, May 1998) concluded that while older people may become accustomed to hazards in their own home they posed real risks to the carers. In the absence of conclusive evidence about the kinds of environmental hazards that cause falls an overview of research concludes:

'Home visiting to identify and remedy environmental and personal risks for falling may reduce the risk of falling. The type of safety changes could include removal of throw rugs and objects in pathways, and installation of improved night lights and bath non-skid mats. Visits could also be carried out by health visitors, nurses, occupational therapists, or trained volunteers'.

(Nuffield Institute for Health/NHS Centre for Reviews and Dissemination, 1996, p. 6)

What needs to be done first is an **assessment** of the person to see what changes are needed in the home. A study of assessment of housing needs showed that these often did not take place on discharge from short-stay hospitals and that medical staff tended to assume that a residential care or nursing home would be the most appropriate placement (Parker *et al.*, 1998). Most research identifies the occupational therapist as the key professional involved in the assessment of housing needs (e.g. Allen *et al.*, 1998). The value of multi-disciplinary assessment is widely recognised and this includes the facility of home adaptation 'without undue delay' (British Geriatrics Society *et al.*, 1995). Delays, especially where there is a shortage of occupational therapists, cause bed blocking as well as distress to the older person. While there may be doubt about the relative importance of the home environment as a cause of accidents (see also Parker *et al.*, 1996) attention should be paid to the condition of the home before a patient is discharged from hospital. For example it may be necessary to install a downstairs lavatory or a grab rail. If this cannot be done the person may remain in hospital for longer than necessary. This should be followed by any necessary modification to the home including the provision of **aids and adaptations**.

The Department of Health's Hospital Discharge Workbook states clearly in their check list:

'16. Have any aids and adaptations required by a patient been supplied prior to discharge, and the patient trained in their use?

19. Have arrangements been made to prepare an individual's home prior to their return from hospital?'
(Henwood, 1994).

Research has highlighted the value of aids and adaptations in enabling older people with disabilities to remain in their own homes and that comparatively minor aids and adaptations could make a great deal of difference to people with reduced mobility (Age Concern London 1995a). Research in London found that there was remarkably little reference to the role of local authority housing departments although the role of aids and adaptations was acknowledged (Age Concern London, 1995b).

Speed is of the essence with adaptations and the provision of aids. There is evidence from a number of studies (e.g. Neill and Williams, 1992; Parker *et al.*,

1998) that community care is hindered by the length of time that people have to wait for adaptations and aids. This has serious cost and other implications. The older person may never return to their home as is the case with many stroke patients. As Bond has pointed out almost one-third of patients with a new stroke are discharged to long-term care (Bond, 1998). Although a similar figure is not available for older people who fall and break bones the seriousness for both the faller and carers is well known (Lilley *et al.*, 1995).

The combination of assessment, the provision of appropriate aids and adaptations must be matched by **rehabilitation.** This is illustrated in a recent study of people with a stroke who are discharged from hospital (Ungerson and Baldock, 1994). In a number of cases the problems were purely practical. For example one women discharged with a walking frame found that she could not use it with a carpet; she also needed the lavatory lowering. Instead of helping with these problems the local authority provided a community nurse, a care assistant, an alarm and regular visits to a day hospital, day centre and lunch club. She then lost her remaining mobility partly because she no longer did anything for herself. This case study is borne out by the study by the Leeds Nuffield Institute which found that the lack of real rehabilitation led to solutions which created dependency rather than restoring people's self-care capacity and independence (Nuffield Institute for Health, 1997). This shows the interdependence of services for good housing has to go hand in hand with other services.

The growing emphasis on rehabilitation after a stroke at home has raised important questions which includes issues to do with the home and its possible unsuitability (Young and Gladman, 1995). But this overview of research also illustrates the importance of assessing all the factors together. For example the authors say of home-based rehabilitation provision:

> *'The potential advantages are that it involves no uncomfortable travel for the patient, there is greater opportunity for involvement of family and other community staff in a more flexible process of care. The disadvantages are that the therapist may be professionally isolated, there may be difficulty in forming and sustaining a multidisciplinary rehabilitation team, patients may be housebound and denied the social contact of the hospital rehabilitation department, the intensity of treatment may be insufficient and the home environment and/or lack of specialist equipment may be restrictive.'*
> (Young and Gladman, 1995, p. 334)

The key role of rehabilitation is also emphasised in the Audit Commission report *United they Stand: Co-ordinating Care for Elderly Patients with Hip Fractures* (Audit Commission, 1995). Discussing the various models of rehabilitation they look at early supported discharge where the key is the home. They say:

> *'Only home based rehabilitation services, such as hospital at home or early discharge schemes, offer patients the opportunity to learn to cope in their usual surroundings. This is important; there is a huge difference between the hospital environment with even floors, wide corridors and specially designed, spacious kitchens, and people's own homes with obstacles and limited space. Patients and carers are very aware of the practical problems.'*
> (Audit Commission, 1995 p. 44)

More recent research has shown that progress on hospital discharge has been patchy and problems have included the lack of NHS rehabilitation facilities which has resulted in 'inappropriate and avoidable placements in residential and nursing homes' (Nuffield Institute for Health, 1997). Although not explicitly stated the assumption is that with rehabilitation people would have been enabled to return home. Another study of older people discharged from hospital showed that older people often devised ways themselves of coping with their disabilities who may be less concerned with safety and more with retaining some control over their lives (Clark *et al.*, 1996). This study also showed the dramatic changes that can take place, for good or ill, after discharge. These may be changes in functional ability, confidence or the availability of care. This points to the need for the need to follow up these people after discharge and for reassessment.

Apart from ensuring that any necessary adaptations are done promptly the case for some **interim kind of housing** needs to be examined. While many older people may go to stay temporarily with a family member the role of other kinds of housing is worth considering. For example a study of very sheltered housing found that the provision of one or two flats in a scheme either for people to have a trial stay or to convalesce after coming out of hospital was valuable (Tinker, 1989). The major problem was the lack of full-time night staff. However, attempts to use short-term residential care or nursing homes for rehabilitation have proved problematic (Nuffield Institute for Health, 1997). Research on appropriate settings for particular groups of older people would be helpful.

Hospital at home services, where a patient is cared for at home by a team of nurses and other medical staff instead of occupying a hospital bed, are becoming of interest to commissioning agencies. Recent and ongoing research, however, advocates caution and suggests that the costs may not be less than hospital in care (Hensher *et al.*, 1996; Iliffe, 1997).

8. Specific issues to do with older people who have long-standing or degenerative conditions

There is also interest in those who have long-standing or degenerative conditions such as depression or dementia where, it is suggested in the Briefing Paper, many of these people will have received treatment in hospital. It is the large numbers of older people with long-standing or degenerative diseases that pose the problem rather than the fact that they may have received treatment in hospital. Indeed as the paper by Banerjee (1998) suggests only 10-20% of older people with depression appear to be referred to psychiatric services at any time during their lives.

A Social Services Inspectorate report *Older People with Mental Health Problems Living Alone* has a welcome chapter on housing which emphasises the need for housing that is safe, secure, comfortable, accessible and preferably somewhere which will remain suitable even if health deteriorates (Barnes, 1997). The Dementia Services Development Centre at the University of Stirling has produced advice on design. For older people with depression and dementia the vast majority will live in the community by themselves or with family, often spouses, members. For those that cannot, very sheltered housing has been shown to be a satisfactory alternative (Tinker, 1989; Kitwood *et al.*, 1995). However, research by the Bradford Dementia

Group suggests that residential care may be more appropriate when the following three factors occur in combination:

- severe physical illness in addition to dementia which needs intensive nursing care;

- no support from family and friends in the local community or scheme;

- limited access to social services.

(Kitwood *et al.*, 1995).

KEY RESEARCH FINDINGS WHICH INFORM THE DEVELOPMENT OF THE POLICY AND PRACTICE AGENDA FOR THE CARE OF OLDER PEOPLE AND KEY MESSAGES FOR POLICY AND PRACTICE — SPECIFIC KINDS OF SUPPORTED ACCOMMODATION

1. General points

A disproportionate amount of research which has been specifically on older people and their housing has been on specialised accommodation. This is partly because it is easier to do, i.e. locate people and get access, also partly because a great deal of recent research has been sponsored by housing associations – mainly Anchor who have an outstanding record of funding and undertaking research.

2. Support in mainstream housing

As stated earlier a strict interpretation of supported housing might not include mainstream as opposed to specialised housing. But it has been included because that is where 95% of the older population live and the degree of support can be considerable. This support can come from formal or informal sources. Very little research has been undertaken on people who were highly dependent being supported in homes of their own. In the early 1980s a study undertaken for DOE with co-operation from DOH *Staying at Home: Helping Elderly People* (Tinker, 1984) did look at this and showed very dependent older people being kept at home with a variety of what were then called innovatory schemes such as intensive home care and personal alarms. But what it also showed was that it was the package of care which included the housing circumstances that was important. There remains a need for good basic health and social support services.

'Floating support' has proved to be popular with older people and with other groups. The concept is that support services are provided to people in their own home and then if (or when) they no longer need it it 'floats' to another user (Morris, 1995; Douglas *et al.*, 1998). The support is for the person and is not tied, as it often is in sheltered housing, to the property. The housing support worker provided a range of practical, emotional and moral support and the people receiving it may also receive other kinds of help such as domestic or personal. It is designed to sustain a tenancy. The main reasons for developing floating support schemes were held to be:

- *'to support people moving on from a general needs scheme into general needs;*

- *accommodation to prevent a breakdown of the tenancy;*

- *as an alternative to traditional special needs housing schemes;*

- *for those in general needs accommodation who develop a need for intensive housing;*

- *as part of general diversification as development opportunities for housing associations decrease.'*

(Morris, 1995, p. 1)

Schemes were originally provided by housing associations with revenue funding from the Housing Corporation, Housing for Wales and Scottish Homes for short-term needs but schemes are now more extensive.

Support in mainstream housing may include the older person living with a family. A recent small piece of work here has shown some of the advantages but also the tensions (Healy and Yarrow, 1997). There are also home sharing schemes whereby an older person allows a younger one to live with them in return for some support (*Exchange on Ageing, Law and Ethics (EAGLE)*, 1997). There has, however, been little evaluation to date.

(See also 4 in the first section for a discussion of repairs and adaptations.)

3. Sheltered and very sheltered housing

For those who want to move sheltered housing is an option. Sheltered housing is schemes which have units of accommodation (flats or bungalows) with a resident or non-resident warden and an alarm system. Communal facilities such as a common room, laundry room or a guest room must also be provided. In England out of a total of 641,494 units of subsidised (i.e. local authority and housing association) 51% was sheltered (McCafferty, 1994). Very sheltered or extra care housing has a greater level of provision or care than sheltered. In addition to sheltered housing there may be, for example, meals, extra wardens, care assistants and additional communal facilities such as special bathrooms, sluice rooms etc. This kind of accommodation represents 2% of subsidised special accommodation, compared with 51% conventional sheltered, but was said to be the fastest growing form of provision (McCafferty, 1994).

Five per cent of people aged 65 and over in Great Britain lived in sheltered housing in 1994 and a further 5% lived in housing with a non-resident warden (OPCS, 1996, p. 157).

This most recent very large and important DOE research on both staying at home options and the different kinds of sheltered show that there are some very dependent old people living in this type of accommodation (McCafferty, 1994). Key findings are:

- high levels of overall satisfaction with this form of housing (borne out by much other research, e.g. Riseborough and Niner, 1994);

- there are some people who are living in schemes that give a lot of support but who appear to have little physical or mental incapacity (also found in Tinker, 1989);

- one in five would have preferred to have stayed in their own home and not to have moved;

- (similar proportions have been found in other studies e.g. Tinker, 1989);

- some older people had been enabled to move out of institutional settings (some of these must fall into the categories that form the focus of this study);

- there is a shortfall in the provision of very sheltered housing which is a cost effective option but is more expensive than sheltered or staying at home *unless the costs of informal care are taken into account*. If the latter is done then staying at home is more expensive than sheltered but cheaper than very sheltered.

Previous research using the same methodology which involved a large national survey of all housing authorities in England and Wales *An Evaluation of Very Sheltered Housing* (Tinker, 1989) had shown the value of very sheltered housing. When the costings were done then it was cheaper than residential care. More research is needed on costings and some of this is now being undertaken by the author and colleagues for the Royal Commission on Long Term Care. (See the Main Report of this volume.)

A problem which is only just beginning to be acknowledged is that of difficult to let sheltered and very sheltered housing (Tinker *et al.*, 1995). For example one-third of sheltered housing in the London Borough of Islington was difficult to let in 1998. The reasons for schemes becoming difficult to let are complex and include an inappropriate location, bedsitters rather than a separate bedroom and shared facilities such as bathrooms. Some of the solutions include ones that would be appropriate for the groups we are considering such as turning sheltered into very sheltered but the boundaries between what is housing and what is very like an institution needs careful thought. Other solutions to difficult to let such as bringing in younger people such as men with mental health or alcohol problems have been disastrous for schemes. If whole unpopular schemes were changed to meet special needs that could be useful although careful thought has to go into what happens to the existing tenants. For schemes to be used for frail elderly people a useful appraisal guide has been produced which suggests key issues such as accessibility, design and space standards, services and staff standards (National Housing Federation, 1996).

The dilemma of upgrading unsatisfactory schemes to very sheltered housing is that 'the loss of the sheltered housing may well have consequences in increased demand for domiciliary care, aids and adaptations elsewhere' (Watson and Britain, 1996, p. 90).

Another development which could help would be a greater use by outsiders of communal facilities. This sometimes takes the form of a day centre for older people or allowing the use of special baths. However research shows that there may be problems with existing tenants feeling that their space (home) is being invaded. This was shown to be the case in very sheltered housing (Tinker, 1989) and in a subsequent study of residential care homes (Wright, 1996). A great deal of sensitivity must be exercised when people from outside use communal facilities and some degree of physical separation between the two groups may be necessary.

An example of a housing association which has taken seriously both the problems and potentiality of sheltered housing is Housing 21. In *Remodelling Sheltered Housing* strong arguments are put for remodelling the buildings as well as changing support (Trotter *et al.*, 1997). The main one is so that tenants can remain in their own home in the scheme for life 'without suffering the trauma of moving into residential or nursing accommodation, which some will not survive' (Trotter and Phillips, 1997, p. 7). On the remodelling of buildings the authors argue that changes can take place in the approach, entrance and general layout, the internal layout and the court facilities. In addition staff, particularly wardens, need to be equipped to work more holistically and proactively with and for older people.

The role of wardens is crucial if frail elderly people are to live in sheltered or very sheltered housing (Fletcher, 1991, Fletcher and Gillie, 1991). Seen originally as good neighbours their role has undergone a dramatic change partly in response to the growing needs of tenants but also to the increased professionalism of wardens. In general it seems to be agreed that the warden should be the enabler rather than the provider of services and should have close links with other services. Whatever the role there needs to be clarity about it. Issues to do with who employs the warden i.e. housing or social services for local authority schemes. Useful Codes of Practice have been developed (Centre for Sheltered Housing Studies, 1993; Knight, 1992). Salutary advice is given in one of these codes about the rights of older people including taking risks, not always being sensible, to have privacy and dignity and the right to refuse services (Knight, 1992, p. 5).

4. Granny flats

The only large piece of research on granny flats was undertaken in 1980 (Tinker, 1980). They were all in the public (local authority) sector. While popular with families and the older relative there were a number of problems including what happens when the older person dies or the family move. The potentiality of having a frail older person living by the family yet not in the family home mean that both can have their privacy but help is on hand for both. The reciprocal nature of arrangements should not be taken lightly for they can give a role to the older person if not in baby-sitting but taking in parcels etc.

A small recent research on the private sector showed that there were likely to be fewer problems of one kind but more of others. For example the family can use the granny flat for renting out, an au pair or for other family members when the older person moves out or dies. On the other hand there can be potential legal, financial and planning problems (Morton, 1993). Although there is international interest in granny flats (Lazarowich, 1991) more up to date research is badly needed.

5. Hostels

Among the distinguishing features of hostels are that the accommodation:

- must not be intended for use by residents on a permanent basis;

- is likely to contain some shared facilities;

- is likely to have a degree of support at least equal to intensive housing management.

(Department of the Environment, 1996).

The focus has been mainly on homeless people.

There is very little research on hostels for older people. However, it is held that hostels can play a role both in their own right for isolated people and for people who need supervision and support (e.g. people with dementia) and as a breathing space for people who have gone through some kind of crisis (Cooper *et al.*, 1994). This research, which included Abbeyfield homes, found that the main advantages for the residents was support as sanctuary, as a buffer, as control and as a safety net (Cooper *et al.*, 1994). Two-thirds of the residents mentioned factors in addition to housing need which influenced their move into this form of housing. For older people the availability of staff support was highlighted. The vast majority of elderly residents wanted to stay in their accommodation indefinitely.

6. Grouped living

We should also consider informal arrangements whereby people can live in housing and support themselves in a variety of ways. For example research is currently being undertaken on older women who choose to live together in old age (Brenton, 1997).

7. Retirement communities

A relatively new concept in the UK is that of retirement communities. This is where a number of different kinds of accommodation are included on one site which is exclusively for older people. There may be mainstream housing, sheltered, residential care and a nursing home. In theory all the care that is needed until death is available on one site. The older person can move through the different options and remain in the same community. These communities are more common in the United States of America and Australia than here. A few such schemes have been established here by charities or professional bodies but no systematic evaluation has been carried out.

GENERAL CONCLUSIONS AND KEY MESSAGES FOR POLICY MAKERS

Housing, like much of social policy, has fashions. What would now be tragic would be for there to be a fashion for a particular kind of housing. Even the current emphasis on keeping everyone in their own homes is similar to that in the 1970s when sheltered housing was seen if not as the panacea at least as the preferred option of many old people. What there is especial need for is to consider the next generation of older people as well as the current. The needs of this generation are of course of paramount importance but planning has to take account of those who are now in their 50s, 60s and 70s. This includes such things as their health e.g. will women have better health because of all the emphasis on healthy eating, drinking and exercise or will they be less healthy because of the increase in smoking etc.

1. Housing and improving housing conditions must be taken seriously as part of preventive strategies

There is clear need to put housing at the top of the agenda when it comes to decisions about frail older people of the kind we are discussing to see how they can have their housing made better or allowing (sometimes encouraging) them to move somewhere more appropriate. At the macro level there is need for

Government Departments to consider whether and when housing should be brought in. 'Think housing' would be a good motto for the Millennium. At local level there is even less excuse not to consider housing because there is explicit advice that community care plans must involve housing departments and associations. At an individual level professionals also need to 'think housing' and especially the older person's own home before a knee jerk suggestion of residential care – or even sheltered housing is made.

In the discussion about people who fall and have strokes it was seen that some older people are unable to return to their homes after such an incident. Obviously there are many reasons for this but the absence of suitable housing is likely to be one.

At a major level of improving housing renovation may be needed yet recent research has shown that the number of grants for renovation has dropped to one-third of the level of the early 1980s and may drop even further with pressure on local authority budgets (Leather and Morrison, 1997).

The Housing Corporation have referred to 'the crucial importance of adaptations in maintaining older people's ability to live independently' and the need for the process to be streamlined (Housing Corporation, 1996, p. 29). Research based on statistical returns by the Department of the Environment, the Welsh Office, the Housing Corporation and Care and Repair, England together with a detailed study of 50 local authorities in England and Wales showed that there was much unmet need for adaptations with about one-third of applicants to local authorities dropping out before receiving any assistance (Heywood and Smart, 1996). Others were put off by not knowing that services existed, by informal means testing and by information designed to discourage applicants from even inquiring (*Ibid.*). This research also highlighted the complexity of the grant system with both social services and housing departments having some responsibilities but that the latter had borne the brunt of the increased demand and expenditure without any extra financial help from central government. Demand for adaptations has increased by 15% per year since 1990 and, although a shortage of occupational therapists was a factor in delaying assessments, the major problem was shortage of capital by both housing and social services. Small or medium range adaptations were the most common with hoists becoming increasingly popular. It would, therefore, seem that a relatively small amount of money might allow people to remain at or return home.

2. There must be choice in housing and a recognition that different groups of older people may have different needs

Much of the research on older people who move into another form of housing and/or care shows that they often do so at short notice and on the advice of their family or a professional such as the doctor. The lack of choice is often striking. The Housing Corporation maintain that 'There are strong arguments for retaining a variety of provision both to offer choice to service users, and because some housing options may be more appropriate for a particular household than others' (Housing Corporation, 1996, p. 4). While there cannot obviously be lots of different kinds of housing built which then lies empty waiting for someone to make a choice there is one factor from another field of research (on housing demand) that has relevance. That is the forecasts about future demographic patterns and the likely demand for housing (see 5 in this section). Choice also means between living in a community with people of all ages and in one which is exclusively for older people. Private provision is likely to increase. The choice between different types of social housing is rarely one for the individual but the main growth is in housing association provision compared with local authorities (Watson and Cooper, 1992; Tinker, 1997).

Policies also need to be sensitive to different groups of older people for example women (more likely to be disabled, dissatisfied and poorly housed – but more research is needed) and people from black and ethnic minorities.

3. The views of older people must be taken more seriously

One of the most important themes of community care is that of the involvement of consumers. This is not only at an individual level, as indicated in the section above, but also over wider issues of policy. There is now a growing body of research on how older people can be brought into decision making in a variety of services (see Tinker, 1997 for a summary) but also specifically over housing. One recent piece of research *Sharing power: integrating user involvement and multi-agency working to improve housing for older people* involved workshops with older people, and others, to identify an 'ideal' housing system for older people (Midgley *et al.*, 1997). Groups of managers from the statutory agencies then responded and a template for designing multi-agency systems for local use was produced.

In another piece of research *The Right Home: Assessing Housing Needs in Community Care* the researchers found that there were wide differences in user involvement (Allen *et al.*, 1998).

> *'We found examples where professionals decided on the appropriate form of shelter and used various techniques to ensure that this was implemented, despite opposition from the people themselves. Assessors sometimes set the terms of the assessment and marginalised the input from the people being assessed. Nevertheless, we also came across examples where assessors went to considerable lengths to ensure that people achieved their desired outcome even when this was considered to be inappropriate according to professional criteria.'*
> (Allen *et al.*, 1998, p. 71)

4. Older people need advice and support when making decisions about whether to stay in their own home or to move

The need for advice comes out in many research projects although this is often more oblique than explicit. A decision is often made quickly for example when someone has had a fall or is in hospital when it is suddenly realised that their home is unsuitable to return to. Care must be given to advice over options. Ideally of course everyone should be thinking about the possibilities of being disabled in some way and what can or cannot be done to an existing home or whether a move is the right answer.

5. There is need for the provision of a full range of the different types of housing and for some clarity about the role and limits of different kinds of housing/care

The need for good ordinary small accommodation is made even more important by the projected rise in the numbers of single person households (CSO, 1996, pp. 50-51). Holmans has assessed the effects of population ageing, mortality and migration and other factors (Holmans, 1995a and 1995b). He has estimated a need for a little under a quarter of a million additional new homes in England between 1991–2011. There has been a dramatic decline in housebuilding in Great Britain from a peak in 1968 (ONS, 1998, p. 171). Perhaps more surprising 'given the growth in the number of single-person households, is the reduction in the number of one-bedroomed dwellings being built' (ONS, 1998, p. 182). There is a strong case for two-bedroom accommodation for frail older people including the need for a carer to sleep there sometimes.

Holmans maintains that there will be a slower rate of growth of owner occupation because of uncertain incomes, more mortgage defaults and fewer local authority and housing association tenants being able to afford to buy even under right to buy terms. He estimated the need for the provision of additional social housing to the tune of 90,000 a year in 1991–2001 and 100,000 a year in 2001–2011. The case for more very sheltered housing has already been made.

For older people who need some kind of supported accommodation Watson and Conway (1995) suggest the following:

- temporary supported accommodation with clear access to mainstream housing;

- long-term supported housing (both self-contained and shared);

- direct access into mainstream tenancies, with support as required;

- support services which are independent of specific types of accommodation.

The case for more very sheltered housing is strong although current provision is unequal across the country (McCafferty, 1994). Advice is given in a National Federation of Housing Associations report (Fletcher, 1991 that there should be more provision for frailer tenants including those who are from residential, nursing and long-stay hospitals as long as there is adequate back-up care. Evidence from the DOE study (McCafferty, 1994) shows that a higher proportion of sheltered housing tenants came from these forms of care than in a previous study (Tinker, 1989).

While it may not be possible to define exactly what every sheltered housing scheme should provide it is essential that each scheme is clear about what it provides and the limits. If there are unreal expectations by staff, families and older people this is not helpful to older people who are housed inappropriately (e.g. if people are discharged from hospital to the 'care' of a warden whose role it may not be).

6. There is a lack of knowledge about costs of alternative packages of care

DOE and DOH undertook costings of the alternative types of housing/care in the 1980s and this included staying at home with a package of care, sheltered and very sheltered housing, residential care and hospitals (Tinker, 1984). These were updated in the later study of very sheltered housing (Tinker, 1989). In the recent DOE study only staying at home and sheltered/very sheltered housing were costed. There is urgent need to update these and to include nursing homes. Whether informal costs should be added is another issue. Costings of some alternative packages of care to institutions have been undertaken by the author and colleagues for the Royal Commission on Long Term Care of Elderly People and are in Part 1 of this volume.

7. A co-ordinated approach both at a macro and a micro level is essential

There is now a growing literature about co-ordination although much of it still focuses on health and social care. It shows that inter-agency working is still very limited, different planning and funding cycles are unhelpful, there is still a lack of understanding of the roles of each organisation and that there are different backgrounds and stereotypes of the various professionals involved (see Tinker, 1997 for a summary, also Arnold *et al.*, 1993; Goss and Kent, 1995; Arblaster *et al.*, 1996; Watson, 1997; Means 1998). The recent Audit Commission report *Home Alone: The Role of Housing in Community Care* shows that too many people are falling through the net because of poor collaboration betwen housing, health and social services (Audit Commission, 1998). As indicated previously there needs to be a co-ordinated approach to planning both at the level of policy and practice and at the case management level.

Official policy is that there is need for co-ordination at all levels as the circular Housing and Community Care makes clear (DOE/DOH, 1992). The more recent *Housing and Community Care: Establishing a Strategic Framework* (DOH/DOE, 1997) and *Making Partnerships Work in Community Care: A guide for practitioners in housing, health and social services* (Means *et al.*, 1997) makes this even more explicit. However, no new money has been identified and the lack of carrots and sticks is apparent in the recent Audit Commission report (1998). One of the members of the Advisory Group for that Audit Commission report argues that while much progress has been made, there is need for a much stronger national framework under the auspices of an inter-departmental cabinet committee chaired by a cabinet minister (Fletcher, 1998) (now set up). He also argues for a much stronger set of national outcome standards which local authorities would have to comply with before resources were made available.

At a local level research shows that inter-agency collaboration between housing, health and social services is difficult to achieve and that housing is often excluded (Arblaster *et al.*, 1996). This research identified important factors in this collaboration:

- resources: the need for more good quality social rented housing, more flexible funding and a firmer financial footing for voluntary bodies;

- clarifying the roles of each sector;

- understanding other agencies;

- communication between agencies.

What may be helpful now is both some kind of financial carrot but also practical examples such as Heywood's *Managing Adaptations: Positive ideas for social services* (1996). Imaginative ways of seconding staff between the various agencies and well as joint departments and joint budgets may be helpful. The Chartered Institute of Housing's Good Practice Guide was based on visits to eight local authority areas in England. Case studies were then carried out in these and other areas known to be developing a joint strategic approach to housing and community care for all groups i.e. not just for elderly people. The research identifies the strategic issues at two levels: the *infrastructure* of accommodation and support services and the mechanisms by which people gain access to housing and support (Watson and Conway, 1995). In more detail they suggest six key elements in a comprehensive strategy. They are:

(a) New and additional housing	**(d) Support to individuals**
<ul><li>bids for new capital;</li><li>capital land from local or health authorities;</li><li>increased use of existing properties;</li><li>use of private sector capital/property.</li></ul>	<ul><li>individual care packages;</li><li>domiciliary and home support services;</li><li>resettlement and tenant support;</li><li>staff attached to housing schemes;</li><li>user managed support;</li><li>housing advocacy and advice.</li></ul>
(b) Property related services	**(e) Housing access and allocations**
<ul><li>house adaptations;</li><li>home improvement services;</li><li>community alarm services;</li><li>furnishings and equipment.</li></ul>	<ul><li>organisation of waiting lists;</li><li>allocation and nomination policies;</li><li>'move-on' policies and practices;</li><li>policies on homeless acceptances.</li></ul>
(c) Conversion and upgrading of property	**(f) Transition agreements**
<ul><li>upgrading to provide individual facilities;</li><li>conversion/extension for extra care;</li><li>improvement of private sector properties.</li></ul>	<ul><li>hospital discharge;</li><li>social services needs assessment;</li><li>acceptance as homeless and vulnerable.</li></ul>

Their strategy for independent living is illustrated in Figures 1 and 2.

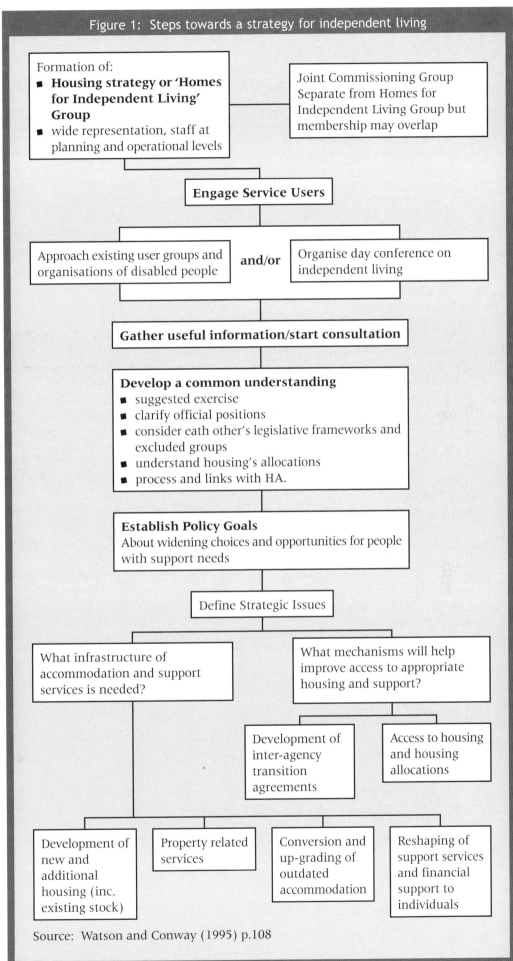

Figure 1: Steps towards a strategy for independent living

Formation of:
- **Housing strategy or 'Homes for Independent Living' Group**
- wide representation, staff at planning and operational levels

Joint Commissioning Group Separate from Homes for Independent Living Group but membership may overlap

Engage Service Users

Approach existing user groups and organisations of disabled people

and/or

Organise day conference on independent living

Gather useful information/start consultation

Develop a common understanding
- suggested exercise
- clarify official positions
- consider eath other's legislative frameworks and excluded groups
- understand housing's allocations
- process and links with HA.

Establish Policy Goals
About widening choices and opportunities for people with support needs

Define Strategic Issues

What infrastructure of accommodation and support services is needed?

What mechanisms will help improve access to appropriate housing and support?

Development of inter-agency transition agreements

Access to housing and housing allocations

Development of new and additional housing (inc. existing stock)

Property related services

Conversion and up-grading of outdated accommodation

Reshaping of support services and financial support to individuals

Source: Watson and Conway (1995) p.108

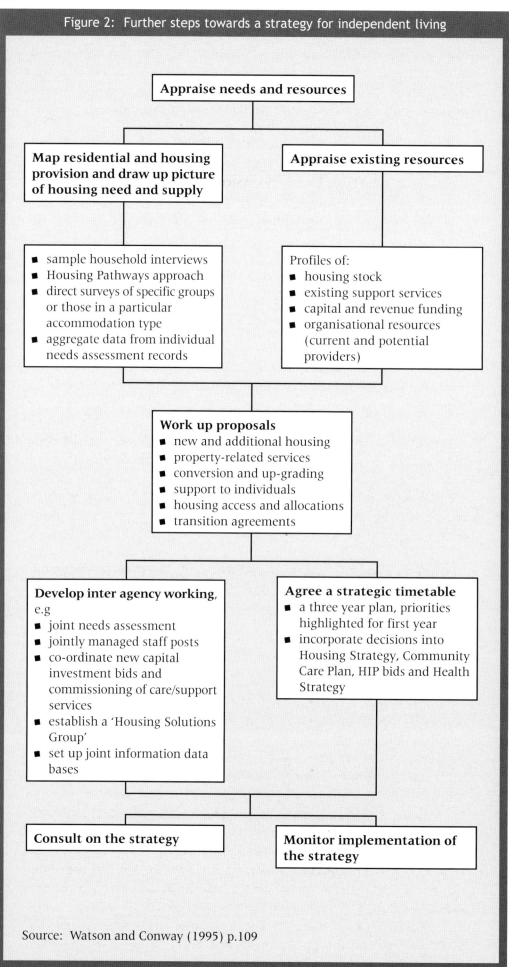

Figure 2: Further steps towards a strategy for independent living

Appraise needs and resources

Map residential and housing provision and draw up picture of housing need and supply

Appraise existing resources

- sample household interviews
- Housing Pathways approach
- direct surveys of specific groups or those in a particular accommodation type
- aggregate data from individual needs assessment records

Profiles of:
- housing stock
- existing support services
- capital and revenue funding
- organisational resources (current and potential providers)

Work up proposals
- new and additional housing
- property-related services
- conversion and up-grading
- support to individuals
- housing access and allocations
- transition agreements

Develop inter agency working, e.g
- joint needs assessment
- jointly managed staff posts
- co-ordinate new capital investment bids and commissioning of care/support services
- establish a 'Housing Solutions Group'
- set up joint information data bases

Agree a strategic timetable
- a three year plan, priorities highlighted for first year
- incorporate decisions into Housing Strategy, Community Care Plan, HIP bids and Health Strategy

Consult on the strategy

Monitor implementation of the strategy

Source: Watson and Conway (1995) p.109

Nor must the contribution of other services be forgotten. It should also be emphasised that housing is only one element in older people's ability to stay at home. A high standard of basic services such as access to good primary and acute care is essential. So is access to support services such as home care although these need not necessarily be provided by the statutory sector. Although innovations in provision must be encouraged this should not be at the exclusion of basic services.

Income levels have an obvious effect on fuel policies, transport and leisure on the ability of frail older people to get out etc. It is outside the scope of this paper to comment extensively on the Benefits System but it should be noted that Housing Benefit is of crucial importance in community care policies for vulnerable people of all ages (see especially Griffiths, 1995; 1997). In a study of a sample of 24 local authority areas in England, Wales and Scotland it was found that Housing Benefit changes had seriously undermined the ability of vulnerable people to be supported in a majority of the supported lodgings, adult placement and supported housing schemes studied (Griffiths, 1997). Housing associations are arguing that changes in the Housing Benefit system will affect the provision of wardens in sheltered housing. The Chief Executive of Anchor Trust commented 'If an older person's right to have their warden's support services paid from Housing Benefit is not guaranteed, the danger is that this money will be reallocated to residential care and heavy-end care, and the key to the preventive agenda will be lost' (Belcher, 1998).

8. A financial arrangement that gives a budget that can be used by whichever agency is the most appropriate is valuable

To avoid the kinds of problems that occur, such as cost shunting, when different agencies are trying to pass the cost of care on to another one, an integrated budget has a great value. Even if it is for small amounts this can help with problems of whose budget something is to come out of.

9. There is need for more research which brings in the housing element and better use made of existing research

The kind of exercise which is being undertaken here both in the seminar and in these extended papers is an excellent example of how research can be brought together and discussed by researchers and policy makers.

Quite rightly funders of research have to keep to their own terms of reference. But it is not easy when a topic crosses boundaries to get funding from more than one Government Department e.g. DOH/DOE

10. Professionals, older people and families must have access to information about different kinds of housing

There is a great lack of knowledge by professionals about the different kinds of housing. For example architects can go through a five-year course and learn nothing about older or disabled people (Hanson, 1998). But other professionals who help older people to make decisions about moving or staying, such as social workers and doctors seem not to know what is available. This was one of the reasons why DOE produced a booklet *Your Home in Retirement: Housing Advice for Older People* (DOE/Welsh Office, 1993). What is needed is a broad brush knowledge e.g. what can be expected of levels of care for bodies like Abbeyfield and what is available locally. There is particular ignorance about the role of sheltered housing and its limitations for very frail people.

Professionals also need to be trained to observe home surroundings. In one study of falls this was aided by the use of a video camera which was used in the homes of elderly people who had had an accident (Adams *et al.*, 1991). It was possible to see potential hazards in the home in a more leisurely way than in a quick visit.

CONCLUSION

For all the topics discussed a research agenda is badly needed. It is suggested that this needs to be a multi-disciplinary one. A good model has been that adopted recently by the Engineering and Physical Sciences Research Council. They currently have an initiative, mainly focused on older people, on the Built Environment. This is leading to the funding of a number of interesting and worthwhile pieces of research which would probably have had difficulty in getting funding from one source.

References

Adams, S., Askham, J., Glucksman, E., Swift, C. and Tinker, A. (1991) *Falls and Elderly People: A Study of Current Professional Practice in England and Innovations Abroad*, ACIOG: London.

Age Concern London, (1995a) *Home Comforts*, Age Concern London: London.

Age Concern London (1995b) *Hospital Afterthought: Support for Older People Discharged from Hospital*, Age Concern London: London.

Allen, C., Clapham, D., Franklin, B. and Parker, J. (1998) *The Right Home: Assessing Housing Needs in Community Care* Centre for Housing Management and Development, Department of City and Regional Planning, Cardiff University: Cardiff.

Anchor Trust (1998) *Killer Homes: Facing Up to Poor Housing as a Cause of Older People's Ill-health*, Anchor Trust: Oxford.

Appleton, N. (1996) *The Value of Handyperson's Schemes for Older People*, JRF Findings, 179, May: York.

Arblaster, L., Conway, J., Foreman, A. and Hawtin, M. (1996) *Inter-agency Working for Housing, Health and Social Care Needs of People in General Needs Housing*, Joseph Rowntree Foundation (JRF) Research Finding, 183: York.

Arnold, P., Bochel, H., Brodhurst, S. and Page, D. (1993) *Community Care: The Housing Dimension*, JRF: York.

Askham, J., Glucksman, E., Owens, P., Swift, C., Tinker, A. and Yu, G. (1990) *A Review of Research on Falls Among Elderly People*, Department of Trade and Industry, London

Audit Commission (1995) *United They Stand: Co-ordinating Care for Elderly Patients with Hip Fracture* HMSO: London.

Audit Commission (1998) *Home Alone: The Role of Housing in Community Care* Audit Commission: London.

Banerjee, S. (1998) 'Depression in Old Age' Paper for the DOH Policy Research Meeting, 27.3.98.

Barnes, D. (1997) *Older People with Mental Health Problems Living Alone*, Social Services Inspectorate, Department of Health: London.

Belcher, J. (1998) Reported in *Community Care*, 30.4- 6.5.98, p. 9.

Bond, J. (1998) 'Pathways Through Care: Facilitating Effective Discharge and Supporting Older People with a Stroke or Fractured Neck of Femur at Home' Paper for the DOH Policy Research Meeting, 27.3.98.

Bonnet, D. (1996) *Incorporating Lifetime Homes Standards into Modernisation Programmes*, JRF Research Finding 174, JRF: York.

Brenton, M. (1997) Paper to the British Society of Gerontology Annual Conference September.

British Geriatrics Society, The Association of Directors of Social Services and the Royal College of Nursing (1995) *The Discharge of Elderly Persons from Hospital for Community Care: A Joint Policy Statement*, Wolverhampton Council: Wolverhampton.

Butler, A. (1989) 'The growth and development of alarm systems in sheltered housing' in Fisk, M. (ed.) *Alarm Systems and Elderly People*, The Planning Exchange, Glasgow, pp. 8-19.

Calling for Help Group (1994) *A Survey of Community Alarms*, Calling for Help Group: London.

Central Statistical Office (1996) *Social Trends No. 26* HMSO: London.

Centre for Sheltered Housing Studies (1993) *Code of Practice for Wardens and Other Workers in Sheltered Housing*, Centre for Sheltered Housing Studies, Bewdeley, Worcestershire.

Clark, H., Dyer, S. and Hartman, L. (1996) *Going Home: Older People Leaving Hospital* Policy Press: Bristol.

Clemson, L., Cumming, R. and Roland, M. (1996) 'Case-control study of hazards in the home and risk of falls and hip fractures' *Age and Ageing* Vol. 25, No. 2 pp. 97-101.

Cobbold, C. (1997) *A Cost Benefit Analysis of Lifetime Homes* JRF: York.

Community Care (30 April – 6 May, 1998) 'New demands on long-term care', p. 7.

Cooper, R., Watson, L. and Allan, G. (1994) *Shared Living: Social Relations in Supported Housing* Joint Unit for Social Services Research, University of Sheffield: Sheffield.

Crane, M. (1990) *Elderly Homeless People in Central London* Age Concern England and Age Concern Greater London: London.

Crane, M. (1993) *Elderly Homeless People Sleeping on the Streets in Inner London: An Exploratory Study* ACIOG: London.

Crane, M. (1997) *Homeless Truths: Challenging the Myths about Older Homeless People* Help the Aged and Crisis: London.

Cullen, K. and Moran, R. (1992) *Technology and the Elderly* European Union: Brussels.

Davey, J. (1996) *Equity Release: An Option for Older Home-owners* The Centre for Housing Policy, University of York: York.

Department of the Environment (1993) *English House Condition Survey 1991* HMSO: London.

Department of the Environment (1996) *The Provision of Hostels by Local Authority Housing Departments* DOE Housing Research Summary, No. 50.

Department of the Environment (1997) *Local Authority Housing Allocations: Systems, Policies and Procedures* DOE, Housing Research Summary, No. 74.

Department of the Environment/Department of Health (1992) *Housing and Community Care* DOE 10/92, DOH LAC (92) 12, HMSO: London.

Department of Health/Department of the Environment (1997) *Housing and Community Care: Establishing a Strategic Framework* DOH: London.

Department of the Environment and the Welsh Office (1993) *Your Home in Retirement: Housing Advice for Older People* DOE.

Douglas, A., MacDonald, C. and Taylor, M. (1998) *Living Independently with Support: Service Users' Perspectives on 'Floating' Support*, The Policy Press/JRF and *Community Care*, Biblios Publishers' Distribution Services Ltd.: West Sussex.

Dupuis, A. and Thorns, D. (1996) 'Meanings of home for older home owners', *Housing Studies*, 4, 485-501.

Edinvar Housing Association (1998) *Assisted Interactive Dwelling – House: Edinvar Smart Technology Demonstration Project* Leaflet from Edinvar Housing Association: Edinburgh.

Exchange on Ageing, Law and Ethics (EAGLE) (1997) 'Homesharing – An innovatory scheme for the elderly people who want to remain at home', August/September, pp. 16-17.

Fletcher, P. (1998) 'Care comes into focus' *Housing Today*, 28.5.98.

Fletcher, P. (1991) The Future of Sheltered Housing – Who Cares: Policy Report National Federation of Housing Associations: London.

Fletcher, P. and Gillie, D. (1991) *The Future of Sheltered Housing – Who Cares: Practice Guide* National Federation of Housing Associations: London.

Goss, S. and Kent, C. (1995) *Health and Housing: Working Together? A Review of the Extent of Inter-agency Working* Policy Press: Bristol.

Graham, H. and Firth, J. (1992) 'Home accidents in old people: the role of the primary health care team' *British Medical Journal*, 4.7.92, Vol. 305, 30-32.

Green, H. and Hansbro, J. (1995) *Housing in England 1993/94* HMSO: London.

Griffiths, S. (1997) *Housing Benefit and Supported Housing: The Impact of Recent Changes* York Publishing Services: York.

Griffiths, S. (1995) *How Housing Benefit can Work for Community Care* JRF: York.

Gurney, C. and Means, R. (1993) 'The meaning of home in later life' in *Ageing, Independence and the Life Course*, Arber, S. and Evandrou, M. (eds.), pp. 119-131, Jessica Kingsley: London.

Hamnett. C, (1995) 'Housing equity release and inheritance' in Allen, I. and Perkins, E. (eds.) *The Future of Family Care for Older People*, pp. 163-180 HMSO: London.

Hancock, R. (1998a) 'Housing wealth, income and financial wealth of older people in Britain' *Ageing and Society*, Vol. 18, Part 1, pp. 5-34.

Hancock, R. (1998b) 'Can housing wealth alleviate poverty among Britain's older population' *Fiscal Studies*.

Hancock, R., Askham, J., Nelson, H. and Tinker, A. (forthcoming) *Home Ownership in Later Life – Benefit or Burden?*

Hanson, J. (1998) *Lecture to MSc Gerontology students King's College London*, January.

Healy, J. and Yarrow, S. (1997) *Family Matters: Parents Living with Children in Old Age* Policy Press.

Hensher, M., Fulop, N., Hood, S. and Ujah, S. (1996) 'Does hospital-at-home make economic sense? Early discharge versus standard care for orthopaedic patients' *Journal of the Royal Society of Medicine*, Vol. 89, pp. 548-551.

Henwood, M. (ed.) (1994) *Hospital Discharge Workbook* DoH: London.

Heywood, F. (1994) *Adaptations: Finding Ways to Say Yes* School for Advanced Urban Studies: Bristol.

Heywood, F. (1996) *Managing Adaptations: Positive Ideas for Social Services* The Policy Press: Bristol.

Heywood, F. in collaboration with Smart, G. (1996) *Funding Adaptations: The Need to Co-operate* The Policy Press: Bristol.

Holmans, A. (1995a) *Housing Demand and Need in England 1991-2011* JRF: York.

Holmans, A. (1995b) 'The rising number of households requiring homes – the national and regional picture' in Wilcox, S. (ed.) *Housing Finance Review 1995/96*, pp. 16-24, JRF: York.

Housing Corporation (1996) *Housing for Older People* The Housing Corporation: London.

Housing Corporation (1997) *The Provision of Supported Housing by Registered Social Landlords* Housing Corporation: London.

Hudson, J., Watson, L. and Allan, G. (1996) *Moving Obstacles: Housing Choices and Community Care* The Policy Press: Bristol.

Iliffe, S. (1997) 'Hospital-at-home: buyer beware' *Journal of the Royal Society of Medicine*, Vol. 90, No. 4, pp. 181-182.

Institute of Health Services Management (1998) *Telemedicine and Telecare: Impact on Healthcare* Institute of Health Services Management: London.

Joseph Rowntree Foundation Findings (1997) *Building Lifetime Homes* JRF: York.

Kelling, K. (1991) *Older Homeless People in London* Age Concern Greater London: London.

Kitwood, T., Buckland, S. and Petre, T. (1995) *Brighter Homes* Anchor Housing Association: Oxford.

Knight, J. (1992) *Sheltered Housing: The Positive Choice — A Professional Care Guide for Wardens* Anchor Housing Association.

Langan, J., Means, R. and Rolfe, S. (1996) *Maintaining Independence in Later Life: Older People Speaking* Anchor Trust: Oxford.

Lazarowich, N. (ed.) (1991) *Granny Flats for the Elderly: International Perspectives* The Haworth Press: New York.

Leather, P. (1997) 'Home improvement agencies: working strategically with local authorities' in *Care and Repair Newsletter*, No. 53, December.

Leather, P., Littlewood, M. and Munro, M. (1998) *Make Do and Mend: Explaining Home-owners' Approaches to Repair and Maintenance* Policy Press: Bristol.

Leather, P. and Mackintosh, S. (1995) *Encouraging Home Maintenance in the Private Sector* School for Advanced Urban Studies: Bristol.

Leather, P., Mackintosh, S. and Rolfe, S. (1994) *Papering Over the Cracks* National Housing Forum: London.

Leather, P. and Morrison, T. (1997) *The State of UK Housing: A Fact File on Dwelling Conditions* The Policy Press: Bristol.

Lilley, J., Arie, T. and Chilvers, C. (1995) 'Special review: accidents involving older people: a review of the literature' *Age and Ageing*, 24, 346-365.

Mackintosh, S. and Leather, P. (1995) *Home-owners' response to a repair and maintenance service* JRF Findings, No. 137, JRF: York.

McCafferty, P. (1994) *Living Independently: A Study of the Housing Needs of Elderly and Disabled People* HMSO: London.

McCrone, G. and Stephens, M. (1994) *Housing Policy in a European Perspective*, JRF Findings 129 JRF: York.

Means, R. (1997) 'Home, independence and community care: time for a wider vision? *Policy and Politics*, 25, No. 4, 409-419.

Means, R. (1998) *Older People and the Housing Dimension of Community Care* Paper to Nuffield Foundation Conference, Oxford, 16-18 March.

Means, R., Brenton, M., Harrison, L. and Heywood, F. (1997) *Making Partnerships Work in Community Care: A guide for practitioners in housing, health and social services*, Policy Press: Bristol.

Midgley, G., Munlo, I. and Brown, M. (1997) *Sharing Power: Integrating User Involvement and Multi-agency Working to Improve Housing for Older People* The Policy Press: Bristol.

Morris, J. (1995) *Housing and Floating Support: A Review* York Publishing Services: York.

Morton, J. (1993) *Planning a Granny Flat: Pitfalls and Procedures* ACIOG: London.

National Housing Federation (1996) *Appraisal Guide for Sheltered Housing* National Housing Federation: London.

Neill, J. and Williams, J. (1992) *Leaving Hospital: Elderly People and their Discharge to Community Care* HMSO: London.

Nuffield Institute for Health (1997) *Inter-agency Collaboration: 1. Hospital Discharge and Continuing Health Care* Nuffield Institute for Health, University of Leeds: Leeds.

Nuffield Institute for Health/NHS Centre for Reviews and Dissemination (1996) *Effective Health Care: Preventing Falls and Subsequent Injury in Older People* Nuffield Institute for Health, University of Leeds and NHS Centre for Reviews and Dissemination, University of York: York.

Office for National Statistics (1997) *Living in Britain: Results from the 1995 General Household Survey* HMSO: London.

Office for National Statistics (1998) *Social Trends 128.* Stationery Office: London.

Office of Population Censuses and Surveys (1996) *Living in Britain; Results from the 1994 General Household Survey* HMSO: London.

Parker, J., Allen, C., Franklin, B. and Clapham, D. (1998) *The Right Home: Assessing Housing Needs in Community Care* The Centre for Housing Management and Development, University of Wales, Cardiff.

Parker, M., Twemlow, T. and Pryor, G. (1996) 'Environmental hazards and hip fractures' *Age and Ageing*, Vol. 25, No. 4, pp. 322-325.

Riseborough, M. (1997) *Community Alarm Services Today and Tomorrow* Anchor Trust: Oxford.

Riseborough, M. and Niner, P. (1994) *I Didn't Know You Cared!* Anchor Housing Trust: Oxford.

Salvage, A. (1993) *Cold Comfort* Age Concern England: London.

Smart, G. and Means, R. (1997) *Housing and Community Care: Exploring the Role of Home Improvement Agencies* Anchor Trust: Oxford.

Tinker, A. (1980) *Housing the Elderly: How Successful are Granny Annexes* HMSO: London.

Tinker, A. (1984) *Staying at Home: Helping Elderly People* HMSO: London.

Tinker, A. (1989) *An Evaluation of Very Sheltered Housing* HMSO: London.

Tinker, A. (1997) *Older People in Modern Society* Longman: London.

Tinker, A., Wright, F. and Zeilig, H. (1995) *Difficult to Let Sheltered Housing* HMSO: London.

Trotter and Phillips (1997) Remodelling Sheltered Housing, Housing 21, Beaconsfield, Bucks.

Ungerson, C. and Baldock, J. (1994) *Becoming Consumers of Community Care: Households within the Mixed Economy of Care* JRF/Community Care: Poole, Dorset.

Warburton, R. (1994) *Home and Away: A Review of Recent Evidence to Explain why Some Elderly People enter Residential Care Homes while Others Stay at Home* DOH: London.

Watson, L. (1997) *High Hopes: Making Housing and Community Care Work* JRF: York.

Watson, L. and Britain, A. (1996) *Homes for Independent Living: Housing and Community Care Strategies in Scotland* Chartered Institute of Housing: Coventry.

Watson, L. and Cooper, R. (1992) *Housing with Care: Supported Housing and Housing Associations* JRF: York.

Watson, L. and Conway, T. (1995) *Homes for Independent Living: Housing and Community Care Strategies* Chartered Institute of Housing: Coventry.

Which (1997) 'Calling for help' March, pp. 28-31.

Wilcox, S. (1997) *Housing Finance Review 1997/98* JRF: York.

Wilson, D., Aspinall, P. and Murie, A. (1995) *Factors Influencing the Housing Satisfaction of Older People* The Centre for Urban and Regional Studies, University of Birmingham: Birmingham.

Wright, F. (1996) *Opening Doors: A Case Study of Multi-purpose Residential Homes* HMSO: London.

Young, J. and Gladman, J. (1995) 'Future directions in stroke rehabilitation', Reviews in *Clinical Gerontology*, Vol. 5, No. 3, pp. 329-337.

Diagrams 1 and 2 are reproduced with the permission of the Chartered Institute of Housing.

Note: This work was undertaken by Professor Anthea Tinker who received funding from the Department of Health; the views expressed in this paper are those of the author and not necessarily of the Department of Health.

Appendix 3

Housing and Housing Organisations: A Review of their Contribution to Alternative Models of Care for Elderly People

Professor Robin Means
Associate Dean (Primary and Community Care)
Faculty of Health and Social Care,
University of the West of England

INTRODUCTION

The focus of this Appendix is upon the contribution of housing and housing organisations to the development of alternative models of care for such elderly people.

The Griffiths review of community care (1998) paid little attention to housing issues and merely stated that the responsibilities of housing agencies should be limited to arranging and sometimes managing the 'bricks and mortar' of housing required for community care purposes (p. 15). However, the White Paper on community care (Department of Health, 1989) differed considerably from the Griffiths Report in this respect. 'Suitable good quality housing' was seen as essential to social care packages (p. 9) and it was argued that 'social services authorities will need to work closely with housing authorities, housing associations and other providers of housing of all types in developing plans for a full and flexible range of housing' (p. 25). Nevertheless, it is only in recent years that serious government consideration has been given to the importance of housing to the achievement of community care objectives (Department of Health, 1994, Audit Commission 1998).

This Appendix focuses on housing issues from the perspective that housing is an essential element of community care. However, the emphasis is not solely on what is usually called 'special needs', sheltered or supported housing, but will also include a consideration of much broader issues such as the meaning of home and the impact of general housing policies upon frail elderly and disabled people.

THE MEANING OF HOME

Community care policy in the United Kingdom is based on the belief that nearly everyone prefers to live in ordinary housing rather than in institutions because institutions lack the capacity to be a home. Higgins (1989) went so far as to argue that the very concept of community care should be abandoned because 'the real distinction is actually between the institution and home which differ markedly in terms of their core characteristics' (see Table 1). Ordinary houses (homes) are preferable to institutions because they offer more privacy, informality, freedom and familiarity.

Table 1: The key characteristics of institutions and home	
Institutions	**Home**
1. Public space, limitations on privacy	1. Private space, but may be some limitations on privacy
2. Living with strangers, rarely alone	2. May live alone or with relatives or friends, rarely with strangers
3. Staffed by professionals or volunteers	3. Normally no staff living there but they may visit to provide services
4. Formal and lacking in intimacy	4. Informal and intimate
5. Sexual relationships discouraged	5. Sexual relationships (between certain family members) accepted
6. Owned/rented by other agencies	6. Owned/rented by inhabitants
7. Variations in size but may be large (in terms of physical space and numbers living there)	7. Variations in size but usually small
8. Limitations on choice and on personal freedom	8. Ability to exercise choice and considerable degree of freedom
9. Strangeness (of people, place, etc)	9. Familiarity (of people, place, etc)
10. 'Batch' or communal living	10. Individual arrangements for eating, sleeping, leisure activities which can vary according to time and place

Source: Higgins (1989) p. 15

In making this point, one is immediately struck by the complexity of the term 'home'. Thus Rapoport (1995), drawing on the work of Hayward (1976), shows how the simple question of 'what does home mean to you?' can generate the following wide set of responses:

1.   as a set of relationships with others;

2.   as a relationship with the wider social group and community;

3.   as a statement about self image and identity;

4. as a place of privacy and refuge;

5. as a continuous and stable relationship with other sources of meaning about the home;

6. as a personalised place;

7. as a base of activity;

8. as a relationship with one's parents and place of upbringing;

9. as a relationship with a physical structure, setting or shelter.

The extensive literature on the home emphasises how responses will vary according to gender, class, ethnicity, country and age of the respondent, and that ideas about 'home' are constantly changing and evolving within any given society (Means, 1997a).

In terms of older people, it is clear that 'home' has a negative connotation for a minority because of the misery of their housing conditions or from the fact that 'home' is where elder abuse can take place free from surveillance (Biggs *et al.*, 1995). However, for the majority, home is associated with positive experiences. Thus, Langan *et al.* (1996) in their study of 31 elderly households from a range of tenures found that many stressed home as a place of privacy and refuge:

> Mr: *It's a place of retreat really.*
>
> Mrs: *. . . and home's always been a place where you want to go back to, however humble it is. Even when we go to town, we're still glad, well I am, to get back . . . It's a place of our own.*
> (p. 6)

Another respondent saw home as a place where you had 'freedom to do what you want, when you want' (p. 6).

It has often been shown that many older people see home in terms of a strong emotional attachment to a specific house lived in for much of the life course:

> *'Home was the old armchair by the hearth, the creaky bedstead, the polished lino with its faded pattern, the sideboard with its picture gallery, and the lavatory with its broken latch reached through the rain. It embodied a thousand memories and held promise of a thousand contentments. It was an extension of personality.'*
> (Townsend, 1963, p. 38)

Such views may at first appear dated and hence irrelevant to present-day debates. However, thirty years later, Australian researchers were uncovering similar sentiments among some older Australians when invited to talk about their homes:

> *'The home is often a collection of memories. One woman comments, "I'm very fond of it; it's got lots of memories". Another man, on the thought of moving, remarks, "all the memories are here; well, I can keep going and I'd just as soon stay here".'*
> (Davison *et al.*, 1993, p. 51)

The Langan, Means and Rolfe study (1996) found similar views from many of those who had lived a long time in one house. One such woman reflected that 'I only get out of it for two or three hours and I can't wait to get back' (p. 6). In this study, such emotions and feelings were not restricted just to owner occupiers. An 89 year old had lived in the same three bedroomed council flat for 43 years. She felt she had 'all my home comforts' in a quiet town block 'with no noisy teenagers running all over the place' (p. 6). She had no intention of moving into sheltered accommodation.

However, in placing this emphasis upon the link between 'feeling at home' and attachment to specific houses, great care must be taken not to overgeneralise. There is strong evidence that the majority of older people do manage to re-establish a sense of home when they move into good quality sheltered housing (Riseborough and Niner, 1994). Two of the ten households who moved into sheltered housing in the Langan *et al.* (1996) study, stressed that they felt at home because they felt secure from burglaries and theft while another stressed it 'started to feel like home when my old friends visited me here' (p. 7).

There is also extensive evidence that owner occupiers who move to a different part of the country on retirement establish a sense of home in their new accommodation and environment. Again drawing on the Langan *et al.* study, two households had moved from the Midlands to Lake District villages. One stressed that 'I love my little cottage, you know' while the other stressed the friendliness of her village which also had excellent facilities including a shop and easy access to a GP practice. It seems likely that many middle class older people are used to moving house periodically for career and other reasons, and perhaps have always seen their house as an asset through which wealth can be released as a result of trading down in later life (Means, 1997b). Such individuals are likely to have learnt the skill of how to transport one's sense of emotional security from one building (home) to another.

Very little research has been carried out on the meaning of home to older people in rented accommodation. Are attachments to particular homes less strong? Certainly, elderly council tenants are often under pressure to move from their house where they brought up their children in order to release family housing to those on the waiting list. Many such tenants have been willing to consider a move to modern prestigious sheltered housing schemes (Means, 1997b), yet seem increasingly willing to reject offers from older schemes, many of which are becoming hard to let (Tinker *et al.*, 1995). However, very little is known about the emotional feelings experienced by older people on leaving rented accommodation. One key factor is almost certainly the quality of rented accommodation lived in the past, and the extent to which there has been a single 'family' home rather than a whole series of moves into different rented accommodation during the life course. For many elderly people, their present rented accommodation may hold little emotional attachment and for some the memories may be largely negative. A move in later life may represent an opportunity to actually establish a sense of home for such people.

Another key issue for elderly people irrespective of whether they rent or own is likely to be whether the proposed move is to a home or to an institution. Willcocks, Peace and Kellaher (1987) suggest that strong emotions and attachments to their houses are expressed by elderly people when they feel threatened by a possible move into residential or nursing home care since 'to leave homes which may be inconvenient and difficult . . . would be to relinquish a hold on a base from which personal power can be generated and reinforced' (p. 8). Or, as Steinfield (1981) explains, housing moves in later life are often linked to negative rather than positive status passages and hence the desire of many to 'stay put'.

This whole debate points to the question of what is an institution, and how neatly it can be distinguished from a home and ordinary housing. More bluntly in terms of the focus of this appendix, do the 500,000 or so units of sheltered housing in England (McCafferty, 1994) essentially offer institutional care or a home? Where do they fall in the Higgins typology and to what extent does the bulk of this accommodation provide a non-stigmatising home for those who live there? With regard to sheltered housing, high levels of satisfaction amongst most residents continue to be recorded (Riseborough and Niner, 1994) but this has to be balanced against growing evidence that bedsit schemes, schemes in unpopular localities and those with outdated facilities (e.g. shared bathrooms) have been rejected by most older people and hence are now 'difficult to let' (Tinker et al., 1995).

Some commentators believe the problems of sheltered housing and other forms of supported housing are about much more than just the 'out of date' nature of some schemes. For these critics, many of whom are disabled activists committed to the social model of disability, all such schemes should be rejected as inherently stigmatising:

> 'Segregated provision, whether it is bricks and mortar, care or equipment has adopted and applied the "special needs" label with regard to disabled people. In terms of "special needs" housing for disabled people, this economy includes residential and nursing homes, group homes and hostels, sheltered and very sheltered accommodation and housing association property. This "special needs" provision is often geographically distinct from ordinary housing, is often inaccessible and denies disabled people the opportunity and right to participate in remunerative employment and fulfilling person relationships.'
> (Macfarlane and Laurie, 1996, p. 8)

But are such negative views of sheltered housing held by most older people? Midgley et al. (1997) draw upon separate focus group interviews with older people, their carers and professionals to identify the desired properties of an ideal housing and community care system. They were found to include the following:

- independent living and decent housing should be seen as basic rights;

- choice for older people should be maximised;

- housing should normally be provided to a mixed age group, with the 'special needs' of older people being met as part of this;

- new houses should be built with lifetime needs in mind.

This did not mean that all older people want to continue to live in general needs housing since some older people wanted 'the choice of going into specialist, segregated accommodation if they prefer' (p. 9). This suggests that there is a role for sheltered housing as one option for some people, but an option which needs to be developed in a way more fully integrated into mainstream housing and other services. In this respect, it is interesting to note the emergence of housing associations as major providers of residential and very sheltered housing (see later discussion for more details). One of their arguments seems to be that they treat frail older people as tenants and not residents, and hence still part of the community.

A few commentators take the radical perspective of stressing the opportunities offered by collective lifestyles. Dalley (1996) believes this can mean an escape from the oppressions of the nuclear family rather than inevitably having to involve a regimented lifestyle with no personal space. Scepticism has been expressed about the practical relevance of these alternative lifestyles on the grounds it is unclear 'how these understandings derived from other societies and other periods can directly influence our thinking about the ways care for dependent people in contemporary Britain should be organised' (Baldwin and Twigg, 1991, p. 128). However, recent research by Brenton (1997) has not only demonstrated the growth of co-operative living schemes amongst older women in America, Canada and the Netherlands but has shown how this might be developed as a policy option in the UK. Although the details of such schemes vary, their essence tends to be self-contained units with some communal support facilities in which each scheme member knew each other prior to moving in. Thus these innovative schemes build upon existing friendships and networks rather than artificially creating a community of strangers.

Perhaps the overall message is that people with support needs require a range of housing and support options to choose from. However, the majority will want to live in mainstream housing and so access to affordable, appropriate and flexible housing will be pivotal to their quality of life.

MAINSTREAM HOUSING AND COMMUNITY CARE

This section, therefore, looks at mainstream housing provision in terms of availability, affordability, repair and access, and draws out the implications for the users of community care services. The context for doing this is of course Conservative housing policies from 1979 through to May 1997, particularly as expressed through the Housing Act 1989, the Local Government and Housing Act 1989 and the Housing Act 1996. Owner-occupation was presented as the preferred option of nearly everyone (Department of Environment, 1995) and this period saw the sale of around 2.2m council houses into owner occupation (Office for National Statistics, 1997). There has also been the emergence of housing associations as the preferred developer of new housing for social renting but in a form which has required them to borrow heavily from the private market as well as the increasing tendency of local authorities to transfer voluntarily part or all of their housing stock to other social landlords. Above all, the period saw a massive decline in housing investment through public expenditure. Hooton (1996) estimated that 1997/98 housing investment plans meant 'cumulative cuts . . . since 1992/93 now add up to more than £7 billion, or put another way, 220,000 new rented homes and nearly 400,000 renovated homes' (p. 18).

1. Availability

Whether or not there is a shortage of housing in England and Wales is a more difficult question than it first appears since it requires much more than checking the overall number of units against the overall number of households. To be used by existing or potential households, houses must be affordable, in the right part of the country and of an appropriate design and size, as well as being in good condition. Studies which try to take all these factors into account suggest major housing shortages exist.

Thus, Holmans (1995) has come up with the following figures for England:

- To meet the demand for homes by private owners, and the need for subsidised renting, about 240,000 new homes a year will be required in the two decades 1991-2001 and 2001-2011.

- The demand for new homes by owner-occupiers is forecast as 150,000-160,000 in 1991-2001 and 130,000-140,000 in 2001-2011.

- The proportion of households that are owner-occupiers will continue to grow, to around 70%; the absolute number of owner-occupier households will increase by 2.7m in the two decades together.

- The need for additional 'social' housing will average 90,000 homes a year in 1991-2001 and 100,000 a year in 2001-2011 to keep the backlog of unmet need at its 1991 level. These estimates compare with the Department of the Environment's published estimates of 60,000 to 100,000 for 1991-2001.

- The figures rise to an average of about 117,000 homes every year for the 20-year period if the backlog of unmet need for separate homes – between 400,000 and 500,000 in 1991 – is to be eradicated over the two decades.

In terms of the focus of this appendix, it is interesting to speculate how many elderly people with support needs could manage in mainstream housing if it was available, affordable and in reasonable repair, and if the necessary support services could be brought to such housing. Although numerous attempts have been made to estimate the need for supported housing (McCafferty, 1994; Watson, 1996), all such estimates depend upon assumptions about the respective roles of sheltered housing, residential care and nursing homes and their relationship to the option of 'staying put with care support from social services (Hoyes *et al.*, 1996). However, it would seem that there is an adequate supply of basic sheltered housing (or even over supply) in many localities but that there is a significant need for more schemes which offer 'extra care'. This was estimated to be in the region of 56,000 units by the McCafferty (1994) study.

2. Affordability

Issues of the affordability of housing and community care are most visible in terms of rented property. Both the Housing Act 1988 and the Local Government and Housing Act 1989 had the effect of driving up rents significantly in all types of rented accommodation. The aspiration of central government was to allow markets to determine appropriate rent levels, and then to develop means-tested subsidy systems (Housing Benefit) to support those on lowest incomes. For example, the 1988 Act established a new funding regime for housing associations which presets the amount of public subsidy prior to scheme commencement and requires them to raise the remainder from banks and building societies. This had the inevitable result of higher rents (Randolph, 1993) and to make many tenants highly dependent on the housing benefit system.

A new financial regime for local authority housing in England and Wales was introduced by the Local Government and Housing Act 1989. This involved the creation of a housing revenue account ring-fenced from the general funds of the local authority. It has generated some major rent rises, and council rents rose by an average of 30% in England during the first two years of the new system (Malpass, 1993). Again, increased dependency on Housing Benefit was an inevitable outcome of these trends for low-income people.

As early as 1990, Maclennan *et al.* (1990) were able to demonstrate that almost half of the households in social housing in Britain did not have access to employment and they argued that 'this yawning gap in the sources of income has to be at the forefront of any discussion of the housing benefit system' (p. 36). These words have proved prophetic. The concentration of the unemployed, disabled people, low income elderly people and people with multiple problems within the social rented sector has continued to occur, partly because homelessness has become a key route into new tenancies. The London Federation of Housing Associations (1995) estimated that 60% of new tenants housed by their general needs housing associations could be defined as vulnerable. A key concern of the Labour government has been how to tackle the subsequent problems of social exclusion experienced by multiply deprived neighbourhoods.

The vast majority of 'vulnerable' tenants in the public and private sectors are likely to be able to afford their accommodation only because of the housing benefit system. This can be seen in a very positive light:

> 'Housing Benefit is uniquely adaptable to the accommodation-related needs of people who require support to live in the community. It is cost-effective – payments can be tailored to the type of supported accommodation required as the individual's capacity for community living increases or diminishes over time.'
> (Griffiths, 1997, p. 23)

However, the response of governments has been the opposite of this. Housing benefit costs have grown considerably and hence there have been numerous attempts to limit entitlement. The impact of this upon the standard of living of people with support needs has been substantial. In terms of older people, Marsh and Riseborough (1995) found that 'even where housing costs are paid by housing benefit, tenants find themselves with very limited incomes, often below income support levels' (p. 56). One reason for the low standard of living of these elderly people, despite housing benefit support, was the high cost of the service charge and a key area of tension has become the extent to which housing benefit is subsidising the 'support' as well as the 'housing' element of supported accommodation (Oldman *et al.*, 1996).

Housing Benefit is now the subject of an inter-departmental government review. In terms of supported housing, nearly everyone agrees on the need for a more coherent system. As Boyle (1998) explains, opening a new project under the present arrangements requires drawing upon some combination of the following:

■ finding ways to fudge what is rental and what is service charge;

- persuading other funders to pay for services which housing benefit had not been expected to cover;

- accepting lower staffing levels than had been planned;

- housing people with lower support needs than those for whom the scheme was originally designed;

- opening up social services funding sources through registration under the Registered Homes Act;

- the contortion of jobs to enable them to fit eligible service definitions;

- the use of reserves to cover operating deficits.

As Boyle stresses, what is needed is 'a permanent solution which clearly describes who should pay for what' (p. 20). The Chartered Institute of Housing (CIOH) has argued that this requires a new 'supported housing benefit' to pay for the whole range of specified support services with a separate benefit covering the housing related element. Individuals would be able to claim either or both benefits (Simpson, 1998). Both the CIOH and the National Housing Federation fear that the eventual solution might see the transfer of responsibility for funding support services to social services authorities who will have to apply rigid eligibility criteria because of the overall resource pressures upon them. This would have the consequence of squeezing out future schemes wishing to include those with low and medium dependency needs (Hirst, 1998).

HOUSING CONDITIONS

Leather and Morrison (1997) profiled the state of UK housing and found that:

- some 1,638,000 occupied dwellings in the UK were either unfit for human habitation or below the Scottish tolerable standard – this represented about 7% or one in 14 dwellings in the UK;

- problems of disrepair are more widespread than unfitness, with almost one in five dwellings in England having urgent repair costs of more than £1,000;

- people on low incomes are the most likely to live in poor housing conditions and this includes many older people especially after the age of 75;

- houses in poor condition are to be found across all tenures (see Table 2).

The *English Housing Condition Survey*, 1996 (DETR, 1998) has just been published and has indicated only marginal improvements in the situation. The survey found one in 13, or 7.3%, of council homes unfit, compares to one in 14 in 1991. The private rented sector continued to have the greatest share of unfit homes at 19.3%, and this compared with 6.3% of owner occupied homes and 5.2% of housing association stock.

The implications of such poor housing conditions are immense. In terms of council housing and other socially rented estates, a concentration of people with social and health difficulties into poor housing has helped to generate an almost total environmental and social collapse requiring broad strategies of estate regeneration to tackle the resultant problems rather than just the repair of the housing stock (Stewart and Taylor, 1995). There are also very negative health consequences for individual older people in poor housing which can easily generate a need for hospital care (often followed by residential or nursing home care) or worse. Thus a recent report from Anchor Trust (1998) surveyed research on this subject and concluded that:

■ poor housing conditions affect both physical and psychological health, particularly for older people;

■ older people living in poor housing are more likely to have accidents and falls while dampness, condensation and mould can cause chest problems.

■ In 1996/97 there were 44,800 excess winter deaths including 356 deaths from hypothermia amongst those aged 65 and over in England and Wales;

Table 2: Dwellings in poor condition by tenure, England and Wales (1991/93)				
	Percentage dwellings in each tenure group			
	Owner-occupied	**Private rented**	**LA rented**	**HA rented**
England				
Unfit	5.5	20.5	6.9	6.7
Urgent repairs over £1000	17.3	41.0	15.1	12.7
Northern Ireland				
Unfit	8.5	27.9	2.0	2.1
Urgent repairs over £1000	15.5	38.9	5.6	1.4
Wales				
Unfit	11.9	25.6	15.8	6.0
Repairs over £1500	19.9	34.3	18.7	8.4

Notes: Figures for England are for 1991; figures for Wales are for 1993.
    Excludes vacant dwellings. Comparisons cannot be made between countries.
Source: Leather and Morrison (1997, p. 32)

For those in owner occupied housing, and especially for low income elderly people, there is a constant pressure about how best to maintain property to a reasonable standard. With regard to the latter group, Leather and Morrison found that the proportion of households living in unfit housing in England rises from 6.6% for households where the head is aged between 60 and 64 to 13.2% for households where the head is aged over 85. People on low incomes including elderly and disabled people can apply for repair help through the home improvement grant system. However, this system is complex and many elderly and disabled people lack the knowledge, expertise or confidence to apply for a renovation grant or home repair assistance and then to organise the subsequent building work (see Figure 1 for more details).

Figure 1: Repair and renovation

A Name of grant	B Purposes	C Who eligible?	D Terms	E Conditions
Renovation Grant	To make fit. To put into good repair. To provide insulation, heating system, safe internal arrangement, means of escape from fire, and radon remedial measures. There is also power for the Secretary of State to specify other measures.	Owner-occupiers or tenants of private landlords.	Discretionary. No limits specified. Test of resources prescribed by the Secretary of State.	Property to be at least 10 years old. Applicant must have owned or (if tenant) lived for at least 3 years in the property (except grant for fire escape – or if property is in a Renewal Area or other exceptions). Grant to be repaid if house sold within 5 years of date of grant approval (with exemption in certain circumstances). Local authority has discretion to disregard all these conditions.
Home Repair Assistance	To carry out works of repair, improvement or adaptation. Help may be in the form of cash grant, or provision of materials or both.	Owner-occupiers, all tenants except council tenants and people with the right to occupy for a least 5 years, who, in each case, are aged 18 or over and in receipt of a means-tested benefit. Includes owners or tenants of houseboats or mobile homes if certain conditions are met. Any owner or non-council tenant who is elderly, disabled or infirm – they do not have to be on benefits. Any owner or non-council tenant – they do not have to be on benefits – who needs the work in order to care for someone who is elderly, disabled or infirm.	Discretionary. Applicant or partner must be in receipt of Income Support, Family Credit, Housing Benefit, Council Tax Benefit or Disability Working Allowance unless they are elderly, disabled or infirm, or the grant is to care for someone who is elderly, disabled or infirm. No further means test. Maximum £2,000 per grant or £4,000 in 3-year period (may be altered by the Secretary of State).	Applicant must have lived in property for at least 3 years unless assistance is for fire escape, or to enable elderly, disabled or infirm person to be cared for or property is in a Renewal Area.

Note: This table is provided only as a guide. Full details need to be checked in the 1996 Housing Grants, Construction and Regeneration Act, Part I and in subsequent Circulars.

Source: Based on the work of Heywood in Means *et al.*, 1997, p. 64

An option increasingly used in this situation is for elderly and disabled people to turn to a specialist home improvement agency (HIA) for advice. These are non-profit making bodies which offer independent advice and support on how to repair, improve and adapt homes (Bradford *et al.*, 1994). Such agencies are often called Care and Repair or Staying Put projects although some agencies use other names. There are 200 such agencies in England and they are supported in their work by a national co-ordinating body called Care and Repair (England). A further 25 HIAs are to be found in Wales and these are co-ordinated by Care and Repair (Wales).

HIAs are used extensively by people with support needs. For example, Poor Housing: Who Cares? (Care and Repair, 1994) looked at the characteristics of nearly 20,000 clients and discovered that 18% of the single older clients and 28% of the older couples had been in hospital during the last 12 months. These clients also included 6,080 who were registered or who were eligible to be registered as disabled under the Chronically Sick and Disabled Act 1970. This client profile has meant not only an expanding role in home adaptation (see next section) as well as home improvement but also the development of a range of new services such as handyperson, home security and home safety schemes (Smart and Means, 1997).

Owner-occupation in later life will be a boon to many. With the mortgage paid off, housing costs will drop at a time when weekly income is reduced, thus avoiding a major decline in living standards. For many, there is the prospect of a move from a family home to a smaller property, thus releasing equity to be used in a variety of ways, including meeting future care needs. But others will be trapped in poorly repaired property of limited value with few assets with which to develop a maintenance and repair strategy in later life. The housing dimension of community care needs to include a strategy for offering support to elderly and disabled people facing these kinds of repair problems.

ACCESS (NEW BUILD AND ADAPTATION)

In discussing issues of access, a distinction is often made between wheelchair and mobility standard housing. Mobility housing is suitable for ambulant disabled people, while wheelchair housing is suitable for the permanent accommodation of people who are wheelchair users. The late 1980s saw a decline in new build housing meeting either of these standards despite the stress of central government about the importance of independent living. The McCafferty (1994) study estimated a shortage of 13,000 units of wheelchair housing and 7,000 units of mobility housing (this was in addition to needing 56,000 units of very sheltered housing as mentioned earlier).

In recent years more and more commentators have argued that improved access requirements for new domestic dwellings should be built into planning law and building regulations. The aim is to build houses, flats and bungalows which are flexible, adaptable and accessible, and hence:

'. . . designed either to meet the changing needs occurring throughout one family's lifetime – raising small children, accommodating the teenager with a broken leg, having

grandparents to stay, mobility difficulties in old age – or to meet the varying needs of numerous changes of occupier in the same home.'
(Brewerton and Darton, 1997, p. 4)

More specifically, the concept of lifetime homes has been developed and such homes have 16 design features (see Figure 2). A cost-benefit argument is being made that the resultant increased building costs can be offset by saving in terms of wider economic benefits (eg reduced home care, health and adaptation costs) as well as major social benefits such as improved quality of life (Cobbold, 1997).

Figure 2: The lifetime homes standards

Access

1. Where car parking is adjacent to the home, it should be capable of enlargement to attain 3.3 metres width.
2. The distance from the car parking space to the home should be kept to a minimum and should be level or gently sloping.
3. The approach to all entrances should be level or gently sloping. (Gradients for paths should be the same as for public buildings in the Building Regulations).
4. All entrances should be illuminated and have level access over the threshold, and the main entrance should be covered.
5. Where homes are reached by a lift, it should be wheelchair accessible.

Inside the home

6. The width of the doorways and hallways should accord with the Access Committee for England's standards.
7. There should be space for the turning of wheelchairs in kitchens, dining areas and sitting rooms and adequate circulation space for wheelchair users elsewhere.
8. The sitting room (or family room) should be at entrance level.
9. In houses of two or more storeys, there should be space on the ground floor that could be used as a convenient bed space.
10. There should be a downstairs toilet which should be wheelchair accessible, with drainage and service provision enabling a shower to be fitted at any time.
11. Walls in bathrooms and toilets should be capable of taking adaptations such as handrails.
12. The design should incorporate provision for a future stairlift and a suitably identified space for potential installation of a house lift (through-the-floor lift) from the ground to the first floor, for example to a bedroom next to the bathroom.
13. The bath/bedroom ceiling should be strong enough, or capable of being made strong enough, to support a hoist at a later date. Within the bath/bedroom wall, provision should be made for a future floor-to-ceiling door, to connect the two rooms by a hoist.
14. The bathroom layout should be designed to incorporate ease of access, probably from a side approach, to the bath and WC. The wash basins should also be accessible.

Fixtures and fittings

15. The living room window glazing should begin at 800mm or lower, and windows should be easy to open/operate.
16. Switches, sockets and service controls should be at a height usable by all (i.e. between 600mm and 1,200mm from the floor).

Source: Cobbold (1997, p. 2)

The Labour government has been sympathetic to these arguments and has amended Part M of the Building Regulations for new homes so as to be able 'to allow people to be able to invite disabled people to visit them in their own homes, and for home owners to be able to remain in their own homes longer as they become less mobile as they get older' (DETR Press Release, 9th March 1998). The amendment covered a range of measures including level entry to the principle, or a suitable alternative, entrance; an entrance door wide enough to allow wheelchair access; and WC provision in the entrance or first habitable storey. These changes have been criticised by groups such as RADAR for the emphasis upon the front entrance so that 'a house would be considered suitable for a disabled person if the front door was accessible, but access to the garden via the back door was impossible' (Director of RADAR quoted in Inside Housing, 24th April 1998).

A complementary approach to using new build schemes to increase mobility and wheelchair access is to emphasise the importance of adaptation to existing properties. The main public subsidy for adaptation work is now through the disabled facilities grant. Figure 3 outlines the main features of this complex grant which has been criticised on a number of fronts. Many complain that the means-tested element discourages some applicants, especially since major outgoings such as mortgage payments are not taken into account in considering what the applicant can reasonably afford (Sapey, 1995). Also, the complexity of the system is often criticised in terms of the failure to co-ordinate the various professional inputs (Mackintosh and Leather, 1994) in a context in which there is often dispute between housing and social services about the best way to proceed (Heywood, 1994) and how this might best be funded (Heywood with Smart, 1996).

Figure 3: Home adaptation

A Name of grant	B Purposes	C Who eligible?	D Terms	E Conditions
Mandatory disabled facilities grants.	To facilitate use by disabled people of their homes. Specifically to provide: ■ access to building; ■ making dwelling safe for disabled persons or others ■ access to and provision of living room, bedroom, lavatory, bathroom (including use of bath and/or shower) and wash hand basin; ■ providing suitable cooking facilities and suitable power, lighting and heating controls; ■ improving or providing suitable heating system; ■ movement around dwelling in order to care for someone ■ other purposes as may be specified by the Secretary of State.	Anyone over 18 in any tenure who is either disabled themselves or needs the grant to allow them to adapt the house for a disabled person. The definition of disabled person for purposes of this grant is given at Section 100 of the 1996 Housing Grants, Construction and Regeneration Act. It includes a very broad range of older and disabled people, including disabled children.	Mandatory for the purposes defined in Section 23, a-1 of the 1996 Housing Grants, Construction and Regeneration Act. Maximum grant £20,000 (but NB discretionary grant for mandatory purposes may be added on). Test of resources as prescribed by the Secretary of State. Housing authorities must be satisfied that works are (a) 'necessary and appropriate' and (b) 'reasonable and practicable'. In deciding (a) they shall consult the social services authority if it is a different authority. Payment of grants may in exceptional cases (ie where it would not cause hardship to the applicant) be deferred for 12 months from the date of application.	Disabled person (or parent if the disabled person is a child) must complete a test of resources which takes into account their income and that of their partner or spouse. This means test does not take existing outgoings into account, and there are therefore serious problems for people with mortgages or other debts. DoE Circular (4)97 provides for test of resources to be applied to people over 16 and under 19, in receipt of Income Support and no longer at school, in their own right, even if they are living with their parents.
Discretionary disabled facilities grant.	Either to augment a mandatory grant for purposes described above or to make the building suitable for the 'accommodation, welfare or employment' of the disabled occupant.	As above.	Discretionary. Test of resources as above.	As above.

Note: This table is provided only as a guide. Full details need to be checked in the 1996 Housing Grants, Construction and Regeneration Act, Part I and in subsequent Circulars.

Source: Based on the work of Heywood in Means *et al.*, 1997, p. 71

Heywood (1994) talks of 'this kaleidoscope of possible permutations' in which 'getting from "A" (needing an adaptation) to "B" (securing the necessary adaptation) may mean encountering occupational therapists, grants officers, technical officers, agency workers, planners, builders, stairlift companies and work inspectors' (p. 5). The recent Audit Commission (1998) report on housing and community identifies existing home adaptation policy and practice as a central weakness in present arrangements and a major factor in some elderly and disabled people drifting into residential and nursing home care.

A number of studies have stressed the need to develop a culture which Heywood calls 'finding ways to say yes'. Thus the Pieda Plc report (1996) outlined a range of options for improved liaison such as the creation of joint teams, regular liaison meetings between social services staff and grants officers, joint training initiatives and common information systems. A further two possibilities also need to be mentioned. First, the work of home improvement agencies (see previous section) is increasingly focused upon helping elderly and disabled people through the whole process of obtaining an appropriate adaptation (Smart and Means, 1997). A second option relates to developing disabled persons' accommodation agencies. These equally offer expertise in obtaining an adaptation but many of them are also involved in developing comprehensive registers of adapted and mobility housing within their localities (Means *et al.*, 1997).

HOUSING ASSOCIATIONS AND COMMUNITY CARE: THE EMERGING CONTRIBUTION OF SHELTERED HOUSING

This section focuses down upon exciting developments in sheltered housing which are being developed primarily by registered social landlords such as housing associations (this is not to deny the existence of similar developments by some local authorities).

1. Remodelling sheltered housing

Reference has already been made to the growing problems that exist in terms of letting units in many of the older sheltered housing schemes. This has lead the Housing Corporation (1996) to call for scheme-by-scheme action plans based upon an option appraisal approach to include a range of possibilities to include demolition, change of use and a radical upgrading to meet modern sheltered housing standards.

A number of housing associations have committed themselves heavily to remodelling programmes, often linked to a more general review of where sheltered housing should fit into community care. Thus, Housing 21 (1997) argue in *Remodelling Sheltered Housing* that all older people, including those in sheltered housing, should have the choice of their present accommodation being a 'home for life'. A key component of this strategy being to equip and develop sheltered housing schemes 'so that care can be delivered to tenants rather than tenants having to move to where the care can be provided' (p. 7). A major capital investment in the existing housing stock is seen as enabling the 'difficult to let' problem to be overcome and to ensuring that in the future large numbers of elderly people do not have to move into residential and nursing home care because the limitations of original design restrict the delivery of care. However, the capital investment required and the likely reduction in unit numbers within remodelled schemes mean that rents may well have to rise. This is likely to lead to yet a further reliance on Housing Benefit for individual elderly tenants even if some of this is offset by reductions in lost revenues from previously empty properties.

The remodelling of sheltered housing is not just about redesigning old buildings but it is also about the repositioning of sheltered housing within community care. More and more housing associations stress that such accommodation should be a 'home for life' and that tenants should be enabled to 'stay put' as their health deteriorates. This requires the bringing of health and social care services into their present accommodation rather than having to access such support through a move into residential or nursing home care.

2. Very sheltered housing

This 'Home for Life' philosophy places a high emphasis upon the need to invest in staff and to develop care services as well as to re-equip buildings. However, some remodelling schemes go further than this and consider the option of a change of use to what is increasingly referred to as very sheltered housing in which all tenants have high dependency needs at their point of entry into the scheme.

The recent review by Laing and Buisson (1997) estimated there to be around 17,000 units of very sheltered housing in Britain, the vast majority of which is in the social rented sector. There is a growing consensus that such schemes combine housing with the availability of high levels of care, and that this requires a formal partnership between the housing association and social services. This partnership usually takes the form of social services having nomination rights into the scheme and these nominations are restricted to people who would meet local social services eligibility criteria for residential care. In other words, very sheltered housing is presented as a homely, non stigmatising and usually cheaper alternative to residential care.

However, the growth of new schemes through large specialist housing associations such as Anchor and Hanover has been mainly through new build rather than the remodelling of old schemes. Unlike residential care, the tenant retains a small independent flat usually with living room, bedroom, shower room and kitchen. Detailed design guidance now exists for new build very sheltered housing schemes to ensure they 'have no obvious features which are blatantly institutional or medical' (Robson *et al.*, 1997, p. 16).

The viability of such schemes is very much dependent upon partnerships with social services in which social services agree to meet most of the care costs of residents in return for their control over nomination rights. However, mechanisms for achieving this can vary considerably. Age Concern (1998) in their evidence to the Royal Commission outlined how this differed for two schemes, one ran by Hanover and the other by Anchor.

> *'Hanover has very deliberately maintained a total separation between the housing and care provision within the scheme, with social services wholly responsible for care, in order to clarify funding responsibilities for the various parties involved. At the Anchor scheme, Anchor staff provide the care although this is largely funded by social services by a mixture of a block contract for a certain number of care hours plus additional spot contracts to meet individual's assessed needs.'*
> (p. 10)

One reason for this difference is that Anchor has for some time wished to expand its own home support services (Quilgars *et al.*, 1997). Such services might provide care support in very sheltered housing schemes but also be available to support older people more generally in the local community either on a fee basis from the client or through a contract with social services.

Laing and Buisson's (1997) review of housing with care in the UK indicates that it is 'the recent activity by the major voluntary sector providers which will increase the stock significantly' (p. 41). The reason for this growth is clear. Very sheltered housing is being presented as a homely cost effective alternative to residential care. However, it would appear that although these schemes save money for social services, there is more uncertainty over whether they are 'cheaper' than residential care in terms of the overall public purse. This is, of course, a central concern of the main report but in this Appendix it is important to stress that these schemes also need to be judged in terms of the quality of care they provide for tenants. Have they finally resolved the dilemma of how to provide 'homely' care in a group setting for highly dependent elderly people or do many of the traditional problems of residential and nursing home care remain?

3. Developing the role of the warden

Sheltered housing tenants are becoming older and frailer across all schemes, and not just remodelled schemes and new build very sheltered housing schemes. This is requiring a major review and rethink by housing associations of the role of the sheltered housing warden. A campaign supported by 34 housing organisations have recently focused on this changing role. This emphasised how wardens have shifted from poorly trained 'good neighbours' to key professionals who are:

- housing professionals with responsibilities towards buildings and tenants;

- managers of sheltered housing, not hands-on carers;

- there to enable older people to live independently with privacy, dignity, security and fulfilment;

- able to assist with communication solutions due to sensory impairment, language or illness (including dementia);

- trained to encourage older people to ask for support, to respect refusal of offers of help and to give information on the availability of and access to services;

- ideally placed, with tenants' agreement, to contribute to assessments and the monitoring of care packages.

This changing role is often reflected in new job titles including residential manager (Housing 21), estate manager (Hanover), sheltered housing officer (Hyde), sheltered scheme manager (Metropolitan Housing Trust) and scheme manager (Sanctuary).

However, it is the substance of the role which really matters if wardens are to play their part in enabling tenants to remain in sheltered housing despite deteriorating health rather than being expected to move into residential or nursing home care.

Perhaps, one of the biggest challenges faced by such staff is how to support tenants who develop dementia. The research of Petre in Kitwood *et al.* (1995) has shown how sheltered housing can 'be a successful environment in which many of those with dementia can live with well-being even at high levels of cognitive impairment' (p. 67) so long as the dementia develops after they move into the scheme. Success was also found to depend on well-trained and well-supported wardens who have a clear understanding of dementia and an ability to explain this to other tenants.

HOUSING ORGANISATIONS AND COMMUNITY CARE — THE NEED FOR STRATEGIC AND OPERATIONAL CO-ORDINATION

This Appendix has emphasised the importance of the housing dimension of community care, and hence the need to draw housing agencies and housing professionals into the centre of community care at both the strategic and operational levels. This requires an integrated response in terms of central government as well as the local level. The recent report from the Audit Commission (1998) places a high emphasis upon the need for central government to establish a coherent policy framework especially in terms of roles and responsibilities, funding and the regulatory framework. For example, the Commission identify that the four main central government departments (Department of Health, DETR, the Department of Social Security and the Home Office) are presently drawing on 25 funding streams in relation to housing and community care. In terms of this appendix, it has been shown how the dominant need is to find a way to respond to the concerns of the government about housing benefit without undermining the funding base of sheltered housing and other forms of innovative housing and support scheme. This will depend upon a higher level of co-ordination of policy across government departments than has been achieved up to now.

The second integration challenge involves the need for improved strategic and operational working at the local level. At the moment, this is often undermined by tensions around the issue of who should provide the care and fund the care of people whose housing and support difficulties are not so great as to ensure they meet the priority criteria of social services for care management and a care package. Thus, housing may define a single homeless person as in priority need on the grounds of old age, mental health problems, learning difficulties, physical impairment or major health problem. They may feel such an individual will fail to retain any offered tenancy and drift back into homelessness unless offered additional support. But social services will often feel unable to respond, and hence housing workers and housing agencies feel they are being 'dumped upon'. Such feeling can be especially acute amongst wardens/managers of sheltered housing schemes as residents become more frail and some develop symptoms of dementia. They can feel great bitterness at the apparent assumption of both health and social services that they should be able to cope (Langan and Means, 1995).

A number of studies have pointed to the extent to which there has been a failure to address these and other issues relating to the integration of housing into the

community care agenda. The government's own study of community care and
housing/homeless devoted a chapter to joint assessment and found that:

> *'Although housing agencies are beginning to be engaged in community care
> implementation, housing solutions for people with "special" needs and homeless people are
> still being developed in isolation, and links between community careand housing
> assessment procedures are rate.'*
> (Department of Health, 1994)

Arblaster *et al.* (1996) carried out a national postal survey backed up by three case
studies on inter-agency working to address the housing, health and social care
needs of people in ordinary housing. They found a lack of effective
communication between agencies, caused partly by both a lack of conceptual
understanding about the overall functions of each other combined with a lack of
awareness of what each other did in practice on a day-to-day basis. Lund and
Foord (1997) studied the housing strategies and community care plans of a range
of local authorities and concluded that further progress required an improved
integration of assessment procedures, a systematic recording of need and 'robust
performance indicators' which are 'relevant to community care' (p. 47).

Such studies tend to claim that some limited progress has been made and most
are able to offer examples of good practice. Central government has proved
willing to encourage the further integration of housing into the community care
agenda through the publication of both strategic and operational guidance which
is supported by both the DETR and the Department of Health. The aim of *Housing
and Community Care: Establishing a Strategic Framework* (DH/DoE, 1997) was 'to
provide a framework to help housing, social services and health authorities to
establish joint strategies for housing and community care so that at a strategic
level, the necessary co-ordination between housing, social services and health is
achieved' (p. 1). The positive message of the guidance was that effective joint
working at the strategic level maximises available resources and can also enable
agencies to both meet their own aims as well as joint objectives. Watson and Torr
(1998) have very helpfully produced a strategy guide to planning services for older
people to help local authorities work with other key agencies on this task, and this
places a high emphasis upon information planning and needs assessment and
hence the necessity to project future housing and care/support needs.

*Making Partnerships Work in Community Care: A Guide for Practitioners in Housing,
Health and Social Services* (Means *et al.*, 1997) looks at many of the same issues from
an operational perspective and with an emphasis upon the need for field level staff
to map their localities because it is essential for them to have an awareness of how
a wide range of agencies might be able to contribute to meeting the housing,
health and support needs of service users. The guide also argues for a much
clearer view of the housing and care management interface than attempted by
most discussions of the 'failure' of joint assessment. The starting point is to clarity
respective roles:

Why bring in housing?

- The care manager is not sure of their client's housing needs and hence wishes to access a specialist housing needs assessment, e.g. of the damp in the house, of their tenancy rights, of their entitlement to a home improvement grant, of whether they are homeless as defined by housing legislation, of whether their housing is inappropriate.

- The care manager wishes to access housing or housing services for their client, e.g. a council house, a housing association property, a housing with support scheme, a home adaptation.

- The care manager needs to work with the housing professional to address issues of, for example, rent arrears, housing repair and maintenance or conflict with neighbours etc.

Why bring in social services?

- The housing professional is not sure of the care and support needs of their client and hence wishes to access a specialist community care assessment.

- The housing professional wishes to access services provided or funded by social services such as home care, respite care or a place in a residential or nursing home.

- The housing professional needs to work with the care manager to sort out her/his tenant's existing care package, to address issues relating to the distressing behaviour of neighbours known to social services or to assess whether the housing situation is exacerbating his/her social care needs etc.

(Means *et al.*, 1997, pp. 38-39)

The guide argues that it might be helpful to think in terms of the complementary assessment roles of both housing and social services staff. It also underlines that joint working between housing and social services raises issues throughout the care management process and not just with regard to assessment. From such a perspective, the key task is clarity about the basic knowledge about housing that should be held by social services staff and the basic knowledge about community care that is needed by housing workers (see Figure 4). From such an agreed base, it becomes possible for each to know when to refer on for a more specialist assessment and support.

Figure 4: Housing and social services staff: key knowledge and skills

Housing staff need to have the following skills and knowledge in such situations:

- awareness of how social services and health are organised locally, what their priorities are and what they might realistically be likely to provide;

- knowledge of how to make appropriate referrals to health and social services, including information required by social services;

- knowledge of signs of possible dementia and when to seek further advice;

- ability to recognise possible signs of crisis and vulnerability;

- alternative sources of help and advice (advocacy groups, organisations of service users/disabled people, specialist voluntary agencies, etc);

- a commitment to work in partnership with the tenant, housing applicant or their advocate

Housing staff cannot demand that health and social services provide services, but they can encourage a specialist assessment to be made where they have concerns about a client or tenant.

Social services staff need to have the following skills and knowledge:

- awareness of how housing is organised locally, what their priorities are and what housing agencies might realistically be likely to provide (NB: housing authorities must provide free copies of a summary of their housing allocation schemes);

- this awareness to include an understanding of both options for homeless people and vulnerable tenants, together with options for those seeking advice on home improvement and/or adaptation;

- knowledge of how to make appropriate referrals to housing agencies;

- knowledge of how to respond appropriately to referrals from housing agencies;

- awareness of alternative sources of help and advice (advocacy groups, organisations of service users/disabled people, specialist voluntary agencies, etc);

- commitment to work in partnership with service users and their advocates.

Social services staff cannot demand a response from housing agencies but they can encourage a (re)assessment to be made where they have concerns about their client's housing situation

Source: Means *et al.*, 1997

CONCLUSION

The publication of central government guidance on joint working is encouraging in terms of improving the robustness of the housing dimension of community care at the local level. Elsewhere the author has referred to an emerging agreed vision for housing and community care (Means, 1996) in terms of a commitment to independent living and a growing recognition that 'nobody . . . should be expected to change their permanent residence simply in order to obtain the services which they need' (Wagner Report, 1988, p. 114). It would appear that the overall situation is improving.

However, the inadequacy of what has been achieved needs to be recognised in terms of the limitations of the overall housing stock of this country and the resultant knock-on consequences of this for the quality of life for many people with support needs. The result is homelessness and misery for more and more (Bines, 1994; Crane, 1997). But it also leads to misery for many others because of expensive, poorly repaired and inflexible housing. From such a perspective, joint working and integrated responses are still to be encouraged as the way to make best use of existing resources but they are no substitute for also tackling the 'bricks and mortar' issues raised by this Appendix. Elderly people with support needs deserve good quality houses, flats and bungalows which help them develop a sense of home, security and independence, and which maximises the likelihood of them avoiding the need for expensive residential and nursing home care.

References

Age Concern (1998) *Beyond Bricks and Mortar: Dignity and Security in the Home*, Submission to the Royal Commission. Age Concern England: London.

Anchor Trust (1998) *Killer Homes: Facing Up to Poor Housing as a Cause of Older People's Ill-Health*. Anchor Trust: Oxford.

Arblaster, L., Conwa,y J., Foreman, A. and Hawtin, M. (1996) *Asking the Impossible? Inter-Agency Working to Address Housing, Health and Social Care Needs of People in Ordinary Housing*. Policy Press: Bristol.

Audit Commission (1998) *Home Alone: The Role of Housing in Community Care*. Audit Commission: London.

Baldwin, S. and Twigg, J. (1991) 'Women and community care – reflections on a debate', pp. 117-135 in Maclean, M. and Groves, D (eds), *Women's Issues in Social Policy* Routledge: London.

Biggs, S., Philipson, C. and Kingston, P. (1995) *Elder Abuse in Perspective*. Open University Press: Buckingham.

Bines, W. (1994) *The Health of Single Homeless People*, Discussion Paper No. 9. Centre for Housing Policy, University of York.

Boyle, H. (1998) 'Near Miss', *Inside Housing*, 22 May, pp. 19-20

Brenton, M. (1997) 'Choice, mutual support and autonomy in old age: older women's cooperative living arrangements'. Unpublished paper delivered to *Elder Power in the 21st Century*, annual conference of the British Society of Gerontology, 19-21st September at the University of Bristol.

Brewerton, J. and Darton, D. (1997) (eds) *Designing Lifetime Homes*. Joseph Rowntree Foundation: York.

Care and Repair (1994) *Poor Housing: Who Cares?* Care and Repair: Nottingham

Cobbold, C. (1997) *A Cost Benefit Analysis of Lifetime Homes*. Joseph Rowntree Foundation: York.

Crane, M. (1997) *Homeless Truths: Challenging the Myths about Older Homeless People*. Help the Aged and London: Crisis: London.

Dalley, G. (1996 edition) *Ideologies of Caring: Rethinking Community and Collectivism*. Macmillan: Basingstoke.

Davison, B., Kendig, H., Stephens, F. and Merril, V. (1993) *It's My Place: Older People Talk About Their Homes*. Australian Government Publishing Service: Canberra.

Department of Environment/Welsh Office (1995) *Our Future Homes – Opportunity, Choice, Responsibility* HMSO: London.

Department of the Environment, Transport and the Regions (1998) *The English House Condition Survey 1996*. DETR: London.

Department of Health (1989) *Caring for People: Community Care in the Next Decade and Beyond*. HMSO: London.

Department of Health (1994) *Implementing Community Care: Housing and Homelessness*. DoH: London.

Department of Health/Department of the Environment (1997) *Housing and Community Care: Establishing a Strategic Framework*. Department of Health: London.

Griffiths Report (1988) *Community Care: An Agenda for Action*. HMSO: London.

Griffiths, S. (1997) 'Bringing the house down' *Community Care*, 29 May – 4 June, pp. 22-23.

Hayward, D. (1976) 'Dimensions of home' in Weidemann, S. and Anderson, J. (eds) *Priorities for Environmental Design Research*. EDRA: Washington DC.

Heywood, F. (1994) Adaptations: Finding Ways To Say Yes. SAUS Publications: Bristol.

Heywood, F. and Smart, G. (1996) *Funding Adaptations: The Need to Cooperate*. The Policy Press: Bristol.

Higgins, J. (1989) 'Defining community care: realities and myths', *Social Policy and Administration*, vol. 23, no. 1, pp. 3-16.

Hirst, J. (1998) 'Reform threatens supported housing', *Community Care*, 30 April-6 May, pp. 8-9.

Holmans, A. (1995) *Housing Demand the Need in England, 1991 to 2011*. York Publishing Series: York.

Hooton, S. (1996) 'Nightmare on Clarke Street' *Inside Housing*, 6 December, pp. 18-19.

Housing 21 (1997) *Remodelling, Sheltered Housing*. Housing 21: Beaconsfield.

Housing Corporation (1996) *Housing for Older People*, Policy Report No. 3. Housing Corporation: London.

Hoyes, L. and Means, R. with Hawes, D., Smart, G. and Smith, R. (1996) *Supported Housing and Community Care*. Housing Corporation: London.

Kitwood, T., Buckland, S. and Petre, T. (1995) *Brighter Futures*. Anchor Trust: Oxford.

Laing and Buisson (1997) *Housing with Care in the UK: From Sheltered Housing to Assisted Living*. Laing and Buisson: London

Langan, J. and Means, R. (1995) *Personal Finances, Elderly People with Dementia and the 'New' Community Care.* Anchor Trust: Oxford.

Langan, J., Means, R. and Rolfe, S. (1996) *Maintaining Independence in Later Life: Older People Speaking.* Anchor Trust: Oxford.

Leather, P. and Morrison, T. (1997) *The State of UK Housing.* Policy Press: Bristol.

London Federation of Housing Associations (1995) *Managing Vulnerability: The Challenge for Managers of Independent Housing.* London Federation of Housing Associations: London.

Lund, B. and Foord, M. (1997) *Towards Integrated Living? Housing Strategies and Community Care.* The Policy Press: Bristol.

Mackintosh, S. and Leather, P. (1994) 'Funding and managing the adaptation of owner occupied homes for people with physical disabilities', *Health and Social Care in the Community* Vol. 2, No. 4, pp. 229-239.

Maclennan, D., Gibb, K. and More, A. (1990) *Paying for Britain's Housing.* Joseph Rowntree Foundation: York.

Malpass, P. (1993) 'Housing policy and the housing system since 1979' pp. 23-38 in Malpass, P. and Means, R. (eds), *Implementing Housing Policy.* Open University Press: Buckingham.

Marsh, A. and Riseborough, M. (1995) *Making Ends Meet: Older People, Housing Association Costs and the Affordability of Rented Housing.* National Federation of Housing Associations: London.

McCafferty, P. (1994) *Living Independently: A study of the Housing Needs of Elderly and Disabled People.* HMSO: London.

McFailane, A. and Laurie, L. (1996) *Demolishing 'Special Needs: Fundamental Principles of Non-Discriminatory Housing.* British Council of Organisations of Disabled People: Derby.

Means, R. (1996) 'Housing and Community Care for Older People – Joint Working at the Local Level' *Journal of Interprofessional Care* Vol. 10, No. 3, pp. 273-283.

Means, R. (1997a) 'Home, Independence and Community Care: Time for a Wider Vision?' *Policy and Politics* Vol. 25, No. 4, pp. 409-419.

Means, R. (1997b) 'Housing options in 2020: a suitable home for all?' pp. 142-164 in Evandroum, M. (ed) *Baby Boomers: Ageing in the 21st Century.* Age Concern England: London.

Means, R., Brenton, M., Harrison, L. and Heywood, F. (1997) *Making Partnerships Work in Community Care: A Guide for Practitioners in Housing, Health and Social Services.* The Policy Press: Bristol.

Midgley, G., Munlo, I. and Brown, M. (1997) *Sharing Power: Integrating User Involvement and Multi-Agency Working to Improve Housing for Older People.* Policy Press: Bristol.

Office for National Statistics (1997) *Social Trends 27* (London: HMSO)

Oldman, C. *et al.* (1996) *Housing Benefit and Service Charges* Research Report No. 55 Department of Social Security: London.

Pieda plc (1996) *An Evaluation of the Disabled Facilities Grant System*. HMSO: London.

Quilgars, C., Oldman, C. and Carlisle, J. (1997) *Supporting Independence: Home Support Services for Older People*. Anchor Trust: Oxford.

Randolph, B. (1993) 'The re-privatisation of housing associations', pp. 39-58 in Malpass, P. and Means, R. (eds), *Implementing Housing Policy*. Open University Press: Buckingham.

Rapoport, A. (1995) 'A critical look at the concept of home' pp. 25-52 in Benjamin, D. and Stea, D. (eds) *The Home: Words, Interpretations, Meanings and Environments*. Avebury: Aldershop.

Riseborough, M. and Niner, P. (1994) *I Didn't Know You Cared! A survey of Anchor's Sheltered Housing Trends*. Anchor Housing Trust: Oxford.

Robson, D., Nicholson, A-M. and Barker, N. (1997) *Homes for the Third Age: A Design Guide for Extra Care Sheltered Housing*. SPON: London.

Rolfe, S., Leather, P. and Mackintosh, S. (1993) *Available Options*. Anchor Trust: Oxford.

Sapey, B. (1995) 'Disabling homes: a study of the housing needs of disabled people in Cornwall'. *Disability and Society* Vol. 10. No. 1, pp. 31-86.

Simpson, M. (1998) 'Counting the Cost of Care' *Inside Housing* 17 April, p. 15.

Smart, G. and Means, R. (1997) *Housing and Community Care: Exploring the Role of Home Improvement Agencies*. Anchor Trust: Oxford and Care and Repair: Nottingham.

Steinfield, E. (1981) 'The place of old age: the meaning of housing for old people', pp. 198-246 in Duncan, J. (ed), *Housing and Identity: Cross Cultural Perspectives*. Croon Helm: London.

Stewart, M. and Taylor, M. (1995) *Empowerment and Estate Regeneration: A Critical Review*. Policy Press: Bristol.

Tinker, A., Wright, F. and Zeilig, H. (1995) *Difficult to Let Sheltered Housing*. HMSO: London.

Townsend, P. (1963 edn) *The Family Life of Old People*. Penguin: Harmondsworth.

Wagner Report (1988) *Residential Care: A Positive Choice*. HMSO: London.

Watson, L. (1996) *Housing Needs and Community Care: The Housing Pathways Pilot Programme*. NFHA: London.

Watson, L. and Torr, G. (1998) *Housing and Care Links: A Strategy Guide to Planning Services for Older People*. Housing 21: Beaconsfield.

Willcocks, D., Peace, S., and Kellaher, L. (1987) *Private Lives in Public Places*. Tavistock: London.

Appendix 4

The Role of Assistive Technology in Alternative Models of Care for Older People

Dr. Donna Cowan and Dr. Alan Turner-Smith
Centre of Rehabilitation Engineering,
King's College London

INTRODUCTION TO ASSISTIVE TECHNOLOGY

This paper outlines Assistive Technology (AT) that is currently available to enable older people and carers to retain an independent lifestyle. Much of this technology is designed to aid activities within the home. In this context 'Home' includes sheltered housing but not hospital or residential care. We will discuss its application within context, and present possible future developments in the field. The report excludes technology used exclusively for diagnosis and palliative care, although some of the devices described do also have great value in these areas, for example in monitoring or warning about dangerous medical conditions.

1. Terminology

Assistive Technology: is an umbrella term for any device or system that allows an individual to perform a task they would otherwise be unable to do or increases the ease and safety with which the task can be performed. This report will focus on **devices** rather than systems. A number of terms have been coined to describe technology associated with the reversal or amelioration of the declining capacities of older people. These include:

Healthcare technology: a broad term encompassing all technologies used in health care.

Telemedicine: has traditionally referred to the application of medical practice by telematic means, but has recently been enlarged to include all telematic healthcare technology.

Gerontechnology: describes the whole gamut of Assistive Technologies for older people.

Care provider technology: Assistive Technology for the family or personal carer, who is often the forgotten key to care of older people, and the on-going professional service provider.

Independence and security technology: specifying particular relevant functional elements of Assistive Technology.

Rehabilitation Technology: refers to rehabilitation services, which might be more correctly understood as 'habilitation' services because they aim to bring people to their maximum well-being, regardless of their initial condition.

Wellness Technology: a term used to correct the negative connotations of 'technology for disability'. It is particularly associated with technology for the prevention of deterioration, for example by encouraging physical exercise, enabling appropriate changes in lifestyle and changed roles in work, or allowing improved social contacts.

A technical classification of AT has been given in ISO 9999 (EN29999). An alternative classification given by the World Health Organisation (ICIDH, 1997; ICIDH-2, 1998) places more emphasis on the social aspects of disability. A helpful classification in the context of understanding the role of AT has been given in the HEART report (Azevedo *et al.*, 1994) reproduced on the right. Devices that may be of particular use to older people are highlighted. AT that is currently or soon to be available is described in the section on 'Current and coming Assistive Technology'.

Communication
Interpersonal
Computer Access
Telecommunications
Multimedia
User Interfaces
Environmental Controls
(Seating and positioning)

Mobility
Manual Mobility Aids
Powered Mobility Aids
Private Transportation
Public Transportation
Motor Function
Seating and Positioning

Manipulation
Recreational/Sports Devices
Robotics
**Environment Control/
 Adaptation of Houses**
ADL Devices
Motor function

Orientation
**Orientation and
Navigation Systems**
Telecommunications
 (e.g. video telephones)
Robotics

Cognition
Time aids
Planning aids

2. The aims of Assistive Technology

Each of the terms coined above was chosen to reflect or to correct a particular approach to the issues of wellbeing of one group within the community. In this report we will use the term Assistive Technology (AT) in an entirely neutral manner and will comment on the significance of its application as necessary. The aims of AT are to allow older people to maintain their autonomy and dignity, to enable pursuit of self-fulfilment, to allow an independent life and valued membership of society.

The implication of these aims is that a 'medical model' is inadequate to describe the needs for AT. Appropriate AT will be chosen with regard to differences of environment, personality and culture. These requirements will change both with age and with changing conditions and expectations of society. These moving goal posts imply that the provision of AT must be timely and appropriate if it is to be effective and its use regularly reviewed to reflect these changes. In medical terms, successful AT requires adequate service provision that allows early intervention, and thorough, holistic assessment as well as delivery of devices. Support services must however be of paramount importance as a need or requirement is rarely fulfilled by the provision of a single piece of equipment.

The social model of disability recognises that people may have difficulty in defining themselves as disabled or in need of special equipment, so they may not look for an aid or take up a service offered with the best of intentions. The aim of assistive technology design is therefore to create a device that is attractive to own and adds ability without removing status. Such a device will often be happily paid for in preference to an equivalent, statutorily provided device that meets medical need but attracts social stigma.

Assistive Technology can be costly and many of the items mentioned below are available through statutory services. Prospective users however should be aware that the range of devices available through these sources could vary greatly from one local service to another. Eligibility criteria can also vary as can the contribution requirement from the user.

The issue of design and acceptance or rejection of AT will be addressed in the section 'Assistive Technology Issues'.

CURRENT AND COMING ASSISTIVE TECHNOLOGY

In this section we review some of the AT devices currently available, those that are expected to arrive on the market within the next few years and consider the medium and long-term future of AT.

1. Mobility aids

Reduced mobility is one of the major disablements that often accompany old age. The growth in prosthetic joint replacement in the lower limb, which is costly to the individual as well as society, and its application to younger age groups testifies to the importance of pain-free mobility. Orthotic support is a form of AT that is constantly improving thanks to new stronger, lighter materials (e.g. carbon fibre), improved fabrication techniques and innovative design. Knee and ankle orthoses are generally custom-made, however, and therefore tend to be expensive.

Some items of AT are accepted readily by most users as they serve both able and disabled users. Reclining chairs and adjustable beds are examples that can restore near-normal function when close supervision would otherwise be necessary.

When self-supported mobility becomes difficult walking aids can assist. These range from simple sticks, crutches, and walking frames through to rollators with various accessories. The popularity of these devices sometimes rests on their double functionality, as when shopping baskets are attached to a rollator.

Wheelchairs are provided by an extensive nation-wide service to both occasional and full-time users, in manually powered and electrically powered versions, depending on need. Recent legislation in the UK has provided for indoor-outdoor powered chairs and also enabled users to add to the basic prescription by paying for customisation or special designs through a voucher scheme. The choice of equipment available depends on the arrangements that the local wheelchair service has made with their healthcare purchaser, manufacturers and local maintenance contractors.

Stair lifts or through-floor lifts are major items of AT that can restore access to a previously uninhabitable home. These are designed to fit one premises and so, like much house automation, are much cheaper if installed during construction.

2. Aids to Daily Living (ADL)

There is a wide range of equipment available for people who find operating or handling everyday items more difficult. These items are used in a wide range of daily activities such as personal care, housework, and leisure activities. Many aids to daily living are available through social services however, as stated above, the range and eligibility criteria are highly variable.

Some of these items (e.g. adapted cutlery, tap adapters, dressing aids) have over the past five years become easier to purchase and are now sold through a few well known high street retailers. Specialist stores who sell only these items have also become established around the country. Mail order is often available from them to encourage use.

Costs for ADL items can be as little as a few pounds for items such as hairbrushes or adapted taps to several thousand pounds for items such as special shower and toilet facilities.

Information about these devices is available from a number of sources, some of which are listed under 'Bibliography'. However, like most AT, the sources refer to 'disability' rather than 'changing need'.

3. Environmental control systems (ECS)

Environmental Control Systems are devices that allow the user to retain control of their environment within the home despite changing physical abilities. In general they allow control of any household item which can be controlled by using a remote control. The most frequently encountered items with this type of interface are audio-visual equipment i.e. televisions, stereo equipment and video recorders. Other devices can however be adapted to function from a infra-red input such as heating controls curtain openers, door locks and openers, intercoms, telephones, electrical power points and a host of other items.

ECS are currently available through the NHS to people with severe and complex physical disabilities (BSRM, 1994). The provision process varies from area to area however it generally involves a referral from one of a number of people (e.g. users, carers, consultants, GPs, social services workers) followed by an assessment. The assessor decides whether there is need for the system and which system would best suit the user depending on the user's abilities and requirements in the home.

An ECS may be upgraded in that a simple system controlling only a few items may at first be prescribed until the user gains confidence with their system and then extra items may be added as realisation of the potential of the systems grows.

The systems usually consist of a control pad that can vary in shape, size and format depending on the user's abilities and are generally operated using a single switch. The options available appear as a list to the user e.g. light, fan, TV, radio, telephone and a scanning method is employed to offer the range of options to the user.

Infra-red (or radio frequency) operated power modules are plugged into standard electrical sockets in the home and the device to be controlled by the user (e.g. a fan or radio) is then plugged into these modules. The control pad stores the codes to operate each of the devices to be operated in the same way that a standard remote control can store all the codes required to operate a video recorder. Some systems use radio frequency signals instead of infra red, in this way line of sight is not required between the transmitter and the receiver.

Currently only three manufacturers hold contracts with the NHS to supply these systems, and therefore the range available through this service is limited (Medical Devices Agency (MDA), 1995). A wider range is available commercially and may be purchased privately.

As already stated, this service is intended only for people with severe disabilities, however the concept of operation that an ECS offers could usefully be employed by someone with a less severe disability. For example the user may have difficulty operating a standard remote control. A large pad remote control may ease the operation of individual items or an 'all in one' remote suggested to replace the three or four control pads operating separate devices in the home. There are a variety of these available from high street stores. The most common simply have stored within them thousands of manufacturer's codes for different devices. The appropriate codes can be selected by following simple start-up procedures. Some remote controllers are able to 'learn' new codes. Device control codes can be input therefore making a single remote capable of operating a TV, video, lighting system and curtain operator.

Many DIY stores stock items such as curtain openers that can be operated by remote controls which are easily installed.

Lighting switches can sometimes be a problem for those with reduced finger power or dexterity. Again DIY stores stock infra-red controlled switches, roller or touch sensitive pad switches, all of which can be used to operate main overhead lighting. Another component of an ECS which is widely used is a remote controlled door release and intercom system. This allows those who are immobile to control access to their home. By including a closed circuit television the user can see who is at the door before opening it.

Costs for the above items can range from £20 for a multifunction remote control to several thousand pounds for an environmental control system with speech output.

4. Communication

This can cover a wide range of equipment, from relatively common hearing aids to high-tech computer-based speech synthesised text to speech output systems. One problem commonly associated with the more sophisticated systems is that they can be bulky and so are predominantly aimed at non-ambulant users.

Communication aids centres are located around the country to provide assessment and advice. Some provide follow-up sessions or training courses on the use of aids for therapists etc, others keep strictly to the prescription and assessment stage of the process. The cost of the assessment is not inconsiderable in some cases and therefore referral is through a professional, usually speech and language therapist or GP.

Having been assessed, the provision of the prescribed item may depend on the availability of charitable funding or the user's ability to pay for their own device as there is little official funding for communication aids. As with all types of equipment, support in the use and maintenance of the device is vital and because of the lack of funding this is often a reason for the disuse of devices.

Recent technical advances have led to an improvement in communication systems in general which could potentially reduce the isolation encountered by older people or indeed anyone who may have reduced mobility. Most of these possibilities are due to the development of the Internet. An example of this is in the use of video conferencing. To date this has been an expensive tool available only for commercial use, but recently software has become available to enable cheap video links via the Internet (for about £1000). It has been suggested as an effective way of forming self help groups for older people and carers alike (Magnusson *et al.*, 1998).

The use of computers to provide entertainment already combats loneliness. In the section 'The Future' we consider this further. Home shopping via cable TV and the Internet is already available, bringing back the old concept of delivery to the door. The Internet is also proving to be a useful means to enable continued participation in cultural life. People can share artistic, education and the creative arts: pictures, video, sound, electronic publishing with other homebound friends or able-bodied people (Klöve *et al.*, 1998).

5. Security: Telephones, Telephone/Alarms, and Alarms

Telephones, once considered a luxury are now seen to be an invaluable tool for all. They allow the less mobile to keep in contact with relatives and friends, enable business transactions (using services such as telephone banking) and allow people who may otherwise be restricted, to initiate social contact. Like all AT, however, the provision of a single piece of equipment should not be viewed as a total solution to the problem of communication but rather, in the case of telephone equipment, as an addition to face to face communication to prevent increased isolation (Cullen, 1992).

A wide range of products are available to users who have disabilities (both sensory and physical), and those who are older requiring adaptation to existing systems (British Telecommunications, 1998). As with many other forms of assistive technology, available services and adaptations can often be overlooked by older people who may be experiencing problems using their telephone effectively and yet do not consider themselves to be 'disabled'. They may require a simple alteration such as a large button pad to compensate for decreased dexterity when dialling numbers or reduced visual acuity. A number of 'options' are available in an effort by the industry to provide service and access for all including various handsets and adaptations, priority services and alternative services for people who have sensory impairments.

For those with a visual impairment, enlarged number pads and labels for handsets can be used. For those with a hearing impairment, alternatives such as loudspeakers and visual and vibrating alarms are available. Acoustic amplification is available and inductive coupling units (magnetic amplification) for users who have hearing aids. Where amplification is not the answer a number of alternatives exist. Text output devices such as message pagers or fax machines may be a solution, alternatively, more specialised equipment such as textphones. These usually consist of a standard QWERTY keyboard and a screen. The user types what they have to say and receives what the recipient types at the other end and so a written conversation takes place between users with compatible equipment. The problem existing with this is compatibility allowing world-wide communication (COST 219 Final Report, 1992). Text phone users can communicate with users of standard telephones via the TypeTalk service. This is a relay service currently operated by the RNID (Royal National Institute for Deaf People) in the UK.

Videophones consist of a standard phone with a video link. Although this technology has been available since the early 1960s, videophones have had little impact on every day life. This has been due to a number of factors including bulky equipment and high costs, however, the introduction of ISDN (Integrated Systems Digital Network) is likely to have a significant impact on this technology and aid its further introduction. Some European countries already have already introduced an internal videotelephony service (Cullen, 1992)

For users with mobility impairments, solutions such as extension sockets and cords to allow the telephone to be moved throughout the home, and cordless or mobile phones enable users to keep the phone near at all times.

For those with dexterity impairments large number pads are available as well as phones which allow 'hands free' operation. These have in-built microphones and loudspeakers allowing two way conversation without the need to keep hold of the receiver. Similar telephones are used as part of ECS described above.

For users with impaired or without speech, telephones are available which output recorded messages by pressing buttons on a keypad. Others allow users with communication aids that have speech synthesised output, e.g. a Liberator[1] or Cameleon2, to make calls unaided using a single switch.

An advisory committee on telecommunications for disabled and elderly people (DIEL) exists which provides information and advice to Oftel. Although they do not provide a comprehensive information service to the public they do provide information packs on what telecommunication products are available for older and disabled people.

Telephones are often considered for use as an alarm as it enables the user to summon help in an emergency. Their use however is limited if the user falls or needs assistance when out of reach of a telephone or indeed if the user cannot gain a reply from their call for help (Thornton and Mountain, 1992). A development from the stand-alone telephone has been that of community alarm systems/services (Riseborough, 1997)

A community alarm system/service has three components:

1. Means of calling for help

This is usually a small portable trigger (usually radio frequency) which is carried at all times, usually worn around the neck as a pendant. When activated an alarm unit is triggered (situated by the phone). This unit is programmed to contact a central control point using the standard telephone network.

In most systems an amplified speech link is opened between the caller and the operator.

2. The control centre operator interpreting the call and initiating action

Operators at the control centre talk through the problem with the user and if necessary initiate action by arranging for an appropriate 'visitor' to call.

The call receiving equipment is generally linked to a database holding information about the user

3. Respondents

If necessary designated people then visit the user and assess the situation/offer help. The people doing this vary depending on the service. Sometimes they are employed by the answering service or else designated by the service user e.g. family members, neighbours. The action taken by the visitor also varies i.e. may give physical aid or simply act as a key holder to enable others to enter the user's premises.

A wide range of alarms is available commercially for users to buy from a variety of sources. These range from personal alarms which emit high volume sound when activated (costs from £10) to mobile pagers which directly contact another person (costs from £200). Home based alarm systems equipment such as that described above can be bought for on average £250. Extra costs may include the installation of a phone line.

Alarms are also available that are activated if the user falls, a particular hazard for older people. A positional sensor determines the angle of the alarm and hence user relative to the horizontal. Activation occurs if it is less than 20 degrees, or if the user is prone or supine for more than a specified time period (information from the DLF database, 1998).

'Wander' alarms are also available. These devices can be useful by reducing the anxiety associated with wandering for a wide range of carers e.g. people caring for those with learning disabilities, with some forms of dementia and for parents with young children. In general these alarms take the form of pendants or clip-on sensors, which emit a radio frequency signal. If a detector within a specified distance does not receive the signal either continuously or at predetermined intervals, the alarm is activated. Costs for these types of alarms vary from £25 to £6K and upwards for a residential installation. Alternatively, a mat with implanted sensors across a doorway can be used to alert carers if someone leaves a specified area (costs up to £230).

6. Cognition

It is sometimes thought that people with cognitive impairments cannot manage new technology, which could account for the small range of products developed for this group. However, AT is becoming available for and being used by people with learning disabilities (e.g. reminder systems, special clocks, pictogram and diary systems to help them to plan their own day[3]) demonstrating that this is not the case. Although still a rather small area the equipment available could be used for people who become confused or suffer from a cognitive impairment. Future developments of computer and software technology will increasingly allow cognitive support to become a natural and life-enhancing reality.

7. Integration: Smart Houses

'Smart Housing' is a term used to describe the electronic and computer-controlled integration of many of the devices within the home. (The term 'domotics' is used to mean domicile/domestic technology). Smart Housing for older and disabled people has and is being been tested at a number of sites around Europe (Elger and Furugren, 1998; Bonner, 1998). Validation includes cost-benefit analysis of a wide mixture of technology and service organisation (Ng-A-Tham, 1998).

It allows the integration of environmental controls for effective control of a building, either by deliberate control or automatically. This includes door and window openers, curtains and blinds, heating, lighting, security devices including motion sensors and video surveillance, telephone and communication, water taps, cooker, bed warming. Monitoring of activities can even be extended to daily health checks, for example an instrumented toilet has been developed to measure heart rate, temperature, and nutrition (Tamura *et al.*, 1998).

Although the basic technology for domotics has been available for many years, the software systems and network standards have not yet converged to the point where systems can be sold in large numbers to reduce cost. Low-cost systems such wireless and radio control are available but currently not reliable enough for safety-critical AT applications.

Builders do not want to commit to any new design so economies of scale are not available. Consequently installation is strictly needs led. The future domestic market, however, is likely to be led by entertainment rather than necessity.

If smart house technology is installed as an AT solution, someone must be technically responsible for the **whole** system of equipment otherwise individual suppliers will argue when system breaks down. Statutory bodies providing AT are naturally reluctant to take on this new and costly commitment.

Although smart housing has been promised for many years, current international discussions are at the stage that a standard is likely to emerge before the millennium. Once the smart house concept has been adopted, the smart neighbourhood is not far away.

ASSISTIVE TECHNOLOGY ISSUES

1. Awareness and Accessibility/Availability

It has long been acknowledged that the uptake of assistive technology is dependent on a number of factors, one of these being the availability of current and easily-accessible information about availability, cost, assessment procedures and funding sources (Mandelstam, 1990). A number of sources are available (see the Bibliography), however whether they will be used or not depends on the users perception of themselves. For example, a large number of potential users of 'aids to daily living' would be older people who require some support and assistance in everyday life yet are unlikely to define themselves as disabled. A second group would be older people with disabilities (having had a disability form birth or acquired later in life). The first group may be hesitant or simply not consider going to a resource centre for information about what they would consider 'aids for people with disabilities' or referring to an organisation such as the Disabled Living Foundation for information. However many of the information sources that carry relevant material about these aids are offshoots from charities or organisations associated with a particular disability, condition or illness.

To ensure relevant design and uptake of technology, older people have to be given power to influence developments for themselves. This is being addressed by centres such Centre of Applied Gerontology at the University of Birmingham who provide a consultancy service to industry. In addition, the spending power of older people will increasing apply pressure to the design process.

2. Attraction and Affordability — Economics

In deciding allocation of resources for new technology, do we use the judgement of society, of carers, or of older people? It is generally recognised that in the context of increasing possibilities for medical care and an ageing population, society alone cannot and should not be the sole funder of AT. Without waste of resources, how can investment on care in the home be encouraged? Residential care is already expensive with respect to AT in the home, so further incentives such tax concessions will have little effect. It can also be difficult to define AT. The most efficient way of increasing resources for home care may be by raising awareness of the possibilities and attraction of AT through information spreading and teaching by example. Inclusion of AT in TV soaps can have a major impact on the awareness and desirability of AT.

Broadcasting a purely technical model of AT disability may also pose a threat, encouraging technical push where disability applications can be just a decoration. Healthcare services are all too aware that once a technology (tool of support) has been adopted, it is difficult to dispose of!

Ability to live at home is an issue of quality of life. This is not best measured in an entirely healthcare or medical model of an individual, but in some more holistic model that includes empowerment of older persons who are suffering a loss of influence, status (importance to others) and sense of self worth. The model should also include the wellbeing of their family or nuclear social group, and the wealth (in the highest and broadest sense) of their society. As a consequence, holistic funding becomes essential. Funding through one channel (e.g. health or social services) creates distortions due to budget competition, or inefficiency due to duplications, holes in support, and incompatible technical or social solutions.

3. Assessment and Acquisition

It is always wise to get advice on a purchase from an independent or professional source. The contact information list (section on 'Some National and International Services') contains a number of sources, however the user's requirements and condition must be considered before recommending one rather than another. For example, someone who simply requires a jar opener due to reduced strength has a different need to someone with a deteriorating condition requiring help with mobility. In the latter case a GP might refer a requirement for a wheelchair first to the local wheelchair service to have needs properly assessed whereas the former could simply buy a jar opener from a local store. Appropriate routes to information have to be established in order for the user to get the fastest and most appropriate response. Information about Assistive Technology has traditionally been aimed at the professional rather than the user (e.g. Hamilton Index). It is this lack of user awareness which may account for the engineered rather than the designed appearance of some products (Mandelstam, 1996). This approach is being challenged and documents such as the Department of Health booklet (1996) attempts to give a user details of how to go about getting specialist equipment. As well as this information provided by charities and support groups often provide factsheets about AT and where to go for further advice. The Contact Information section contains a selection of organisations that provide this type of service.

Many of the services listed have websites that are freely accessible to those with a computer and internet connection (see Bibliography). However, as most older people are still without this form of communication, fact sheets and telephone helplines are offered by many of the organisations.

4. Acceptance, Use and Rejection

It is well recognised that assistive technology often remains unused (Korpela *et al.*, 1993, Sonn *et al.*, 1996). This may be because the technology was incorrectly prescribed or imposes too great a burden in use. Often, however, it an important reason for rejection is the stigma attached to an assistive product. Services provide technology to meet a 'need', but users (and their carers) will most readily use technology that is desirable because it enhances their social status as well enabling them to do things or making them feel better. It is because design for older and disabled people at home has to be based on want, not an assumption of need, that much research in AT is currently aimed at exploring acceptance.

'I am ashamed of the (adapted) bathroom, when anybody goes, I feel like, oh it's so terrible, you know . . . You see, I'm not a normal person!'
(Lebbon and Boess, 1998)

The importance of social awareness is hard to over-estimate. To this end the MediaAge news service was launched in 1998 at European Social Policy Forum in Brussels to inform journalists, non-governmental organisations and older people.

Legislation can also help. The alteration of fashion and social perception has been a major benefit of the Americans with Disability Act (1990).

5. Europeanisation and Standardisation

According to the White Book of the European Commission (COMM, 1994) the intention is to promote the integration of people with disabilities. The Commission will also derive a suitable instrument to confirm and support the UN's Standard Rules on the equalisation of opportunities for persons with disabilities. One of the rules concerns support services.

> *'States should ensure the development and supply of support services, including assistive devices for persons with disabilities, to assist them to increase their level of independence in their daily living and to exercise their rights.'*

Thus the role of AT in support of older people is well recognised.

The market in assistive technology currently suffers from being small and fragmented, which results in generally high prices and under-developed design. Europe, however, is the largest potential market for AT products in the industrialised world. In 1995 about 26 million potential consumers of AT products can be expected. Between 1995 and 2020 the estimated number of people, who are potential users of AT will increase more than 25% according to Carr *et al.,* (1993). A single European market in assistive technology will have a great economic impact, from which industry, administration and the users will benefit. A single European market will also improve the possibilities for export outside the European Union. This enlarged market will benefit users by reducing costs and improving design.

A larger market is attractive for many reasons, but the differences between national service delivery systems, and national social and psychological preferences renders progress to a single market difficult. People in different countries have different preferences to input mechanisms. For example, PAM-AID is a walking aid for frail and visually impaired people, the development of which involved user requirement studies in UK Ireland and Sweden (O'Neill *et al.,* 1998). The study showed that users in the UK preferred finger and thumb operated switches for input whereas in Sweden people prefer using a finger alone. So items produced for a mass European market will still require modification for different preferences.

When technical issues alone are paramount, standardisation can be a major assistance to market development. As mentioned in Section 2.5 above, a number of text telephone systems are available throughout Europe but incompatibilities inhibit communication between them. Agreements are being sort in most technical spheres. For example a new EU standardisation work is starting in Sept/Oct 1998 for accessibility to IT following Medical Devices Directive 93/42/EEG.

The Medical Devices Directive on the design and manufacture of medical devices has important implications for AT. Most AT devices are designated 'class 1', i.e. presenting low risk. Since June 1998 the manufacturers of these devices have had the responsibility of registering with the appropriate authority in their member country and ensuring that devices used in healthcare meet certain design and manufacturing requirements. Some fear that this harmonisation process may cause the rate of innovation in the market to decrease. However the quality of products will be enhanced and they will be able to be marketed across national boundaries in Europe.

6. Education and training

It is sadly true that not all professionals advising on AT are adequately trained or knowledgeable about what AT can do. One reason for this is that up-to-date specialised education and training has largely been unavailable, except in Sweden and the UK (HEART Study Line E, 1995). Efforts are currently underway to stimulate education across Europe to utilise the total competence within Europe, in order to lead to a higher quality and uniformity of care within service provision.

Carers and users also require information and training. Some carers develop their skills over a long time as an older relative gradually becomes more dependent, for example. Others are thrown into the job, for example when their partner becomes suddenly disabled following a stroke. The latter group in particular needs training and network in a hurry. In this respect interactive video links in the home can provide welcome information, training and a network to others with similar problems or solutions to share (ACTION).

Even before a product is made available, those involved in the design process need training. It is desirable to involve older people and carers in the formation of engineers and designers as well as consulting them in the design process itself (see, for example, Poulson *et al.*, 1996). They are, after all, the experts on everyday life. The best designs emerge from an informed network of designer, consumer, manufacturer and provider.

Take-up of AT depends critically on knowledge of its availability, so information technology and the education of professionals, older people, and carers is another essential lubricant to appropriate adoption of AT.

Beyond those immediately involved we have already mentioned the stigma associated with some AT. This is where social education is required – a task for schools, charities, and the media as well as AT professionals.

THE FUTURE

1. Discussion

We cannot predict the future, but there are certain trends that indicate likely technical possibilities. Using these we present here a few ideas that may stimulate thinking. A forecast to 10-20 years is generally considered 'long term' and highly unreliable, but we do well to remember that to foresee the possibilities for the next generation of older people we need to think 30 years ahead. Such long-term prediction is made even more difficult by the fact that the needs of older people, the capabilities of their carers, and the shape of their society will also change. For example, are the expectations and fitness of today's 40-year-olds compatible with the heavy caring role that demographics suggests they may be called on to undertake in 20 years, let alone their own requirements as older people in 40 or 50 years? Will advances in medicine change the nature of the demand for Assistive Technology?

As a background to technological change it is worth noting that computing power has been roughly doubling every year for the last 15 years. In 20 years it is reasonable to expect we could have 10 times the power of today's fastest multimedia personal computer available in a package the size of a credit card for the cost of a newspaper. The development of mechanical technology is not so rapid and has been aided in recent years chiefly by the use of information technology in design or by the use of electronic control to overcome limits of mechanical tolerances.

SMART house technology has the potential for immediate application. Once a common standard emerges it is possible to see this becoming a standard for new buildings. Building design for all, i.e. designing a building to suit all ages of people, is a new concept that is likely only to be adopted on a significant scale in the short term through building regulations. This is because builders get their return from the first buyer, not the whole spectrum of buyers who might occupy the property through the years. Mixed housing stock suitable for creating communities of all ages is a possible intermediate solution.

In the process of housing design, virtual reality is a new tool that will increasingly enable architects and AT designers to build more age-friendly housing. It will also enable older people to assess their ability to live independently.

Orientation and navigation within buildings will be assisted by intelligent signage or signage aids (e.g. signs that show the way to the toilet when asked, or even when they detected that it might be necessary based on a previous pattern of movement or physiological condition).

In all future scenarios it is important to remember that AT is not just to enable an older person to live alone, but to maintain autonomy when living with his or her family or carer.

Take-up of technology by older people is not related solely to chronological age, however it is true that familiarity with a technology makes it easier to learn. With this in mind we can expect future older people to be as comfortable with computer controls as the present generation with telephones. We need to think of the technology being used extensively by the current generation to think of the implications for next generation of older people.

We are moving into an information age where although we are developing tools to order information (e.g. hypertext) we are also being swamped by more information than even, thanks to increasing connectivity (e.g. Internet). In the future we can expect it to be easy to find detailed information about AT devices, to find how to use them and to locate and interact with a human network that is experienced in using.

It should always be remembered that the opportunities and equalities created by technology, where physical strength or memory does not matter so much, also creates barriers. For example new interfaces that fully-abled people can enjoy may be unusable by older people with cognitive problems, vision, hearing, manipulation or other infirmity. We have seen the dangers of the 'windowing' systems used now for computer displays that might have created insuperable problems for partially sighted people. Fortunately these issues are being actively addressed at the core of the operating systems thanks to active lobbying and technical assistance from disabled groups worldwide.

The evolution of computer games and interactive television will provide a stimulating and ultimately very worthwhile form of entertainment. Further, in the future it is possible to imagine a world in which it becomes rather difficult to defining 'reality'. It will certainly not confine its inhabitants to the limitations of a human body. We may then wonder what the importance of mobility will be. We can think of digital shared memory albums: provokers that will stimulate memories with sounds and smells, texture and shape as well as vision. A personal virtual reality diary will enable older people to re-live and share their experiences more effectively with each other, with their grandchildren, or whoever.

Although we do not need to move as much as we do now, it seems that physical meeting of human beings is still of paramount importance. We are social animals, so mobility aids may still be important in the future. But mobility is limited by the imperatives of physics: it does take a significant strength and energy to move people from place to place. At the same time, encouraging mobility will certainly still be important for our physical wellbeing. Technology may be used to encourage a healthy lifestyle rather than compensate for the results of an unhealthy one.

2. European Research projects in the field

TIDE: *Telematics for Disabled and Elderly People* is an applied research programme under TAP, the Telematics Application Programme of the European Commission Directorate-General XIII. TIDE aims to develop applications that provide support for independent living, autonomy and social integration opportunities and to open up society to older people and individuals with disabilities. Focusing on assistive technologies, the sector is developing systems that improve mobility and interpersonal communications, and which shape the immediate environment to suit individuals' needs. From Braille or acoustics displays for personal computers, to robot arms for wheelchairs, informatics or communications technologies can enhance quality of life and tailor state-of-the-art technology to the specific needs of the user.

ACTION *'Assisting Carers using Telematics Intervention to meet Older persons Needs'* project aims to determine needs of informal carers and then to develop an expert system which will give access to practical assistance in developing competency i.e. safe lifting etc. It will define the choice and process of eliciting respite care help, financial resource availability and improvement of coping skills. The project will show that through a combination of familiar technologies e.g. TV remote control units and use of additional i.e. video reception and transmission, fast computer processors and access to interactive communication – on line effective care information communication can become a reality for formal and informal carers.

CERTAIN *Cost effective rehab tech through appropriate indicators* plans to develop methodology of evaluation of cost effectiveness and cost utility of rehab technologies and will then validate the methodology. It aims to provide a robust method to prove cost effectiveness of AT.

COST 219 bis *European co-operation in the field of Scientific and Technical research* is a framework for scientific and technical co-operation in Europe. The main aspect is a co-ordination of the national research on an European level. COST Actions consist of basic and pre-competitive research as well as activities of public utility. From an initial 7 Actions in the beginning COST has grown to 123 Actions in February 1996. At the moment the COST co-operation consists of 25 member countries: The 15 EU Member States, Iceland, Norway, Switzerland, The Czech republic, Slovakia, Hungary, Poland, Turkey, Slovenia, Croatia and The European Commission.

DAILY aims to develop an interactive CD-ROM that supplies information about assistive devices to the elderly with minor mobility problems who want to remain independent. Provides knowledge about types of technology and how to use and furnish their home with them – enabling individuals to take the initiative in defining his or her own needs. Users can choose among different subjects and problems they want to solve.

EUSTAT: – *Empowering users through Assistive Technology* – aims to develop a training model set of curricula and basic educational material for the education of end users of assistive technology. This will enable end users to make informed choices about AT and improve skill of peer counsellors and professionals.

FACILE aims to produce the definition, the realisation and the experimental application of support tools for the design and management of living spaces provided with automated telematics systems and external services, targeted to elderly and disabled (end-users).

FACILE will develop a catalogue of home environment systems concerning home automation systems and available products. Also a design guide for the modification of the home environment.

HOME aims to produce an intelligent multimodal and multimedia user interface providing a new dimension of natural man machine communication able to remotely control and even tele-operate (via mobile phone) all home appliances, usable by the vast majority of elderly and disabled users.

PAM-AID is a mobility aid for partially-sighted people which will enable users to improve their personal autonomy and remove the need for complete dependence on carers.

SAFE 21. Care and security for elderly people at home in Europe is fragmented. Social alarm systems only provide an emergency response to a call initiated manually by the user. SAFE 21 aims to take social alarms in Europe into the 21st century, using the existing infrastructure to deliver much broader assistive technology and extending availability to users who are currently excluded.

TELEMATE: Telematic Multidisciplinary Assistive Technology Education. This programme is developing a framework for the design, conduct and continued maintenance of modular courses in Assistive Technology for people from all disciplines involved with its across Europe.

Footnotes

1 Liberator Ltd, Whitegates, Swinstead, Grantham, Lincolnshire NG33 4PA.

2 Cameleon: Cambridge Adaptive Communication, The Mount, Toft, Cambridge CB3 7RL

3 http://www.handitek.se/html/eng/WATCH.HTM#download

References

ACTION: EC DGXIII TAP project DE 3001: *Assisting Carers using Telematics Interventions to meet Older persons Needs*.
http://www2.echo.lu/telematics/disabl/action.html

Axtell, L. A. and Yasuda, Y. L. (1993) *Assistive Devices and home modifications in geriatric medicine.* Geriatric Rehabilitation 9 (4), 803-821.

Azevedo, L., Feria, H., Nunes da Ponte, M., Wann, J. E. and Recellado, J. G. Z. (1994) Heart Report: Line E – Rehabilitation Technology Training: E3.2 European Curricula in Rehabilitation Technology Training, European Commission: Brussels.

Bonner, S. (1998) Assistive Interactive Dwelling House. In *Improving the Quality of Life for the European Citizen*, Placencia Porrero, I. and Ballabio, E. (eds.). IOS Press, 396-400: Amsterdam.

British Telecommunications (1998) The BT Guide for Disabled People, British Telecommunications PLC: London.

BSRM (1994) Prescription for Independence. British Society for Rehabilitation Medicine: London.

Carr, S., Carruthers, A., Humphreys, J. and Sandhu (1993) *The Market for R.T. in Europe: a Demographic Study of Need* in (Eds.: Ballabio, Placencia-Porrero, I., Puig de la Bellacasa, R.). Rehabilitation Technology, Strategies for the European Union, Proc. 1st TIDE Congress, April 6-7 1993, IOS Press: Brussels, Amsterdam.

COMM (1994) The European Commission COM(94) 333, July 27, 1994.

COST Action 219 (1992) *Final Report – Future telecommunication and teleinformatics facilities for disabled people and elderly.* http://www.stakes.fi/cost219/COSA130.HTML

Cullen, K. (1992) *Technology and the elderly. The role of technology in the prolonging the independence of the elderly in the community context – FAST Report R1992.* The Commission of the European Communities: Brussels.

DAILY: EC DGXIII TAP project DE 3207: *Make Daily Life Easier*
http://www2.echo.lu/telematics/disabl/daily.html

Dept of Health (1996) A Practical Guide for Disabled People – where to find information, services and equipment. Dept. of Health: London.

Elger, G. and Furugren, B. (1998) 'SmartBo' – An ICT and computer-based demonstration home for disabled people. In *Improving the Quality of Life for the European Citizen*, Placencia Porrero, I. and Ballabio, E. (eds.). IOS Press, 396-400: Amsterdam.

EUSTAT: EC DGXIII TAP project DE 3402 *Empowering Users Through Assistive Technology*. http://www2.echo.lu/telematics/disabl/eustat.html

FACILE: EC DGXIII TAP project DE 3207. *Support tools for housing design and management, integrated with telematics systems and services.* http://www2.echo.lu/telematics/disabl/facile.html

HEART Study: Ohlin P, Fagerberg G and Lagerwall T (1995) Technology for Assisting Disabled and Older People in Europe The HEART Study. TIDE 1995.

Home: EC DGXIII TAP project DE 3003. *Home applications optimum multimedia/multimodal system for environment control.* http://www2.echo.lu/telematics/disabl/homep.html

ICIDH (1997) *International Classification of Impairments, Activities and Participation: A Manual of Dimensions of Disablement and Handicaps.* World Health Organization

ICIDH-2 (1998) *International Classification of Impairments, Activities and Participation: A Manual of Dimensions of Disablement and Functioning.* http://www.who.ch/msa/mnh/ems/icidh/index.htm or just http://www.who.ch/

Klöve, L., Lundman. M., and Oderstedt, I. (1998) Culture for Everyone – in the footsteps of Frida Kahlo. In *Improving the Quality of Life for the European Citizen*, Placencia Porrero, I. and Ballabio, E. (eds.). IOS Press, 164-167: Amsterdam.

Korpela, R., Seppanen, R. and Koivikko, M. (1993) Rehabilitation Service Evaluation: A follow up of the extent of use of technical aids for disabled children Disab and Rehab 15 143-150.

Lebbon, C. and Boess, S. (1998) Wellbathing. In *Improving the Quality of Life for the European Citizen*, Placencia Porrero, I. and Ballabio, E. (eds.). IOS Press, 192-197: Amsterdam.

Magnusson, L., Berthold, H., Brito, L., Chambers, M., Emery, D., and Daly, T. (1998) ACTION – Assisting Carers using Telematics Interventions to meet Older persons Needs. In *Improving the Quality of Life for the European Citizen*, Placencia Porrero, I. and Ballabio, E. (eds.). IOS Press, 173-178: Amsterdam.

Mandelstam, M. (1990), How to get equipment for disability. Disabled Living Foundation: London

Medical Devices Agency (1995) *Environmental control systems. Disability Equipment Assessment A14.* HMSO: Norwich.

Ng-A-Tham, S. (1998) Equality service, accessible for all citizens, in prticular Elderly and Disabled. In *Improving the Quality of Life for the European Citizen*, Placencia Porrero, I. and Ballabio, E. (eds.). IOS Press, 189-191: Amsterdam.

O'Neill, A. M., Petrie, H., Lacey, G., Katevas, N., Karlson, M. A., Engelbrektsson, P., Gallagher, B., Hunter, H., Zoldan, D. (1998) In *Improving the Quality of Life for the European Citizen*, Placencia Porrero, I. and Ballabio, E. (eds). IOS Press, 292-295: Amsterdam.

PAM-AID: EC DGXIII TAP project DE 210: *Personal adaptive mobility aid for the frail and elderly visually impaired.* http://www2.echo.lu/telematics/disabl/pamaid.html

Poulson, D., Ashby, M., and Richardson, S. (1996) Userfit – A practical handbook on user-centred design for Assistive Technology. HUSAT Research Institute: Loughborough.

Riseborough, M. (1997) Community Alarm Services Today and Tomorrow. Anchor Trust: Oxford.

SAFE 21: EC DGXIII TAP project DE 3011: *Social Alarms for Europe in the 21st Century.* http://www2.echo.lu/telematics/disabl/safe21.html

Sonn, U., Davegardh, H., Lindskog, A. C. and Steen, B. (1996) The use and effectiveness of assistive devices in an elderly urban population. *Aging Clin.Exp.Res.* 8 176-183.

Tamura, T., Togawa, T., Ogawa, M. and Yoda, M. (1998) 'Fully Automated Health Monitoring System in the Home'. *Medical Engineering and Physics (in press)*.

TELEMATE. EC DGXIII TAP project DE 4103. *Telematic Multidisciplinary Assistive Technology Education.* http://www.telemate.org

Thornton, P. and Mountain, G. (1992) *A positive response to developing community alarm services for older people.* Joseph Rowntree Foundation Community Care: York.

Bibliography

a. Publications

Cook, A. M. and Hussey, S. M. (1995) *Assistive Technologies: Principles and Practice.* ISBN 0-8016-1038-9. 712 pages. Mosby: St Louis.

EUSTAT D3402 Deliverable D03.2: *Critical Factors involved in End-User's Education in relation to Assistive Technology.* Brussels: European Commission DGXIII Telematics Application Programme.

IFMBE News. *Growing old technically – report on the IPTS report for the Committee on Science, Technology and Energy of the European Parliament.* IFMBE News, November 1997 (27), N4-N7.

b. Some National and International Services

Below are just some of the ever-widening group of national and international disability sites and organisations that share information on AT for older people. In addition to these sites there are also countless locally organised information services for people with disabilities.

Centre for Policy on Ageing: Independent organisation aiming to formulate and promote social policies to allow all older people to achieve full potential of their later years http://www.cpa.org.uk/cpa. There is no link to an end-user database e.g. equipment, therefore it is accessed by professionals working in the field. There are links to articles on the use of equipment by older people. A similar site is that of:

Charities such as Help the Aged and Age Concern have extensive websites with information about AT and provide free factsheets. http://www.ace.org.uk, http://www.helptheaged.org.uk

Co-Net AbleData is a North-American based CD-ROM of AT devices. The information it contains is supplied directly by manufacturers.

DesignAge http://DesignAge.rca.ac.uk/ is an action research programme on design for an ageing population based at the Royal College of Art and funded by the Helen Hamlyn Foundation and the EC. This site gives a useful database search of articles including details on articles such as KeepAble superstore etc. fact sheets from Age Concern England.

DIAL (Disability Information and Advice Line) are local services generally run by users for users. These services often have websites associated with them.

DIEL http://www.acts.org.uk/diel.htm is an independent body established by Act of Parliament to advise OFTEL, the Telecommunications industry regulator, on the particular interests and needs of consumers who happen to be either elderly or disabled, or both. It produces free information packs in an effort to make people aware of what is currently available.

Disability Information Trust (Equipment for Disabled People) publishes a series of reviews of AT of many types. The reviews include an assessment of the design and function and are aimed at users carers and professionals alike. The Trust is based at: Mary Marlborough Centre, Nuffield Orthopaedic Centre, Oxford OX3 7LD

Disability Living Foundation: http://www.atlas.co.uk/dlf/ (UK based). This is a major site again predominantly for those with disabilities however the AT covers all aspects of daily living and therefore appropriate for a wide range of users. Contents include a wide range of fact sheets on choosing and fitting equipment, information about disability living centres, training courses aimed at users, carers and professionals, the recently re-established DLF helpline and the DLF equipment and Hamilton index database. There is also a special set of guides for older people.

Disability Net: http://www.disabilitynet.co.uk/ (UK based, Hull). Through this site there is access to a number of other sites providing information on a wide range of subjects from Government policy decisions through to holidays for people with disabilities. This is a site for those who have disabilities and as such may not be used by elderly and carers with minor daily activity/mobility problems.

Disability North: http://www.nagd.org.uk/ this is a site aimed at promoting the work of disability groups based in the north of England. The emphasis is on people with disabilities but there are a number of links to other sites in the UK and Europe and North America. The services of Disability North are based in Newcastle and are available to anyone needing information on disability issues. It is also linked to the local Disabled Living Centre and the information and advisory service covering both equipment demonstration, and general information enquiries.

Disabled Living Centres http://www.dlcc.demon.co.uk/homepage.html are local centres where users and carers can try out and get information and advice about assistive technology. Lists of centres are available from: DLCC, 11 Cranmer Road, London SW9 6EJ.

ENB Healthcare database http://www.enb.org.uk/ is predominantly for professionals involved in the field of care giving.

HANDITEL: http://www.santel.lu/HANDITEL/home.html (Luxembourg based). The aim of this server is to gather and classify web sites related to people who are elderly or disabled. Much of it is from the US and concentrates on the disabilities and illnesses/conditions associated with onset of old age rather than elderly per se. – similarly to the Cornucopia of disability information. http://www.codi.buffalo.edu/

HandyNet is a CD-ROM based inventory of AT available across Europe. Items are classified in a uniform manner and the CD is available in all European languages. Further information on the database and how to order it is available from the Internet website http://www.handynet.org.

MediaAge.net: http://www.MediaAge.net/ is an evolving electronic European news service highlighting issues related to the global age boom. It will bring relevant information and stories to those that can best use them. MediaAge networks are being established across Europe, bringing together different organisations involved with ageing and policy issues as well as media representatives and researchers.

Medical Devices Agency http://www.medical-devices.gov.uk/ publishes occasional assessments of items of AT, critically assessing and comparing the efficacy and safety of products. The reports are not intended as a buying guide and are aimed at informing professionals rather than users. Copies are free to NHS/Social Service employees. MDA Room 2/FO5 Crown Buildings, Surbiton, Surrey KT6 5QN

TAP The Telematics http://www2.echo.lu/telematics/telehome2.html Applications Programme, is one of the European Commission's research programmes and is aimed at stimulating Research and Telematics development on applications of information and/or communications technologies in areas of general interest.

Visual Impairment Service: http://www.ssc.mhie.ac.uk/VISHome.html/ is easy to use information service for all those in and concerned with the visually impaired community. It is run by the Scottish Sensory Centre in Edinburgh in collaboration with Action for Blind People, Sense Scotland and RNIB.

c. Examples of some local services

DIAL Basildon: http://www.thurrock-community.org.uk/tcis/tc500501.htm

DIAL Hampshire: http://www.hants.gov.uk/istcclr/cch16419.html

DIAL Trafford: http://www.disabilitynet.co.uk/groups/dialtrafford/

DISS, Disability Information Service for Surrey: http://dspace.dial.pipex.com/town/square/ad544/

Norfolk Disability Information Federation: http://www.open.gov.uk/ndif/homestuf/homepage.htm/

Printed in the UK for the Stationery Office Limited on behalf of the
Controller of Her Majesty's Stationery Office
Dd 5068537. 03/99. 39462. Job No. 68989